Dr. Sharp —
Happy Holidays — Happy Everydays.
Your small but sincere association,
Jacki + Kitty

By the same author

*A Century of Medicine
in San Antonio*

*The Medical Story
of Early Texas, 1528–1853*

A History of the
Texas Medical Association

PAT IRELAND NIXON, M.D.

A History of the
Texas Medical Association
1853 – 1953

Foreword by MERTON M. MINTER, M.D.

AUSTIN · UNIVERSITY OF TEXAS PRESS · 1953

UNIVERSITY OF TEXAS PRESS
AUSTIN 12

THOMAS NELSON AND SONS LTD
Parkside Works Edinburgh 9
3 Henrietta Street London WC2
312 Flinders Street Melbourne C1
5 Parker's Buildings Burg Street   Cape Town

Thomas Nelson and Sons (Canada) Ltd
91–93 Wellington Street West   Toronto 1

Société Française d'Editions Nelson
25 rue Henri Barbusse Paris Ve

Library of Congress Catalog Card Number 53–6000.

TO THE FOUNDERS OF THE
TEXAS MEDICAL ASSOCIATION

No CLASS of men needs friction so much as physicians; no class gets less. The daily round of a busy practitioner tends to develop an egoism of a most intense kind, to which there is no antidote. The few setbacks are forgotten, the mistakes are often buried, and ten years of successful work tend to make a man touchy, dogmatic, intolerant of correction, and abominably self-centred. To this mental attitude the Medical Society is the best corrective, and a man misses a good part of his education who does not get knocked about a bit by his colleagues in discussions and criticisms.

SIR WILLIAM OSLER, 1897

Foreword

IN THE BROAD FIELD of medicine, which changes rapidly, one might think that a history which began a hundred years ago could contribute but little to our understanding of present progress or future developments. But history is important. To foresee the future with intelligence requires a knowledge of the past. Has anyone given us a better oath than did Hippocrates? With only his senses and his power of observation did not William Withering write an article in 1765 which today can serve as a useful guide in the administration of digitalis? It is refreshing to read the careful observations of Ashbel Smith on yellow fever in Galveston in 1839 and to remember that most medical progress has been made by men using only those senses which all of us have but which we too often neglect.

We can and should study the history of medicine, which is the record of the men of medicine, and we will be inspired to use, as our forebears did, the tools at hand to advance our ability to help our patients.

In this day of dependence on science, we are prone to neglect the art of medicine. The history of medicine can teach us a great deal about the art. It can guide us in re-establishing some of the closeness to the patient which a good physician must have to help those whose illness is not curable by scientific methods alone. We can better understand the science and we can better learn the art if we know what physicians of the past century were doing in medicine.

In 1936, Dr. Pat Ireland Nixon wrote *A Century of Medicine in San Antonio*. In his Preface he stated: "It is obviously impossible and not altogether desirable to dissociate the medical history of Bexar County and the medical history of the State of Texas. With periods of ebb and flow the two have developed simultaneously and

ix

have each exerted a profound influence on the other. However, the desire has been to limit the story to Bexar County as much as possible, leaving the telling of the larger story for someone more familiar with it."

The combination of a competent, busy physician and a trained, excellent historian is infrequent. No one in Texas except Dr. Nixon had both the knowledge and the ability to write "the larger story." He spent a tremendous amount of time in research to make this history a comprehensive one. He applied his considerable writing ability to the arduous task of authorship. He was encouraged and helped by the officers of the Texas Medical Association, who felt that if Pat Nixon did not write the history of the Texas Medical Association in its first century of organized work, it might never be written and would surely never be written so well.

MERTON M. MINTER
Chairman, Board of Trustees
Texas Medical Association

San Antonio, Texas
December 1, 1952

Preface and Acknowledgments

THE MEDICAL HISTORY of Texas has been long and distinguished. From the time of the Indians and Cabeza de Vaca, on through the Spanish and Mexican periods and beyond the years of the Republic of Texas, the medical history went hand in hand with the civil history of the state. As survival amid hunger, the elements, and Indian attacks became more sure, political and economic conditions improved and a higher degree of culture was gradually attained. Likewise, improvements in medical practice were made as physicians from the United States and Europe found their way to Texas in increasing numbers. I have treated the early medical history of the state in *The Medical Story of Early Texas, 1528–1853*. The year 1853 was chosen as a stopping point because it is most important in the medical story of Texas: in this year the Texas Medical Association was organized.

The history of the Texas Medical Association cannot be separated from the history of the state of Texas. The one is part of the cultural development of the other. Dr. Oliver Wendell Holmes, a contemporary of the founders of the Texas Medical Association, has given apt expression to this thought. After maintaining that the history of medicine cannot be isolated geographically or intellectually from conditions and events of the time, he continues: "A geographer who was asked to describe the tides of Massachusetts Bay, would have to recognize the circumstances that they are a limited manifestation of a great oceanic movement. To consider them apart from this, would be to localize a planetary phenomenon, and to provincialize a law of the universe." [1]

The history of the Texas Medical Association is in the main the

[1] Eleanor M. Tilton, *Amiable Autocrat: A Biography of Dr. Oliver Wendell Holmes* (New York, 1947), 300.

xi

medical history of the state, for most of the progress in medical practice has centered in, or been sponsored by, this organization. At certain points in the story, material will be introduced which may not appear to be relevant. In most such instances, it will be seen that this material has been included because it throws light on certain developments which were coeval with the growth of the Association.

This is a narrative description of the Texas Medical Association over a period of one hundred years—its ideals, its ambitions, its steady progress, its controversies, its failures, and its successes. As we project the Association far into the future, our early professional forebears will appear as foundation-layers. And yet, as we read the story, it will be seen that they accomplished much in their own right, that they sincerely recognized and worthily met the obligations and opportunities that were theirs.

As, in imagination's eye, we follow the Texas Medical Association through the intervening century, we can but be impressed with a feeling of awe and admiration that a small band of medical pioneers, amid hardships and difficulties, effected the beginnings of organized medicine in Texas. Too much praise cannot be accorded these early leaders for the vision and the wisdom they displayed, for they laid the foundation on which rests the framework of organized medicine as we know it today. As we write and as we read about these men and what they accomplished, we should rejoice with unceasing reverence and pride that they are our medical forefathers. As the result of their work and as a tribute to their attainments, we should accept our obligations and opportunities with greater assurance and greater courage.

Through the years, occasional suggestions had been made concerning the collection of material for a history of the Texas Medical Association. Credit for keeping this matter alive and for actually making a beginning must go to the Society of Ex-Presidents of the Association. The move was started in 1912, and the next year important data were presented by Dr. Frank Paschal. The influence and energy of men like Dr. Paschal and Drs. J. D. Osborn, R. H. Harrison, L. H. Reeves, and W. B. Russ have played a notable part in the ultimate completion of the project. To Dr. Russ and Dr. Reeves should go our gratitude for their patience and their prodding. As members with me of the committee created in 1949 to write the history of the Texas Medical Association, they have lent enthusiasm and assurance through these several years. All credit goes to them for the part they have played as exhorters. But the plan and the execution of this history—to paraphrase the words of one of our eminent medical forebears, Sir Thomas Browne—were bred among the "weeds and tares" of my own brain and are my sole responsibility.

To document or not to document has been an ever present question in presenting historical data relating to the Association. For the year 1853 and from 1869 to 1905, the *Proceedings* and *Transactions* were published, and every single volume has been made available. After 1905, the *Texas State Journal of Medicine* was the official organ. It is unlikely that many comparable organizations can point to such an uninterrupted recording of their accomplishments. If every item or quotation that I have taken from these publications were to be documented, there would be a tiresome array of references at the bottom of each page—"horse loads of citations," as Milton puts it—and no good purpose would be served thereby. As the story develops, it is obvious from the context that my main sources of information are the publications of the Association. I have therefore omitted documentation of all but a few references to the *Proceedings,* the *Transactions,* and the *Journal.* Anyone interested in data for a certain year can trace the desired information in the deliberations or papers for that year. All references to material in newspapers, manuscripts, books, or other outside sources, on the other hand, have been carefully set down.

Wherever possible, the officers and members of the Association have been allowed to tell their own story. Where they have expressed themselves aptly and incisively, I felt that nothing was to be gained by paraphrasing. Their language typifies their times; to us it may appear ornate or high flown, but to them it was proper and convincing.

Assistance in this historical effort has come from many persons, and to all of them I express my sincere gratitude. They include Dr. George F. Lull, general manager of the American Medical Association; Dr. Chauncey D. Leake, vice-president of the University of Texas; Mr. Dan Ferguson, of Dallas; Mrs. Merle Duncan, of Waco; Mrs. J. F. Lentz, of Marshall; Dr. Samuel W. Geiser, of Southern Methodist University; Dr. Merton M. Minter, Dr. J. B. Copeland, and Mr. C. Stanley Banks, of San Antonio; and Dr. Lyman C. Blair, of Houston. The ever willing and ever capable aid of the following librarians was well-nigh indispensable: Miss Magdalene Freyder, of the American Medical Association; Miss Elisabeth D. Runge, of the Medical Branch of the University of Texas; Mrs. Estelle Parnell, Mrs. Katheryn Wendler, and Miss Pauline Duffield, of the Texas Medical Association; Miss Helen M. Holt, of the Houston Academy of Medicine; and Mrs. Helen R. Branum and Miss Betty Constantine, of the Bexar County Medical Library.

The contributions of Miss Winnie Allen, archivist of the Library of the University of Texas, and her associates deserve special mention. No work on any phase of Texas history can hope to approach completeness without the help and guidance of Miss Allen. She it was who directed the search for medical material in the vast resources of the university library and came up with much that had lain hidden and unused these many years.

Two names, always associated with my historical ventures, require emphasis: those of Olive Read Nixon, my wife, and Mary Johnston, my secretary. Much of the labor involved in handling the details of the present undertaking has been lightened by their loyalty and patience.

Special mention should be made also of the advice and assistance of Mr. W. E. Syers, of Austin. At many times and in many places he has given direction to the Association. Now his wide experience has helped to steer this book through the press with few or no complications.

The officers of the Texas Medical Association have given every co-operation. The official family in Austin have followed the progress of the manuscript with eagerness and interest, notably Dr. R. B. Anderson, Mr. Tod Bates, Miss Harriet Cunningham, Miss Lurine Hightower, and Mr. N. C. Forrester. But it was reserved for Mrs. Lynita Baxter to supervise the project from the beginning. She accepted this assignment seriously and kept a devoted but jealous eye over it.

PAT IRELAND NIXON

San Antonio, Texas
January 17, 1953

xiv

Contents

Illustrations

xviii

ILLUSTRATIONS

A History of the
Texas Medical Association

I

Groping for a Beginning

ON JANUARY 17, 1853, the Texas Medical Association had its beginning. Conditions surrounding this important event were troublous and uncertain. Seventeen years earlier, Texas had become a republic, and by 1853 it had been annexed to the United States for seven years. Rumblings of the irrepressible conflict which was to erupt with fratricidal fury in 1861 could be heard far south of the Mason and Dixon line and far west of the Mississippi River. The vision and courage of our medical forefathers in those troubled times can be applauded. In founding the Texas Medical Association, these men were following a pattern. The British Medical Association had been organized in 1832 and the American Medical Association in 1847. In 1838 had been formed the Medical and Surgical Society of Houston.[1]

As a background, it will be well to take a glance at medical conditions in Texas about the middle of the nineteenth century and to consider some of these conditions as they relate to earlier periods of history.

Principally as the result of financial stringency, Texas' decade of independence was strenuous and uncertain. Yet increase in population and wealth was steady and continuous. In 1836 the population was less than fifty thousand; by 1850 it had increased to well over two hundred thousand. This increase, of course, brought many physicians to Texas during the period.

Medical conditions were of necessity primitive. Hospitals were few in number and limited in equipment. Some of the doctors were

[1] *Telegraph and Texas Register*, August 14, 1838.

well educated for that day, but most were products of the preceptor system. Malaria, yellow fever, cholera, typhoid fever, and smallpox made up the bulk of their practice. Any efforts in the direction of organization or control of the practice of medicine, however inadequate they may appear now, were improvements. Under Spanish and Mexican rule, Texas authorities at various times received instructions concerning medicine, hospitals, and public health. As early as 1795, regulation and licensing of physicians, surgeons, and apothecaries were attempted.[2] This effort, however, could have been little more than a gesture, since these three professional groups were practically nonexistent.

In 1828, in Stephen F. Austin's Texas colony, a more serious attempt at licensing physicians and enforcing certain public health measures was made. Physicians were required to present their diplomas before beginning practice. Cleanliness of private and public places was emphasized as a public health measure. In 1830, in San Antonio, compulsory vaccination of children was required for the first time in Texas and perhaps in the United States.[3] From time to time, over the state, boards of health were created. The first one was in San Felipe de Austin in 1831, and the second was in San Antonio later in the same year. Similar boards were formed at Goliad and Nacogdoches. These boards were, in all instances, the result of panic from epidemic disease, notably smallpox and cholera, and when the epidemic had passed, the health boards ceased to function.

One other regulatory measure had to do with physicians' fees. In 1831, the town council of San Felipe appointed a committee of two physicians to set up "a tariff or fee bill." [4] But the first step which had a tangible effect on the beginnings of organized medicine in Texas was taken in 1837. In that year, by joint action of the Senate and House of Representatives of the Republic of Texas, a Board of Medical Censors was created. This board, in existence for four years, was the predecessor of the present Texas Board of Medical Examiners.

And yet—even though a Houston editor as early as 1837 was calling for the establishment of county medical societies, "composed

---

[2] Bexar Archives, February 10, 1795, Library of the University of Texas.

[3] "Records of the City of San Antonio," February 25, 1830, City Clerk's office.

[4] Eugene C. Barker, "Minutes of the Ayuntamiento of San Felipe de Austin, 1828–1832," *Southwestern Historical Quarterly*, XXIII (1919–20), 306.

4

of regular graduates of medical colleges of the United States and Europe," to help control "damnation round the land" [5] dealt to the people by quack doctors—all these efforts were perfunctory and at best exploratory; they were little more than gropings in the dark for solutions to problems which only time and the processes of evolution could solve.

Prior to 1853, abortive attempts were made to organize the medical profession of Texas by legislative enactment. These I have treated in detail elsewhere and need not repeat here.[6] It is enough to say that in 1848 a group of Galveston doctors petitioned the Legislature to grant a charter to the Medical and Surgical Society of Galveston, and a bill to that effect was introduced. The petition, signed by Ashbel Smith and ten other physicians, set forth the objects of the proposed society as advancement of medical and surgical skill, diffusion of knowledge among its members, creation of higher professional standards, establishment of a library, and control of quackery. These altogether worthy ambitions were patterned after the declarations of the American Medical Association, and it is difficult to understand why the legislators should have objected to any of them. In addition, the society desired to be empowered "to appoint a board of Censors whose duty it shall be to examine and license persons who shall hereafter propose to commence the practice of Medicine and Surgery." During the discussion of the bill the name of the proposed organization was changed to the Medical and Surgical Society of the State of Texas, and the provision relating to the appointment of a board of censors was eliminated. The amended bill read as follows:

SEC. 1ST. Be it enacted by the Legislature of the State of Texas, that John B. Taylor, J. B. Gardiner, W. R. Smith, Ashbel Smith, R. H. Chinn, Wm. McCraven, C. McAnalley, C. G. Keenan, E. W. Rentfro, N. B. Viser, J. B. Robertson, T. J. Heard, E. J. Arnold, J. H. Price, W. H. Beirs, J. H. Lyons, J. E. Elgin, J. W. Robinson, Moses Johnson, D. C. Dickson, J. H. Starr, R. S. Tate, C. B. Rains, ———— Vaught, C. S. Brown, J. L. Johnson, J. J. Johnson, J. H. B. Hoxey, ———— Duncan, Jas. A. Wells, W. P. Smith, J. M. Glasscock, J. M. Ball, A. Ewing, William T. F. Coles, George Gorden, R. J. Walker, Wm. Seybold, Beriah Graham, Franklin L. Yoakum, Lemuel Peters, W. K. Cooke, E. Stephens, F. W. Smith, Wm. M. Carper, L. Randall, Anson Jones,

[5] *Telegraph*, January 24, 1837.
[6] *The Medical Story of Early Texas* (San Antonio, 1946), 466–71.

S. G. Haynie, M. B. Bennett, their associates and successors be and they are hereby constituted a body politic and corporate under the name and style of the "Medical Society of the State of Texas" and in that name may sue and be sued, plead and be impleaded, and may do and perform all things, which bodies politic and corporate under the Constitution and laws, do and perform in their corporate capacities and may have and use a common seal for the authentication of their Acts, with liberty to alter or change the same from time to time, as they may think proper. SEC. 2D. Be it further enacted, That the society may have, receive and enjoy property both real and personal by purchase, donation or otherwise, with power to sell, alienate and convey the same at pleasure; *provided* the amount shall at no time exceed Fifty thousand dollars. SEC. 3D. Be it further enacted, That the first regular meeting of the society shall be held at the City of Huntsville on the 1st Monday of October 1848 and annually thereafter at such place as the members thereof may designate, at which time they shall elect from their body a President, Vice President, Secretary Treasurer and such other officers as the interest of the Society may require, which said officers, shall continue in office one year and until their successors are elected, Provided however, that six members may constitute a quorum to transact business and may adjourn from day to day or have called meetings whenever said quorum deem it necessary. SEC. 4TH. Be it further enacted, That said society may pass by-laws for the government of its members, provided such by-laws are not in conflict with the Constitution and laws of this State and may make such requirements of Physicians applying for membership as they think the prosperity of the society and the promotion of the Science of Medicine may require. SEC. 5TH. Be it further enacted, That the institution hereby incorporated shall be purely literary and scientific and shall continue so long as its object is the promotion of Medicine and kindred sciences. SEC. 6TH. Be it further enacted, That this act take effect and be in force from and after its passage.[7]

The bill was considered at intervals for about a month but was finally defeated. The defeat did not deter the physicians. Their continued agitation for the organization of medicine in Texas, in the face of unsettled and unpromising conditions, testifies all the more to their vision, their wisdom, and their determination.

[7] "Bills of the Second Legislature of the State of Texas," Archives, Texas State Library.

6

II

A Medical Association Is Born

THE FIRST SUCCESSFUL MOVE toward organization of medicine in Texas was made by a group of Austin doctors. On December 11, 1852, in the *Texas State Gazette,* and on December 15, 1852, in the *Texas Monument,* there appeared the following:

The members of the medical profession resident in the city of Austin and county of Travis, had a meeting on the 9th instant, to consider of the propriety of assembling a convention of the profession throughout the State at an early day. After due consultation, it was unanimously resolved to issue the following call. The objects to be attained are of an important character, and we commend the subject to the serious consideration, and prompt action of physicians in all parts of the State:
To all regular authorized Physicians of the State of Texas:
We the undersigned, Physicians of the City of Austin and vicinity, being desirous of promoting the advancement and improvement, as well as elevating the standard of our profession within this State, propose as an object conducive to that end a State Medical Convention, to meet at the City of Austin on the 17th day of January next; for the purpose of organizing a state medical society, and generally to do and take such action then as will be most conducive to these objects.
And we furthermore express the wish and hope that all the members of our profession throughout the State who can, will meet with us at the time and place specified, and aid us in the proposed organization.

This notice was signed by the following Austin physicians: Arthur J. Lott, J. T. Alexander, S. W. Barker, J. F. Duval, Edward McDonnell, S. K. Jennings, Jr., W. K. Brown, J. M. Litten, R. N. Lane, and W. A. Morris. The mere narration of these names fails to do full justice to the memory of this group of men. It has been

7

said that the success of any organization is dependent, in large degree, upon the enthusiasm with which it is begun. These men furnished the enthusiasm. They had the vision. They did something about it. Well can they be called the Fathers of Organized Medicine in Texas./

We have a picture of the Austin of that day:

When, in 1852, as a young lawyer just going into the practice, I came here, Austin was a frontier village of a few hundred people, with none but log cabins for residences and public buildings except a few instances—very few, at that. The Capitol was an old wooden shack, standing on the hill where the City Hall now is built. . . . At that time we had one policeman and he was seldom on duty. The latch string of every home hung on the outside, and the interior of our homes gave a welcome to all comers. There was no such thing as stealing, robbery or violence toward women. Cows and other stock ranged on the hills round about and sometime lawless men would take a cow or kill one, but I do not remember it being considered unlawful until a good many years afterward. The Indians visited us frequently, not as hostiles but as friends, bringing hides and furs for trading purposes. They would camp near the city and stay several days.[1]

On the appointed day, January 17, 1853, the convention was called to order with Dr. S. K. Jennings, of Austin, in the chair and Dr. A. J. Lott, of Austin, as secretary. The meeting was held in the Methodist Church. The Rev. J. W. Phillips opened this meeting and three subsequent sessions with prayer.[2] From our viewpoint, the attendance was small, but it was probably larger than the sponsors had expected. Most of the doctors came from counties close to Austin. Of the thirty-five physicians present, one each came from Anderson, Bastrop, Burleson, Cameron, Collin, Fayette, Freestone, Harris, Harrison, Hays, Lamar, Navarro, Polk, and Williamson counties; two came from Grimes County, three from Milam, four from Comal, and twelve from Travis County.

Dr. Joseph Taylor came from Harrison County, on the Louisiana border. He must have acted quickly, for the time between announcement and meeting was about one month and the distance each way was more than three hundred miles. This long journey, probably

[1] W. M. ("Buck") Walton, in *Austin American*, April 25, 1915.
[2] John W. Phillips was transferred from the Tennessee Conference to the Texas Conference of the Methodist Episcopal Church, South, in 1849.— Macum Phelan, *A History of Early Methodism in Texas, 1817–1866* (Nashville, Tennessee, 1924), 297.

8

on horseback, may have been a factor in his election as the first president of the Texas Medical Association.[3] The following doctors were registered as members of the convention: H. M. Allen, Navarro County; S. W. Barker, Travis County; W. K. Brown, Travis County; Lewis A. Bryan, Cameron County; W. S. Burks, Milam County; J. W. T. Coles, Lamar County; H. W. Davis, Travis County; D. C. Dickson, Grimes County; J. P. Duval, Travis County; W. F. Evans, Polk County; James Gaines, Milam County; W. L. Gammage, Freestone County; G. S. C. Harper, Williamson County; J. L. Holliday, Burleson County; J. T. Jeffries, Milam County; S. K. Jennings, Travis County; W. H. Johnson, Travis County; W. G. W. Jowers, Anderson County; Theo. Koester, Comal County; R. N. Lane, Travis County; J. M. Litten, Travis County; A. J. Lott, Travis County; W. A. Morris, Travis County; Edward McDonnell, Travis County; ———— Nohe, Comal County; Chas. A. Porter, Comal County; R. B. Pumphrey, Travis County; William Remer, Comal County; O. F. Renick, Bastrop County; W. Russell, Hays County; Ashbel Smith, Harris County; W. P. Smith, Fayette County; Joseph Taylor, Harrison County; J. W. Throckmorton, Collin County; and Edward Tucker, Grimes County.

The story of most of these men has been lost in the mists of the intervening century. Ashbel Smith and James W. Throckmorton, who became governor of Texas thirteen years later, stand out above the rest. And yet, when appraised from the present viewpoint, every one of these thirty-five members of the convention made a worthy contribution to organized medicine in Texas. By way of comparison, it is interesting to note that at the organizational meeting of the American Medical Association in New York City in 1847, the number present was eighty.[4] Thirty-five at this Austin meeting was encouraging.

One session was held on the seventeenth, two sessions on the eighteenth, and two on the nineteenth. At the first session a committee of five was appointed to petition the Legislature for a charter. A committee composed of Drs. Taylor, Smith, Litten, and Renick was appointed to draft a constitution and bylaws. By two o'clock the next afternoon this committee submitted its report.

[3] In *The Medical Story of Early Texas* (p. 473) I erroneously stated that Dr. George Cupples, of San Antonio, was the first president.

[4] Morris Fishbein, *A History of the American Medical Association, 1847–1947* (Philadelphia, 1947), 24.

The document was adopted with very few changes, and a committee was appointed to superintend the publication of the proceedings of the convention along with the constitution and bylaws. Such activity and such accuracy are difficult to understand until we are reminded that Dr. Ashbel Smith was a member of this committee and without doubt the author of the committee report.[5]

At the second session of the second day, held at 7:00 P.M., the *State Gazette* was authorized to print five hundred copies of the proceedings and constitution and bylaws. The published work had this wording on the title page: "Proceedings of the Texas Medical Convention together with the Constitution and By-laws of the Texas Medical Association. Instituted at Austin, January, 1853. Austin: Printed by J. W. Hampton, 'Gazette' office, 1853."

The constitution and bylaws, printed as Appendix I in this history, is not an unusual document. But it is of tremendous significance to organized medicine in Texas. It sets out the usual directions concerning the election and duties of officers, the time and place of the annual meeting ("the second Monday of November, at two o'clock, P.M., in the city of Austin"), membership ("every gentleman of the Medical Profession residing within the state," under certain conditions), creation of district societies, assessment of annual dues of five dollars, etc. Preferring with Louise Imogen Guiney

> A short life in the saddle, Lord!
> Not long life by the fire,

the founders provided in the constitution for retirement at the age of sixty, free from "assessments and liabilities of office."

Very interesting and praiseworthy are the "Orders":

1. The Association shall dine together on the day of its annual meeting, at the expense of the Association. Dinner to be provided by a Committee appointed for the occasion by the President.

2. Professional strangers shall be invited to dinner at the discretion of the President.

3. The President, at the meetings of the Association or Counsellors, shall not vacate the chair, unless permitted to do so, or required by some

[5] Ashbel Smith (1805–86), statesman, soldier, diplomat, physician, and educator, was probably the most intellectual physician of all Texas. He received the A.B., M.A., and M.D. degrees from Yale, then spent two years in Europe. He came to Texas in 1837 and for fifty years thereafter rendered distinguished service to his adopted state.

10

urgent occasion; nor speak on any question without first obtaining permission.

4. Members speaking must rise and address the Chair, and sit down when they have done.

5. Members who have spoken, shall always give place to those who have not.

6. No member speaking shall be interrupted, unless to correct a mistake, or to call him to order.

7. All speaking shall cease after any question has been put.

8. No motion shall be considered unless seconded.

9. No vote shall be re-considered at the same meeting by a less number than were present at its passing.

10. Literary gentlemen interested in Medical Science, and Medical Students, shall be publicly invited to hear the annual discourse.

11. All printed publications shall be in the octavo form.

From this pamphlet, much of the material concerning this organizational session was obtained. At the seven o'clock meeting on the second day, the first officers were elected, as follows: Joseph Taylor, Harrison County, president; W. A. Morris, Travis County, first vice-president; Edward Tucker, Grimes County, second vice-president; A. J. Lott, Travis County, corresponding secretary; R. N. Lane, Travis County, recording secretary; O. F. Renick, Bastrop County, assistant recording secretary; J. M. Litten, Travis County, treasurer; and James Gaines, Milam County, orator.

At the first session held on January 19, twenty-four of the thirty-five delegates to the convention were appointed "counselors." [6] The final session was held on January 19, at 8:00 P.M. The prayer was offered by Dr. W. P. Smith.[7] A few routine matters were disposed of, and the meeting adjourned.

Thus the Texas Medical Association was born.

[6] Then, as now, the word *counselor* was confused with *councilor*. These counselors were the forerunners of our present Board of Councilors.

[7] Like Ashbel Smith, but in a less intellectual way, William P. Smith was a man of many talents: physician, soldier, Methodist preacher, politician, farmer, and editor. He came to Texas from Tennessee in 1833. His chief claim to fame lies in the fact that he early attached himself to the army of Stephen F. Austin and did valiant service at the Siege of Bexar in 1835.

III

The Second Meeting

THE CONSTITUTION and bylaws adopted at the organizational meeting of the Texas Medical Association made provision for the formation of district societies, it being thought "important that there should be but one medical organization throughout the state and that the District Societies should be collateral branches of one parent Society." Under this provision, two societies were formed: the first at San Antonio, on September 22, 1853, with Dr. George Cupples as president; and the other at Austin, on October 22, 1853, with Dr. John T. Alexander as president. These were called the Bexar Medical Society and the Travis Medical Society. This was the only recorded progress between the first and second annual meetings of the state association.

As provided in the constitution, the second meeting was held in Austin on November 14, 1853, again in the Methodist Church. President Joseph Taylor being absent, Vice-President W. A. Morris called the meeting to order. The work of the entire meeting consisted in improving the machinery of organization. Three days were consumed in discussing matters of general interest. A revised constitution and bylaws were adopted, no radical changes being made. The dues were raised from five to ten dollars. The name of the organization was changed to "Medical Association of Texas." [1] Another interesting innovation, reflecting the influence of Dr. George Cupples, who was on the revision committee, provided for

[1] In 1869 the name became "Texas State Medical Association"; in 1901, "State Medical Association of Texas." In 1951 the original name was resumed: "Texas Medical Association."

12

PAST PRESIDENTS

George Cupples, 1853 and 1878	T. J. Heard, 1869
R. H. Jones, 1870	D. R. Wallace, 1871

PAST PRESIDENTS

R. T. FLEWELLYN, 1872   D. F. STUART, 1873
A. G. CLOPTON, 1874   H. W. BROWN, 1875

the issuance of a "diploma," or certificate of membership, to each member. In reputedly good Latin, it read as follows:

Societas Medica Reipublicae Texanae, Anno Domini MDCCCLIII Instituta, et Eodem Anno Auctoriatate Reipublicae Confirmata. Omnibus ad quos haec pervenerint salutem. Viro ornato . . . qui in numerum nostrum hoc anno fuit admissus . . . hoc munus liberis sociorum suffragiis, lubentissime conceditur. Diu vivat, et floreat patriae, scientiarumque decus; utque societas haec semper illius, sic ejusdem memor, prestet. In Quorum Fidem has literas, sigillo societatis munitas, subscripsimus Austiniae . . . Anno Domini, 185—.

.... *Praeses.*
.... *Secretarius.*[2]

The code of ethics which had been adopted by the American Medical Association five years earlier was accepted. This code was based on Thomas Percival's *Medical Ethics,* published in 1803.

On the second day the following new officers were elected: George Cupples, of San Antonio, president; S. K. Jennings, Jr., of Travis County, first vice-president; John T. Alexander, of Travis County, second vice-president; R. N. Lane, of Austin, recording secretary; M. A. Taylor, of Austin, assistant recording secretary; A. J. Lott, of Austin, corresponding secretary; and J. M. Litten, of Austin, treasurer.

Dr. Cupples presided for the remainder of the meeting. He appointed a committee on publication, a committee on medical topography, and a committee to draft and have printed certificates of membership.

The report of J. M. Litten, treasurer, was as follows:

To am't dues from members, received	$60.00
Cr. by cash for seal, as per receipt	16.95
Balance in hands of Treasurer	43.05

Number of members who have not paid annual dues, 36; whole number of members, 48.

No definite statement on the actual attendance was made.

[2] Roughly translated, this would read: "Medical Association of the Republic of Texas, organized in 1853 and confirmed by the authority of the Republic in the same year. To all to whom these presents may come, greetings. To this distinguished man who is admitted to our number, this honor is graciously conferred by free vote of our members. May he live long and prosper, a credit to his country and to the sciences, in order that this Association may always hold him in high esteem. In recognition of which, at Austin, we have affixed our names and the seal of the Association."

This report must have been quite discouraging. The membership was only forty-eight, and of these only twelve had paid the dues of five dollars. Besides, the bylaws provided that "the Association shall dine together on the day of the annual meeting, at the expense of the Association." The seal, for which there could have been no urgent need except to keep dignified company with the Latin "diploma," was expensive, and the next day ten dollars would be voted for use of the Methodist Church.

Two Austin doctors, who had signed the original notice for the meeting of the organization ten months earlier, for some reason had become antagonistic to the Association. The following penalizing resolution was read and apparently adopted: *"Resolved,* That the conduct of Doctors S. W. Barker and E. McDonnell, towards the Association, in endeavoring to destroy it by circulating injurious reports to the detriment of said Association, endeavoring to prevent the accession of members, and in refusing to act on the committees to which they had accepted appointments, as, also, to pay their respective contributions, when applied to by the Treasurer, merits expulsion, and that they be expelled accordingly, and that a copy of this resolution be addressed to each of them by the Secretary."

For the apparent purpose of nullifying any opposition to the Association, a committee was appointed to address a circular to the physicians of Texas. Signed by George Cupples, San Antonio; G. S. C. Harper, Georgetown; J. R. Simms, Webberville; J. T. Alexander, Travis County; W. P. Smith, La Grange; J. W. Robertson, Travis County; R. N. Lane, Travis County; W. A. Morris, Travis County; J. M. Litten, Travis County; A. J. Lott, Travis County; and Ferdinand Herff, San Antonio, the circular read as follows:

It is not generally known that a medical organization exists in this State. A convention of Physicians, in accordance with a published request, met in this city on the 17th day of January, 1853, and formed the Medical Association of Texas, which was incorporated by the present Legislature.[3]

The object of this Association, is to elevate the standard of the medical profession within our State; we, therefore, earnestly request the cooperation of the physicians throughout the State, in this important and interesting enterprise. The field before us, for medical observation, is extensive and important. Is it not, then, incumbent upon every

[3] On the correct date of incorporation see below, Chapter 4, and n. 1.

14

member of the profession in the State, to unite with us, and contribute his aid to make it honored and respected? Give us your names and your aid.

The high point of this meeting was the final session, on the night of November 16, 1853, when Dr. Cupples gave his presidential address. Handbills circulating around the streets of Austin invited the public to attend. The address was a masterpiece. It has been described in these words: "Lofty in its ideals, profound in its conceptions, compelling in its erudition, uncompromising in its principles, high in its praise of the profession, this address was more than a promise for the future: it was the consummation of all that had gone before in the medical story of Texas. The doctors of Texas should read it thoughtfully because in it they will find the flowering of medicine in Texas; and because of it they should be grateful for and proud of the medical heritage which Cabeza de Vaca, Federico Zerván, Ashbel Smith, and the many other medical pioneers created for us." Dr. Cupples had this to say about organized medicine in Texas:

The Medical Association of Texas was established, not from any sudden impulse, for the purpose, as has been facetiously conjectured, of raising the fees, or of securing a monopoly, but in prosecution of a plan long contemplated by many physicians in this State, of whom that distinguished ornament of our profession, *Dr. Ashbel Smith* was one. The object of this Association, as then contemplated, and now being carried out, is the organization, of the qualified Medical practitioners of the State, for the purpose of ensuring unity of design and concert of action in devising and carrying into execution such measures as may conduce to the general welfare and improvement of the profession, and the exclusion from its ranks of unworthy and unqualified persons.

Dr. Cupples felt that the medical profession had a deep obligation to the public, especially in the direction of eradicating quackery, in and out of the profession.

Nor can I altogether acquit the Medical profession in this State of blame. The timidity of some—the culpable indifference and selfishness of others, and the dispersion of all over a vast territory, have hitherto prevented our exercising the legitimate influence we possess. I earnestly conjure you to let this reproach attach to us no longer. It is our duty and our privilege to enlighten the people on this subject [quackery], and to call to a sense of their duty the Legislators whose constituents we are. In our collective capacity we yield to no class of the community the palm of superiority in intelligence and education. Let no unworthy dread of offending the prejudices of some and of conflicting with the interests of others, prevent our doing our duty in this matter. Denounce ignorance, happen what may, looking not to consequences but to results. Strong in the conviction that we are right, let us not fear to go ahead.

The standing, social and individual, of medical practitioners as a class, is confessedly lower here than in any other country of Christendom. Charlatanism and imposture, the offspring of ignorance, general and professional, reign rampant in the land; no legislative check restrains the indiscriminate and unregulated practice of physic by unqualified persons, the incredible and destructive abuse of nostrums and secret remedies; humbug is the order of the day. The usual reply to all such representations is, that this is the land of liberty, that every man is free to offer his knowledge and his skill for the acception of his fellow-citizens as he is to offer goods for sale; that it is anti-republican to exact by law any guarantee for the competence of those professing to treat disease; that free competition will always suffice to establish the merit of the deserving, the incompetence of mere pretenders. This is specious but not true, plausible in theory, but destructive in practice.

And yet Dr. Cupples had to the profession a large and unswerving loyalty, which he well expressed toward the close of his address:

Can there be, let me ask you, a prouder privilege, a nobler task than to aid in the attainment of so high an end, than to lighten to our fellow-men the weight of the primal curse? If vast responsibility attach to our ministry, is there no honor in the faithful discharge of its duties, no gratification to be derived from its successful result, save that of our self-love? When after weary days and sleepless nights of torturing anxiety and agonizing suspense, you relieve the heart of the anxious mother by announcing the safety of her darling child, when by a skilful operation or judicious treatment you recall from the confines of the kingdom of spirits the soul that had almost abandoned its tenement, are you not conscious of being indeed invested with a high office, with an holy trust? The man who feels not these things, who regards his profession but as the means of earning a livelihood or of amassing a fortune, ought not to practice an art so fraught with good or with evil to his fellows.[4]

Of this address Frank Paschal was to write: "It is one of the most magnificent addresses that was ever made by any President of any State or National Medical Organization." [5] In this appraisal, which

[4] The address is printed in full in the *Texas State Journal of Medicine*, XIV (1918–19), 7–13, and *The Medical Story of Early Texas*, 482–88.

[5] Remarks before the 1913 meeting of the House of Delegates of the Association at San Antonio. See below, Chapter 15.

he regarded as a "strong statement," Paschal was most sincere and in all likelihood not far from the truth.

Following the presidential address, a resolution was passed thanking Dr. Cupples for "the zeal which has characterized his efforts for the welfare of the Association and for the able and instructive address." After thanks were tendered to the pastor and members of the Methodist Church, "the Association then adjourned till the next annual meeting." Little did any member present think that the next meeting would be sixteen years away.

A Charter and Some Founding Fathers

THE COMMITTEE APPOINTED to petition the Legislature for a charter for the new association evidently performed its mission well. Twelve days after the fall meeting, the Fifth Legislature on November 28, 1853,[1] passed the following bill:

An Act to incorporate the Medical Association of Texas

SECTION 1. Be it enacted by the Legislature of the State of Texas, That Ashbel Smith, M.D., O. F. Renick, M.D., David C. Dickson, M.D., W. P. Smith, M.D., Joseph Taylor, M.D., G. S. C. Harper, M.D., George Cupples, M.D., Edward Tucker, M.D., H. P. Howard, M.D., R. W. Guilmette, M.D., J. M. Litten, M.D., James Gaines, M.D., S. K. Jennings, Jr., M.D., W. Russell, M.D., W. G. W. Jowers, M.D., H. M. Allen, M.D., A. J. Lott, M.D., J. W. T. Coles, M.D., John T. Alexander, M.D., W. F. Evans, M.D., Theodore K[o]ester, M.D., J. W. Throckmorton, M.D., Lewis A. Bryan, M.D., W. A. Morris, M.D., W. Remer, M.D., W. K. Brown, M.D., Charles A. Porter, M.D., M. A. Taylor, M.D., J. J. Roberts, M.D., and John McDonna, M.D., together with all others who now belong to, or shall hereafter be duly admitted or become members of that Association, according to the rules, orders and constitution of said Association, formed or to be formed, shall be and they are hereby declared to be one established body, corporate and politic, in deed and in name, by the name and style of the Medical Association of Texas, and by the same name shall have perpetual succession of officers and members, and a common seal, with power to change, alter, break and make new the

[1] When George Cupples said in his presidential address, November 16, 1853, that "a charter has been granted," he must have spoken too soon.

18

same as often as the said corporation shall judge expedient and the said corporation and its successors shall be able and capable in law to purchase, have, hold, receive, enjoy, possess and retain to itself and to its successors for the term of fifty years, any estate or estates, lands, tenements or hereditaments of any kind or nature soever, not to exceed in value the sum of One Hundred Thousand Dollars, to sell, alienate, exchange or lease the same or any part thereof, as they shall think proper, and may by the same name sue and be sued, implead and be impleaded, answer and be answered unto, in any court of law or equity in this State, and to make such rules and bylaws (not repugnant to the laws of the State) for the benefit of the said corporation, and for the order, rule, good government and management of said corporation as shall from time to time be agreed upon by a majority of the members of the said Corporation.

SEC. 2. That this act shall take effect and be in force from and after its passage.[2]

Approved, November 28, 1853.

For the recovery of a copy of this act and the consequent correction of our knowledge of the early history of the Association, we are indebted to Dr. Frank Paschal.[3] He himself has given a good interpretation of its significance.

The physicians who first organized the State Medical Association of Texas were men of high standing and ability. They looked forward, even at that early day, to building up the standard of our profession and placing it on the high plane of usefulness which each succeeding year has endeavored to attain. . . .

The remarkable part of the first organization . . . is that it was then as it stands today, the parent organization being the State Medical Association of Texas, and the County organizations owing allegiance to the parent, or State organization. The County organization was then as now, the unit of organization. It is indeed remarkable that over one half of a century ago, the entire plan or organization should be exactly like that of today. This again shows the magnificent type of medical men that the pioneers of the profession of this State were. It shows that they knew the necessity of organizing, and the plan of co-operation in order to accomplish the ends that could never have been attained without unity and concert of action.

[2] Copy furnished Dr. Paschal, May 15, 1912, by C. C. McDonald, then secretary of state.

[3] Paschal's contributions to the Association are treated below in Chapter 15. For a great many years this tireless and far-sighted leader worked incessantly at collecting and preserving the early records of the Association. See below, Chapter 17.

The State Medical Association of Texas did not take out another charter until the year 1889, and then again in 1901. It was practically working under the charter of 1853. . . . [We should] acquaint the members of the medical profession, not alone of our own State, but of the entire world, . . . how in this wild and sparsely settled State of those days a plan of organization was conceived of, that was fifty years afterwards, recommended by the American Medical Association in 1901.[4]

It took the doctors of Texas half a century to learn, as the subsequent history of the Association shows, what these founding fathers seem to have known from the beginning. Not until the 1903 meeting of the Association [5] were the members willing to make effective the intended—and, as they then saw, necessary—integral relation of county associations to the state association.

The thirty names in the charter are not simply the thirty-five names of those who attended the first 1853 meeting less five. Twelve of the latter do not appear in the charter: S. W. Barker, W. S. Burks, H. W. Davis, J. P. Duval, W. L. Gammage, J. L. Holliday, J. T. Jeffries, W. H. Johnson, R. N. Lane, Edward McDonnell, ———— Nohe, and R. B. Pumphrey. Barker and McDonnell, as we have seen, had been expelled; but why the other ten do not appear we are not informed. That R. N. Lane was not in disfavor with the Association is suggested by his being one of those appointed to sign the circular addressed to Texas physicians on behalf of the Association. Seven members named in the charter, on the other hand, had not been registered for the first 1853 meeting: John T. Alexander, George Cupples, R. W. Guilmette, H. P. Howard, John McDonna, J. J. Roberts, and M. A. Taylor. Of these valuable additions to membership, at least two, Alexander and Cupples, presidents of the two local societies, were present at the November, 1853, meeting.

Frank Paschal's earnest efforts to unearth information about the founding fathers of the Association were at first unavailing, despite his dedication to the task. "Surely they should not be forgotten," he pleaded in 1913. Yet he was forced to announce that he had "so far failed to get a single line from anyone regarding any of those men." Shortly before his death, in 1925, however, he was able to record some information about them and what their accomplishments meant to organized medicine:

[4] Remarks at San Antonio, 1913. See below, Chapter 15.
[5] See below, Chapter 13.

There are several who were so prominent before the world, that it is only justice to them that their names be again recorded in history for their greatness, their acts and deeds. Among them is that of the revered

Doctor George Cupples

the leader and father of organized medicine in Texas. Doctor Cupples was a native of Scotland. From 1836 to 1838 he was staff assistant surgeon in the Spanish service in the British Auxiliary Legion. In August 1838 he graduated from the University of Edinburgh, Scotland, studying also in the hospitals of London on specialties. After graduating he studied in the University of Paris from 1839 to 1843 for the privilege of occupying any official medical positions in the hospitals of France. In 1844 he came to San Antonio, Texas, from Paris and made this city his home until he died in 1894. In the Mexican war, Doctor Cupples served as surgeon of Hays 2nd. regiment of cavalry, in 1847. In the Confederate army he was first surgeon of the 7th. Texas regiment of mounted volunteers and served in the campaign of New Mexico, 1861–2. In December 1862 he was appointed medical director of the Eastern military district of Texas, and continued in charge until ordered to rejoin the Sibley Brigade, to which he belonged, in Louisiana. Doctor Cupples served as senior chief surgeon of division, and in 1864, as medical director and inspector of Cavalry corps of the Trans-Mississippi department up to the close of the Red River Campaign.

He gave his parole in San Antonio at the time of surrender. He served first on General Green's staff, and afterwards on the staff of General Magruder; then on that of General Wharton, having entered the service as regimental surgeon of the 7th. Texas under Colonel William Steele.

Doctor Cupples was president of the State Medical Association of Texas in 1854 and again in 1878. He was the first to introduce into Texas the use of anesthetics, ether first and chloroform afterwards. He was the first in the United States to perform the extirpation of the tongue for cancer, by Nunnelly's method. The man lived many years. He was the first in the U.S. to perform the operation for ovariotomy in a child under eight years of age and Freund's operation for extirpation of the uterus and ovaries. He was the first in Texas to amputate at the hip joint and knee joint with success. The ovariotomy was performed in the summer of 1874, on the bed in which the child lay. The pedicle was tied off and returned, an unusual procedure in those days. They were then treated extraperitoneally. The diagnosis was accurately made. The tumor was a unilocular cystoma about the size of an adult head. She lived to womanhood and became a mother. The hysterectomy was performed October 14, 1878. The patient lived fifty hours. Then there was no defined method of operating. The operation was abdominal. The broad liga-

21

ments were tied off with silk, piece-meal, using for that purpose an aneurism needle. Today it is not a difficult operation, but was a very difficult one in those days. The operation, ovariotomy, was performed in a boarding-house with no conveniences. There were no hospitals in this city at the time these operations were performed. I had the honor of assisting him in the two later operations. Doctor Cupples was a master in his profession, laborious, careful in all his practice, his reports, his cases, and private records. He was a man of broad culture, familiar with every historic reference, with every royal family and their traditions, a fluent conversationalist. He was the friend of young physicians, kind, considerate, helpful; he was a constant attendant of national, state, and local medical society meetings, and until within a few months of his death, never failed to attend our county society meetings, always taking an active part in its affairs and in the discussions of scientific subjects.

This is not the proper time to eulogize one whose deeds are more lasting than bronze or marble. In years to come it may be that a monument will be erected to his memory, for no physician could be more deserving. There never has lived in this state a member of our profession more entitled to recognition than the father of organized medicine in Texas, Doctor George Cupples.

Doctor Ashbel Smith

was noted, not only as a physician, but as one prominent in the affairs of state and nation. He was a graduate of Yale. Doctor Smith was ambassador to the Court of St. James from the Republic of Texas. He was one of the first in Texas to advocate the establishment of the University of Texas; he was president of the first board of regents. He was a bachelor. Doctor Cupples spoke of him as "an ornament to our profession."

Doctor David C. Dickson was prominent in state affairs. He was Lieut. Governor of Texas in 1853. He ran for Governor in 1855 and was defeated.

Doctor W. G. W. Jowers of Palestine, was also prominent in political affairs. He ran for Lt. Governor in 1855 but was defeated.

Doctor H. P. Howard was a surgeon in the United States Army with the rank of Major. He was the last surviving member of the first State Medical Association. He lived in San Antonio for many years and died in this city. He left a number of children, among them Doctor H. P. Howard, now of Dallas, Texas.

Doctor R. N. Lane was prominent in state affairs; he was secretary of the first Medical Association, wrote and signed the charter of our society. After the reorganization of the State Medical Association on its present plan in 1903, Doctor Lane was president of the Maverick County Medical Society. He called on me, an honor that I appreciated. I showed him

22

the charter granted to the Bexar County Medical Society in 1853 that he had written and signed as secretary. He was visibly affected and tears ran down his cheeks. After so many years of honest labor, with all of his co-workers in the cause of science and humanity, except Doctor Howard and himself, gathered to their fathers, this preserved charter of which we are justly proud, brought to him memories of the cherished past. It would have been impossible for it not to have affected one even of a less impressionable nature than was ... R. N. Lane. He left a family that now fills places of good citizens.

Doctor J. H. Lyons served as Mayor of San Antonio from January 1865 to August 15th, 1865; from that date until October 9th, 1865, San Antonio had no mayor. On October 9th, 1865, D. Cleveland was appointed mayor by Gov. Hamilton, the provisional Governor of Texas. Doctor Lyons was reinstated Mayor by an act of the legislature August 24th, 1866, and served to December 31st, 1866. A charter election was held January 1st, 1867, and Doctor Lyons was elected Mayor and served until November 2nd, 1867. Those were in the turbulent days of reconstruction. Doctor Lyons handled the city affairs in an admirable manner, and during those heated days of hatred between the North and South still rankling in the bosoms of many, and with free men turned loose with equal privileges in law, through sound common-sense, tact, and humane sentiments, Doctor Lyons so managed that there were few, if any disturbances. We should appreciate the fact that one of our profession proved himself in those stormy days to be equal to the task placed upon him. Only those who lived through all of this can realize what it meant to handle public affairs then.

Doctor W. A. Morris was vice-president of the Medical Association of Texas in 1853, and signed the first charter of the Bexar County Medical Society. He was the father of Prof. Morris of the Medical Department, University of Texas.

Doctor J. W. Throckmorton was born in Sparta, Tenn., February 1st, 1825. He studied medicine with success, and maintained a fine reputation; he was surgeon in Major Mike Chevaille's Texas Rangers, in the Mexican War. He located in Collin County and engaged regularly in the practice of medicine until 1859. In 1851 he was elected to the Legislature and re-elected in 1853. In 1857 he was chosen to the Senate for a term of four years. When the question of secession came up, both as a Senator and a citizen, he opposed that mode of redress of Southern grievances, and for the moment was in harmony with Governor Houston against secession. It is written of him that while in the convention assembled to decide the question of secession, he, acting in dual capacity of State Senator and as representative chosen to represent union men who were opposed to secession, when his name was called, voted No. A single person in the gallery almost directly over his seat hissed in the manner of theatrical loafers. Throckmorton instantly arose to his feet, and pointing upwards, said, "Mr. President, the rabble may hiss, while patriots tremble." The repartee was so prompt and so apropos that the whole convention rapturously applauded, and utterly squelched the screech of the unknown disturber of that solemn scene. He was elected Governor of the State June 1866, by a vote of four to one and was inaugurated August 8, 1866. Texas never had a more faithful executive. His acts were wise, just and conservative, embracing every effort to restore peace to the country and renewed friendship between the North and South. But he did not seem to be the desire of the then dominant power controlling the Federal Government, and on the 8th of August, 1867 was deposed by General Sheridan, then in command of military affairs in Louisiana and Texas. Doctor Throckmorton abandoned the practice of medicine and took up law, in which profession he also attained great success.[6]

[6] Undated memorandum, inscribed "Dr. F. Paschal to Dr. Holman Taylor." Manuscript in the Library of the Texas Medical Association, Austin.

V

A Hope That Failed

*W*HY, IT WILL NO DOUBT be asked, did this early organization of Texas medicine fail to function for sixteen years? These organizers had met and overcome the hardships of a rigorous frontier. Of their generation, as they came to Texas, it had been said that cowards never started and weaklings never arrived. These men were neither cowards nor weaklings. Under subaverage conditions, they could have carried through any movement which they initiated. Why, then, were there only two meetings of the early Texas Medical Association? Was the effort at organization premature? This, doubtless, was a factor. But the principal reason probably lay in the social and economic conditions under which these early Texas physicians lived.

First of all, the tremendous distances and poor modes of transportation were factors of importance. Closely associated with these was the ever present danger of Indian attack. More subtle and less tangible was the fact that no high degree of culture had been attained during the days of the Republic of Texas and after. The problem of physical survival left little time for intellectual and spiritual pursuits. Hogan records that in 1845 "not more than one-eighth of the white population were either active or nominal members of Texas churches." [1] Heavy drinking of whiskey was prevalent. Corpus Christi is reputed to have had more than two hundred grogshops. In education, too, Texas lagged. Men like President

[1] William Ransom Hogan, *The Texas Republic* (Norman, Oklahoma, 1946), 194.

Mirabeau B. Lamar, early and late, emphasized the importance of education, but the average citizen had few educational opportunities. In many households, the weekly newspaper was the only medium of information and instruction.

Added to all these factors discouraging cultural development, the characteristic Texan trait of rampant individualism was of prime importance. This feeling of independence and aloofness extended to both cultural and physical phases of life in the state. Dr. Ashbel Smith thus applied it to medicine: "We have, so far as I am aware, no medical organization in our State; nor is there much prospect of any change. Each member of the faculty is a separate independency, and sometimes adopts a sort of armed neutrality system." [2]

Could the action taken against Drs. Barker and McDonnell have played a part in the disruption of the Texas Medical Association? Medical controversies in those days were serious and violent. At a somewhat later date, delegates from New York were refused admission to a meeting of the American Medical Association. It is barely possible that the expulsion of these two members produced a schism which required sixteen years to heal.

A final cause retarding medical organization in Texas was the fact that the black hand of slavery lay heavy on the land, where soon civil war would pit brother against brother. Times were hard, poverty was extreme, patriotism was high. Practically all Texas physicians were loyal to the Confederacy. A few, mostly of German descent, such as Drs. Hermann Nagel, of Milheim and A. M. Dignowity, of San Antonio, cast their lot with the Union. But Ashbel Smith and George Cupples marched proudly and loyally under the Stars and Bars. The result was inevitable, and poverty and patriotism of the Civil War gave way to poverty and reconstruction under the carpetbag regime. Under such conditions, no progress, medical or otherwise, could be expected.

Nevertheless, the reasons for the discontinuance of the Texas Medical Association remain unclear. The factors mentioned above doubtless played their part, but it is difficult to understand why an organization presided over by Dr. George Cupples, with all his drive, intellect, and leadership, should quietly cease to exist. The charter, applied for after the January meeting, was granted on

[2] "On the Climate, etc. of a Portion of Texas," *Fenner's Southern Medical Reports* (New Orleans, 1851), II, 458.

November 28, 1853. This in itself should have assisted in keeping the Association together.

Observers much nearer to the event than we came no nearer to a solution. Dr. H. C. Ghent, in his presidential address of 1885, dismissed the incident with this facetious observation: "I have been reliably informed that the society was organized at the *time* and *place* for the convenience of the doctors who might be in attendance upon the Legislature. No wonder the child became paralyzed and died so early in infancy!" [3] It may be that the Texas Medical Association was in a situation akin to that of the California State Medical Society about the same time: "From 1860 to 1870," says Henry Harris, writing of California, "there was no State Medical Society. It did not have a ten-year period of suspended animation— it simply died." [4]

However, if the activities of organized medicine were dormant, medical thought was making some progress. Several years earlier, Dr. Ashbel Smith had published his valuable papers on cholera and yellow fever. In 1854, Dr. J. C. Massie wrote a creditable book, *Treatise on the Eclectic Southern Practice of Medicine.* A less pretentious publication was F. C. Wilkes's *Manual of Practice for the Diseases of Texas,* published in 1866. The former was published in Philadelphia; but the latter bore a Texas imprint, of Wilkes and Stone, Chapel Hill.

From Harrison County came a report of a successful blood transfusion. At the hands of a Dr. Benedict a woman with far-advanced yellow fever, as evidenced by hemorrhage from the mouth, received blood in her veins from a volunteer who had just recovered from the disease. With pride it was reported: "This, we believe, is the only known case of transfusion in this city, but it is not likely to be the last. Indeed, it would not be surprising if that 'heroic' practice should become as popular, in time, as the opposite practice of phlebotomy was at a former period. It is obvious, however, that none but the most scientific and skillful should ever be suffered to undertake so delicate an operation." [5]

Soule University, at Chapel Hill, began to consider the establishment of a medical department in 1857. Two years later a medical faculty was appointed, but the department apparently did not func-

[3] *Transactions of the Texas State Medical Association,* 1885, p. 63.
[4] *California's Medical Story* (Baltimore, 1932), 154.
[5] *Harrison Flag,* November 19, 1858.

tion until 1869, when the first and perhaps only class was graduated.[6] A projected medical school at Houston in 1861, under the direction of the state, received a charter and chose a promising faculty, including Dr. Ashbel Smith as professor of surgery;[7] but there is no record to indicate that the school was ever opened. J. J. Lane, in his *History of the University of Texas*, makes no mention of such a school. The Galveston Medical College opened its doors in 1865, with twenty-three students in attendance. The professor of surgery, a forward-looking man, Dr. Greensville Dowell, edited and published the *Galveston Medical Journal* from 1866 to 1871. The period of the Civil War and Reconstruction would naturally have been hard on these institutions.

Many newspapers, the usual media for imparting medical information, carried articles on various professional subjects. The ether-chloroform controversy was aired, the conclusion being that the factor of safety lay in the direction of ether, even though chloroform was the favorite of most Texas doctors. Under the heading "A Peep into a Live Man's Stomach," one paper devoted the equivalent of ten large typewritten pages to the story of Alexis St. Martin. The accident, the operation, the remarkable recovery, the epoch-making experiments are all described. At this time Alexis had escaped from Dr. William Beaumont and was in the hands of Dr. John C. Bunting, of Hartford, who was planning to "exhibit this living wonder" to the doctors of Europe.[8]

The newspapers were publishing the usual items of interest concerning physicians, some serious, some trivial. The unfortunate suicide of Dr. Anson Jones, last president of the Republic of Texas, in 1858, was the most tragic. Another Dr. Jones, of Owensville, on a visit to La Grange, was displaying "a magnificent assortment of surgical instruments" and was expressing his willingness "to visit on short notice any part of the State and perform operations." [9] The conscience of Dr. R. H. Lewis, of La Grange, was deeply involved when he addressed the local editor: "Permit me through your paper to say to my friends and the community generally, that I have been on a spree (as it is generally called) for five or six months occasionally, and as I am determined in future to *drink no more,*

[6] "Minutes of the Trustees of Soule University," 26, 41, 113, Southern Methodist University Museum.
[7] *True Issue*, April 11, 1861.
[8] *Texas Republican*, May 23, 1857.
[9] *True Issue*, November 1, 1860.

they may rely, if employed in my profession, upon the best ability and attention I can give as Surgeon or Physician." [10]

One German newspaper had a story about the number of doctors in relation to population. The United States as a whole had 1 doctor for every 617 persons, the proportion varying in the different states from 1 for every 147 in California to 1 for 885 in Maine. "What a dreadful mass of powders and pills the people of California must have to swallow!" commented the editor.[11] Therapeutic nihilism, ahead of its day, came to Texas in 1859 in this quotation from Dr. Jacob Bigelow, of Boston: "I sincerely believe that the unbiased opinion of most medical men of sound judgment and long experience is made up, that the amount of death and disaster in the world would be less, if all disease were left to itself than it now is under the multiform, reckless and contradictory modes of practice good and bad with which practitioners of adverse denominations carry on their differences at the expense of their patients." [12]

Some progress was being made, but it was partially offset by the various brands of quackery that had sprung up. Texas did not escape the lure of newfangled homeopathy. Although she had no Oliver Wendell Holmes to ridicule the claims of homeopathy, ardent adversaries, both lay and medical, were not lacking. Typical of the times was the controversy between Dr. T. A. Stanwood and Dr. James Angell, homeopath. They argued the demerits of the doctrine of Hahnemann pro and con, back and forth, for five or six thousand words. The homeopathic treatment of scabies came in for discussion. If in reality like is cured by like, then, Stanwood argued, the internal administration of louse tea should cure the itch. In fact, he declared, Angell was not even a good homeopath: he was a disciple of "Goitonhisownhookopathy." [13]

About the time a resolution was introduced at an American Medical Association meeting condemning the religious press for publishing "serious homilies on prayer and praise side by side with cures for consumption, cancer, Bright's disease and other incurable diseases," [14] Dr. Persons, "the great magnetic physician," was being touted to the skies by George W. Baines, former president of Baylor University, and by J. W. Whipple, a presiding elder of

[10] *Ibid.*, January 22, 1859.
[11] *Neu Braunfelser Zeitung*, January 14, 1859.
[12] *Ibid.*, February 19, 1859.
[13] *Galveston Weekly News*, July 17, 1855.
[14] Fishbein, *History of the A.M.A.*, 134.

the Methodist Episcopal Church, South.[15] On and on through the press there ran a trail of quackery, with blatant effrontery claiming to cure hydrophobia, cancer, and "all ailments man is heir to." Water cures, steam cures, rupture cures, phrenology, the laying on of hands—all gradations of quackery were represented, and neither laymen nor doctors could do much to combat the situation. Then as today, printer's ink, charlatanism, and credulity united themselves in a formidable combination.

This time, the field was ripe for some sort of medical organization. Politically, however, the situation was still bad. In Texas the Civil War had been followed by years of turmoil and hardship. And the four years of tyranny and bloodshed under carpetbagger Governor E. J. Davis were not to begin until 1870.

In 1869, when many rights and privileges of citizenship were being denied, it took courage even to suggest the formation of an organization which would not be subject to Davis or one of his cohorts. Yet in spite of the fact that liberty of thought and action had been set aside, in that year the call was sent out, and the Texas State Medical Association became a reality.

[15] *Harrison Flag*, February 25, 1869.

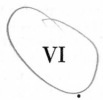

VI

Reorganization in 1869

IN 1856 AN ATTEMPT was made to organize a medical society in East Texas, but no record has been found to indicate that the effort was successful. A call was sent out for a meeting in Tyler on May 18, 1857. A medical society, it was asserted, would elevate the standard of the profession and "inspire its individual members with a laudable desire to emulate the rapid strides of Scientific reformation in the older States." The call was signed by Drs. George Gordon, John McDonna, J. A. Barry, E. S. Look, G. H. Wootten, J. R. Lyons, and W. L. Gammage. The closing paragraph of the newspaper notice contained this modest statement: "The general intelligence of physicians in our midst, is indicative of the fact that we have the embers of a professional literature, that need but the gust of a popular movement of this character, to be fanned into a flame whose brilliancy will not only eclipse the ignorance of a shallow empiricism, but will effectually stay the 'hue and cry' of the pretender and charlatan both in and out of the profession." [1]

In the November 30, 1857, issue of the same paper, this group of doctors published a notice in which they agreed "not to engage family practice by the year" and they agreed to be governed by the following schedule of charges:

Mileage (daytime)	$1.00 per mile
Mileage (nocturnal)	1.50 " "
Town visits	2.50
Prescriptions & medicines	2.00 & upwards

[1] *Tyler Standard,* November 22, 1856.

Obstetrics	15.00
Detention	12.00 for 24 hrs.
Consultation	6.00

Three years later a similar effort was made to organize the Red River County Medical Society at Clarksville. The call was issued by Drs. J. A. Barry, E. S. Look, G. H. Wootten, George Gordon, J. R. Lyons, J. T. King, and George G. Wootten.[2] A week later a meeting was held, and a committee was appointed to draw up a constitution and bylaws.[3] In this deep East Texas county, so close geographically and culturally to the Old South, it is to be doubted whether this effort could have mustered much strength in the year 1860.

Between 1866 and 1869, there are records of county medical societies being contemplated or organized in Galveston, Harrison, Harris, Washington, Smith, Ellis, Dallas, and McLennan counties, and there were probably others. As early as January, 1866, the Galveston Medical Society was in existence. Dr. Edward Randall was president; Dr. T. J. Heard, vice-president; and Dr. C. H. McGill, secretary.[4] The Waco Medical Association was formed on April 30, 1866. The history of this organization has been ably recorded by Dr. W. O. Wilkes. There were ten original members with the following officers: J. H. Sears, president; J. M. Willis, vice-president; E. P. Booth, recording secretary; David R. Wallace, corresponding secretary; and J. H. Caldwell, treasurer. The other five members were S. A. Owens, E. Merrill, A. M. Clingman, J. S. Taylor, and W. E. Oakes. Dr. Wilkes calls attention to two physical characteristics of this group: long beards and high-top boots. A creditable constitution and bylaws were adopted as well as a fee schedule. This latter was quite flexible, as evidenced by these two items: "Office advice and Prescription from $1.00 to $50.00," and "Obstetric Service from $20.00 to $200.00." One wholesome item of the constitution should be mentioned: "It shall be the duty of the members of this Association, at every monthly meeting to present a report in writing of each death that occurs in his practice—giving the name, age, sex and disease of his patient; the general treatment he pursued; and the reasons why, in his opinion, the treatment failed, and to report in writing any case that may recover that is

[2] *Ibid.*, May 19, 1860.   [3] *Ibid.*, June 2, 1860.
[4] *Galveston Medical Journal*, I (1866), 63.

32

of peculiar interest." [5] Dr. Wallace was present in Houston in 1869 when the Texas Medical Association was reorganized, and he and Dr. Sears were later elected presidents of that organization, the former in 1871 and the latter in 1891. The Waco Medical Association continued to meet until 1903, when the final reorganization of the state association led to the formation of the McLennan County Medical Society.

In Harrison County a notice signed by "Many Physicians" was placed in the *Texas Republican* on April 13, 1866, inviting all physicians of Harrison and adjoining counties to meet in Marshall "for the purpose of forming a medical association and other business pertaining to the profession." Nothing seems to have come of this proposed meeting, for a similar notice appeared in the same paper on March 23, 1867. Two years later the Harrison County Medical Association was in existence with the following officers: H. P. Perry, president; E. P. M. Johnson and W. F. Baldwin, vice-presidents; E. J. Beall, secretary; W. G. Thomas, assistant secretary; B. F. Eads, corresponding secretary; and T. M. Marks, treasurer.[6]

The *Texas Republican* of December 11, 1868, carried a notice of a medical organization which apparently held only one meeting: "There was an 'East Texas Medical Convention' at Starville, Smith County, on the 1st of October, at which Professor Morgan E. Looney, of the Gilmer College, delivered an address of unusual interest and elegance."

On August 21, 1869, the following notice appeared in a Dallas paper, signed by "Amor Medicae":

To the Editors of the Dallas Herald:
   In a number of your paper some two weeks since, you referred to the organization of a Medical Society in Ellis county, and very appropriately asked the question "why cannot we have a Medical Society in Dallas?" No just reason can be assigned. Dallas county with the number of physicians now located within her borders, ought not only to organize a society but should take the lead in the advancement of the Medical Sciences in Northern Texas. Three years ago an attempt was made to organize a Medical Society, but it failed through the apathy of the members of the profession. Let us try it again. I would like to hear from some of the profession in our city, and if agreeable to all, suggest that the first Monday in October next be appointed as a proper time for all the

[5] William O. Wilkes, *History of the Waco Medical Association* (Waco, Texas, 1931), 299.   [6] *Harrison Flag*, July 22, 1869.

members of the Medical profession, located in the county to meet in the city of Dallas, and organize. If that time does not suit the majority, let them appoint some other and make it known through the medium of the *Herald*.[7]

Apparently the county organization was formed some months later, for Philip Lindsley writes: "The Dallas County Medical Society was formed about this time, with Dr. A. B. Palmer, president; Dr. J. W. Crowdus, first vice-president, and Dr. Sam Field (now living at Beaumont), recording secretary. Its other members included eleven physicians. It was made the duty of each member to deliver an address, write an essay or report a case once in each year." [8]

These organizational attempts were of a local nature. The effort that was to be successful on a statewide basis was being exerted far to the south. Just as the physicians of Austin led the way toward the formation of the Texas Medical Association in 1853, the physicians of the Houston area took the lead in 1869.

The Houston Medical Association was formed on March 11, 1857, with Dr. J. S. Duval as president. The other four members were Drs. R. H. Boxley, Greensville Dowell, W. H. Howard, and H. W. Waters. The objectives of the association were altogether worthy: "To cultivate the science of medicine and all its collateral branches; to cherish and sustain medical character; to encourage medical etiquette and to promote mutual improvement, social intercourse and good feeling among members of the medical profession." [9] This association is reported to have survived for about two years and to have issued a call for reorganization of the Texas Medical Association in 1859.[10] The claim, however, cannot be confirmed. After this date there is no record of activity of the Houston Medical Association.

On December 8, 1868, the Harris County Medical Association was formed, at a meeting held at the Hutchins House in Houston. In attendance were Drs. L. A. Bryan, W. H. Howard, J. Larendon, D. C. Stuart, T. J. Poulson, R. W. Lunday, Alva Connell, Sr., Alva

[7] *Dallas Herald*, August 21, 1869.
[8] *A History of Greater Dallas and Vicinity* (Chicago, 1909), I, 83.
[9] B. H. Carroll, *Standard History of Houston, Texas* (Knoxville, Tennessee, 1912), 125.
[10] *Ibid.*, 124.

Connell, Jr., J. H. McDonald, W. D. Robinson, T. J. Devereaux, J. M. Morris, and W. P. Riddell, all of Houston. Dr. Ashbel Smith was listed as a member of the association but apparently did not attend this meeting.[11] Again, the report that this group presented itself as a nucleus of reorganization and sent out communications to that effect cannot be substantiated. However, it seems likely that the physicians of Houston did consider such possibility; Carroll, in his *Standard History of Houston,* twice advances this unconfirmed opinion.[12] This notion must have been firmly fixed since Young makes the same claim, setting the date for reorganization as April 15, 1869.[13] But, as will be seen from the following notice in a Houston paper, it was not the doctors of Houston who actually issued the call for reorganization: "The Washington County Medical Association has issued a circular, suggesting that the different medical associations in the state send delegates to the city of Houston at the time of meeting of the Grand Lodge of Masons, on the 26th of June next, for the purpose of taking the initiatory steps for the formation of a State Medical Association. Members of the profession living in counties where no 'Society' organization exists are respectfully solicited to organize a county association and send delegates forward." [14] Thus it is clear that the Washington County Medical Association must be credited with having taken the final step essential to reorganization of the Texas Medical Association, which was thereafter to function continuously through the years.

By way of preparation for the Houston meeting, which was held June 15 rather than June 26, the Harris County Medical Association was called together at the courthouse on June 10. The attendance was reported to be large. A constitution and bylaws were adopted, and the following officers elected: R. W. Lunday, president; D. F. Stuart, F. Hasenburg, and W. E. Cocke, vice-presidents; A. Connell, recording secretary; W. P. Riddell, corresponding secretary; and E. L. Massie, treasurer. A committee on arrangements was appointed, composed of B. Powell, D. F. Stuart, and E. L. Massie. The newspaper account of the meeting contained a sentence which, with evident satisfaction to the writer, was intended to chide the doctors of that era: "The attendance was large and the

---

[11] *Ibid.,* 128–29.   [12] *Ibid.,* 125, 128.
[13] S. O. Young, *A Thumb-nail History of the City of Houston, Texas* (Houston, 1912), 79.
[14] *Houston Daily Times,* May 15, 1869.

proceedings were harmonious, illustrating the fact that doctors do sometimes agree." [15] In other words, it was obvious to the layman that these early Texas doctors would abandon their individualism only with reluctance, but on this occasion they were willing for their conduct toward each other to appear exemplary.

Thus—as the *Proceedings on Organization of the Texas State Medical Association* set out in the first sentence—"pursuant to a call of the Washington County Medical Association, for the purpose of organizing a State Medical Association, physicians representing about twenty counties met at the Hutchins House, in the city of Houston, June 15th, 1869, at 6 oclock P.M." Twenty-four years later, Dr. D. F. Stuart, of Houston, shed further light on this call: "In 1869, almost a quarter of a century ago, Dr. Thomas Morris of Brenham issued a circular, requesting the physicians of the state to assemble in convention in Houston, for the purpose of organizing a state medical association." [16]

The Hutchins House was the leading hotel of Houston. It was located on the corner of Travis and Franklin streets, on the site of the present Southern Pacific Building.

The city of Houston had been founded in 1836 and had been the capital of the Republic of Texas from 1836 to 1839. In 1869 its population was less than nine thousand. "Besides its very creditable schools and churches," it could "justly be proud of its two very successful manufacturing establishments of cotton and woolen goods, the Eureka and City mills." A historian of the time reported that "the merchants of Houston do considerable business with interior merchants, and can calculate when they complete the *ship channel,* so that ocean steamers can come up to Houston as easy as they can enter Galveston Bay, which scientific engineers say can be done, to compete with Galveston as to future growth and commercial importance." [17]

The three days of the 1869 meeting were spent working out details of organization. Attendance was surprisingly good. Twenty-eight names were signed to the constitution and bylaws. Some of those present, however, did not sign. Twelve years later the loyalty of this little band was attested by Dr. A. R. Kilpatrick in his presidential address: eighteen were still members of the Association,

[15] *Ibid.,* June 11, 1869.
[16] *Transactions of the Texas State Medical Association,* 1893, p. 72.
[17] J. M. Morphis, *History of Texas* (New York, 1874), 502.

36

one had withdrawn, and nine had died. The great majority came from Harris and adjacent counties. Fourteen came from Harris County and Houston, five from Washington County, three from Galveston, and one each from Anderson, Ellis, Austin, McLennan, Fayette, Grayson, and Grimes counties. We have a record of the route traveled by the delegates from Waco: "By stage all day to Bremond, staying overnight there, and then an all day journey to Houston by rail." [18] The following names of those in attendance are set down in the order of their signatures: T. J. Heard, Galveston; R. H. Jones, Brenham; D. R. Wallace, Waco; E. L. Massie, Houston; G. Dowell, Galveston; D. F. Stuart, Houston; J. H. Webb, Galveston; W. T. LeGrand, Washington County; James F. Morris, Houston; A. Connell, Jr., Houston; F. Hasenburg, Houston; W. H. Howard, Houston; C. R. Nutt, Houston; R. W. Lunday, Houston; J. Larendon, Houston; W. C. Wathen, Waxahachie; J. F. Matchett, Washington County; G. M. Devereaux, Houston; B. Powell, Houston; Jas. Poulson, Houston; W. G. McGown, La Grange; J. A. Lawrence, Palestine; R. T. Flewellen, Washington County; W. P. Riddell, Houston; Ashbel Smith, Harris County; W. J. Cocke, Bellville; J. B. Robertson, Washington County; and J. A. McQueen, Anderson. Of these, only Ashbel Smith had been present at Austin in 1853 at the organizational meeting of the first association.

Forty years later Dr. S. O. Young, of Galveston, recorded that as a medical student he attended this meeting.[19] Because of discrepancies and because he stated that the printed *Transactions* began in 1872, he seems to have written from memory. According to Dr. Young, only twenty-four were present; the following names listed by him are not listed elsewhere: William D. Robinson, W. J. Locke, J. T. Norris, Alva Connell, Sr., George McDonnell, R. H. Harrison, L. A. Bryan, and J. J. Burroughs. Some or all of these may have been present, since the signed list is not complete, as we know from names of nonsigners appearing on the committees.

J. A. Lawrence, of Anderson County, was chosen as temporary chairman and E. L. Massie, of Harris County, as secretary. A Committee on Constitution and Bylaws was selected, composed of R. T. Flewellen, chairman, W. H. Howard, R. W. Lunday, R. H. Jones, E. T. Bonney, of Austin, W. P. Riddell, W. G. McInnis, of Free-

[18] Wilkes, *History of the Waco Medical Association,* 57.
[19] "A History of the Early Meetings of the State Medical Association of Texas," *Texas State Journal of Medicine,* V (1909), 119–21.

stone, W. C. Wathen, J. F. Matchett, and Alva Connell, Jr. The Committee on Nominations included B. Powell, chairman, R. W. Lunday, J. A. McQueen, T. S. Freeman, of Grayson, and W. C. Wathen.

The second session was held at 4:00 P.M. on June 16, with Dr. Greensville Dowell in the chair. The Committee on Constitution and Bylaws made its report, and its recommendations were accepted after being considered article by article. Likewise, the recommendations of the Committee on Nominations were accepted, and the following officers were duly elected: T. J. Heard, president; R. H. Jones, first vice-president; D. R. Wallace, second vice-president; Alva Connell, Jr., recording secretary; W. P. Riddell, corresponding secretary; and F. Hasenburg, treasurer.

The new constitution and bylaws embodied some changes and innovations at variance with the regulations set down sixteen years before. The purposes of the Association were clearly set forth in the first paragraph: "The name and style of this Association shall be the 'Texas State Medical Association.' It exercises its function by virtue of a voluntary and plighted faith of its members, and shall have for its objects, the promotion of Medical Science, Uniformity of Medical Ethics, and the inculcation of harmony and fraternity in this medical profession, and especially among the members of this Association." The fee of admission was fixed as "five dollars currency," and the next year was added the stipulation that "the annual tax for permanent members shall be one dollar in currency." In keeping with the origin of the revived association, the bylaws required that the annual meeting be held "in the city of Houston, at the time of meeting of the M. W. Grand Lodge of Texas." It will be recalled that the bylaws of 1853 named Austin as the place of meeting.[20]

Membership was open to all physicians in good standing, on recommendation of one or more members. Election was by two-thirds of all votes cast. A similar vote was required for conviction,

[20] The provisions of the 1853 and 1869 constitutions followed rather closely the pattern set by the American Medical Association. However, in both these instances the Texas association deviated. The parent organization, obviously sensing the significance and the seriousness of the war that was becoming imminent, provided in its constitution that the annual meeting could not be held twice in succession in the same place. This provision was to guard "against any liability to become sectional or localized."—N. S. Davis, *History of the American Medical Association* (Philadelphia, 1855), 50–51.

censure, or expulsion. Each county association was allowed two delegates for each ten members and one for each additional five members. All medical colleges with as many as seven professors were allotted two delegates. There was but one medical school, the Galveston Medical College, three of whose ten professors were members of the Association. The code of ethics adopted by the American Medical Association in 1847 was accepted at this meeting, just as it had been in 1853.

The third and final session of this reorganizational meeting of 1869 was called to order by the new president at 11:00 A.M. on June 17. In accordance with the bylaws, these committees were announced by the president:

Committee on the Science and Progress of Medicine: S. M. Welch, Galveston, chairman; B. Powell, Houston; R. W. Brown, Waco; J. P. Norris, Brenham; and W. J. Cocke, Bellville.

Committee on Grievances and Appeals: W. H. Howard, Houston, chairman; J. H. Webb, Galveston; and J. F. Matchett, Brenham.

Committee on Publishing, Finance and Claims: R. W. Lunday, Houston, chairman; W. P. Riddell, Houston; D. F. Stuart, Houston; F. Hasenburg, Houston; and Alva Connell, Jr., Houston.

Committee on Record of Cases: G. Dowell, Galveston, chairman; J. E. Morris, Houston; J. M. B. Gwinn, Cherokee County; W. C. Wathen, Ellis County; and George C. Red, Washington County.

Committee on Climatology and Epidemics: R. M. Swearingen, Chapel Hill, chairman; George Cupples, San Antonio; J. M. Reuss, Indianola; J. H. Sears, Waco; S. Eagan, Marshall; R. DeJarnette, Jefferson; W. A. East, Anderson County; W. D. Kelly, Galveston; E. L. Massie, Houston; W. G. McGown, La Grange; and D. R. Wallace, Waco.

Some idea of the problems and prospects of the Association as they appeared to this early group of physicians meeting in Houston can be gained from the number and type of these committees.

With the business of the Association completed, President Heard "asked all who were willing to do so to make reports of such medical cases or on such subjects as they might consider interesting"; whereupon "Dr. R. W. Lunday, who had served as surgeon of the Fifth Texas Regiment, Hood's Brigade, in Virginia, made an interesting talk on gunshot wounds of the lungs and chest. Dr. Lunday was followed by Dr. Ashbel Smith, who commanded the Second Texas

Infantry during the last three years of the war, and who had acted as much surgeon as colonel of that regiment, who made a most learned and interesting talk on the treatment of malarial fever by the use of leaves and bark of the willow tree as a substitute for quinin. Other short talks were made by several members." [21]

As this important meeting drew to a close, it was obvious that pride of accomplishment was asserting itself. Dr. R. H. Jones felt that the Committee on Publishing should be authorized to publish in pamphlet form the proceedings of the Association, along with the constitution and bylaws, and that the pamphlets should be distributed according to the best judgment of the committee. Dr. William H. Howard moved an amendment, which was accepted: "That these pamphlets be distributed to the more intelligent portion of the citizens; also, in order that they may the better appreciate the relations existing between the physicians and themselves, as shown in the Code of Ethics."

"A short time was taken up in the discussion of Specialists, but the sense of the American Medical Association on the subject not being known, the question was laid over until the next annual meeting." To those who think that specialization is of comparatively recent origin, this discussion is somewhat surprising. Hardly less surprising is the factor of compulsion implied in this motion: "Dr. Lunday moved that this Association require of the Subordinate Associations of the State to make it obligatory upon their members to report all cases of peculiar interest to their respective Associations, and that the Publishing Committee of such Associations be required to make a digested report of said cases; and that said digested reports be furnished by said Association to the Publishing Committee of the Texas State Medical Association, and that the same be published annually in the proceedings of the said Association."

All in all, the meeting was satisfactory. The presence and influence of men like Ashbel Smith, George Cupples, D. R. Wallace, T. J. Heard, and Greensville Dowell would seem to insure permanency of organization, and this expectation was fulfilled.

[21] Young, in *Texas State Journal of Medicine,* V (1909), 120.

VII

Years of Struggle, 1870–74

ENTHUSIASM WAS NOT an outstanding feature of the early days of the Texas State Medical Association, if we may judge from the small attendance at its meetings. Certainly there was much to discourage the early leaders. For instance, at the first session of the 1870 meeting only twenty-five were present, and in 1871 the attendance was twenty-six. Of this loyal group, seventeen were present at both meetings. The 1872 meeting was held in Houston with eleven members answering the initial roll call, and then the meeting place was changed each year so as to cover more of the state. The first meeting outside of Houston was held in Waco, with only seven present at the opening session. Subsequent meetings were held at Dallas, Austin, Marshall, Galveston, San Antonio, Sherman, and Brenham. The Dallas meeting in 1874 found "fully one hundred members in attendance." In Austin, "about fifty" were present; in Marshall, a large number; in San Antonio, thirty-three. In Galveston, Sherman, and Brenham, it was noted that a quorum was present.

It can confidently be assumed that failure to attend these annual meetings did not indicate a critical lack of interest in the state association, for by 1877 its membership had risen to 263. In all likelihood, these attendance records were affected by some of the same factors that prevented the Association from meeting between 1853 and 1869: distance, slow transportation, hazards of the journey, and stringent times of adjustment after the Civil War and the carpetbag regime. The panic of 1873 prostrated an already crippled industry and commerce; the Texas state debt of $3,167,000 in 1874 increased to $5,500,000 in 1879.

It is significant that during these difficult years the annual meetings of the Association continued to be held. The number in attendance should not be viewed critically from this distance; the remarkable fact is that the leaders, with persistence and purpose, held the Association together through long years of trial. Discouragements and disappointments came here and there. Some indifference and apathy on the part of the profession were constantly in evidence; less than 10 per cent of Texas physicians listed in the 1880 census were members of the Association.[1] Yet through hardships, uncertainties, and difficulties, the Association made progress to the point where continuance was assured.

The annual meetings of 1870, 1871, and 1872, all held in Houston, were devoted principally to matters of organization and policy. Twenty-two new members were admitted at the 1870 meeting. Fortunately, some interesting information about these men has been preserved in the *Proceedings,* including their names, medical schools, and years of graduation: W. G. McInnis, Tennessee Medical College, 1859, University of Louisiana, 1870; L. Hudspeth, Galveston Medical College, 1866; J. T. Norris, Jefferson Medical College, 1852; G. W. Foster, University of Louisiana, 1869; W. J. Cocke, Jefferson Medical College, 1853; G. T. Ross, University of Memphis, 1854; J. E. Prince, Jefferson Medical College, 1852; W. C. Blanchette, King's College, London, 1847; H. P. Downman, University of Louisiana; Sam. H. Towney, Galveston Medical College, 1869; A. E. Leger, University of Louisiana, 1870; J. R. Pettus, University of Tennessee, 1840; J. M. Callaway, University of Louisiana, 1854; Robt. T. Sweat, Galveston Medical College, 1869; J. N. Baylor, Jefferson Medical College, 1853; S. A. Owens, University of Missouri; S. M. Welch, Jefferson Medical College, 1855; W. D. Kelly, University of Pennsylvania, 1848; M. Campbell, Jefferson Medical College; S. O. Young, New Orleans School of Medicine, 1870; F. T. Jeager and W. D. Robinson, no schools listed.

The bright lights of the city must have served as an enticing counterattraction—the Houston which Abbé Emmanuel Domenech

[1] The United States Census gives the following figures: in Texas in 1850, 616 physicians and 13 dentists; in 1860, 1,471 and 65 respectively; in 1870, 1,906 and 120; in 1880, 3,003 and 246; in 1890, 4,340 and 398.

twenty-two years before had described as "a wretched little town composed of about twenty shops, and a hundred huts, dispersed here and there, among trunks of felled trees" [2]—for the following amendment was added to the bylaws on motion of Dr. R. W. Lunday: "No member of this Association or delegate shall absent himself from a meeting of the Association without special permission from the President, or from its session without the consent of the Association, the sense of the Association to be taken by vote."

The Committee on Publishing, Finance and Claims made a report on publication of the 1869 *Proceedings,* of which 5,000 copies were printed by the Times Job Printing Establishment of Houston at a cost of $100. This was a profitable transaction, since $240 was collected from advertisements of Houston and Galveston business firms. Among these were three Houston hotels, which offered board and lodging for $2 per day. Of this large number of copies of the *Proceedings,* only two are known to have been preserved.[3]

The presidential address of Dr. T. J. Heard was scholarly and forward-looking. He presented a strong plea for the establishment of a medical school as a branch of the state university, an accomplishment that was not to be realized for twenty-one years. "Should we, as one man," he prophesied, "bend our united energies to the founding and sustaining such a great Medical School in Texas, made equal to the wants of our people, the good resulting, not only to the present generation, but to those who are to follow us, will be greater than the most sanguine now anticipate." He also advocated publication by the Association of a medical journal which would reflect "the observations and opinion of the medical men of Texas." Here again he was many years ahead of his day.

The Committee on the Science and Progress of Medicine made a lengthy but learned report. It was presented, and doubtless prepared, by the chairman, Dr. S. M. Welch. Consider these scattered quotations:

[2] *Missionary Adventures in Texas and Mexico* (London, 1858), 25.

[3] Now in the Army Medical Library and the Library of the Houston Academy of Medicine. Only one copy of the *Proceedings* of the two 1853 meetings has been located, in the Library of the University of Texas in Austin. Copies of the 1870 *Proceedings* are found in the Army Medical Library, the Library of the Houston Academy of Medicine, and the Library of the Medical Branch of the University of Texas, at Galveston. The *Union List of Serials* includes several more copies of the 1869 and 1870 *Proceedings,* but their existence is not certain.

The history of medicine is, to a large extent, the history of civilization from the time of the father of medicine, Hippocrates, to the present period. . . . The extent to which subdivision and specialism have gone will, doubtless, be hereafter looked upon by the professional historian as the distinguishing medical characteristic of the present century. . . . The present is the era of intellectual growth and progression in all branches of knowledge, and may be truly called the Augustan age of medical science. . . . It would perhaps not be an exaggeration to say that as much progress has been made in the department of Therapeutics during the present century as in all the previous eighteen centuries, and as much in the last ten or fifteen years as in all the rest of this century. . . . The word impossible, indeed, is expunged from the vocabulary of modern science.

The following order of business was adopted in 1870:

1. Roll call
2. Reading minutes of previous meeting
3. Report of Committee on Credentials
4. Reception of communications
5. Report of special committees
6. Report of standing committees
7. Report of officers
8. Unfinished business
9. New business
10. Annual address of President
11. Annual essay
12. Miscellaneous discourses
13. Adjournment

It was moved and quickly carried that "only five minutes be allowed each member to speak."

The officers elected for 1870 were R. H. Jones, of Brenham, president; R. W. Lunday, of Houston, first vice-president; W. J. Cocke, of Bellville, second vice-president; Alva Connell, Jr., of Houston, recording secretary; D. F. Stuart, of Houston, corresponding secretary; and W. P. Riddell, of Houston, treasurer.

As we survey this 1870 meeting, stress should be placed on its organizational accomplishments. At the second reorganization of the State Medical Association of Texas in 1903, great emphasis was laid on the fact that the county society was the individual unit of organization and that the aggregate of these units went into the making of the state association. At that time it was intimated that this plan of organization was something new. That such was not the case was shown by Dr. Frank Paschal, who in 1913 pointed out that essentially this plan had been contemplated by the Texas Medical Association in 1853. And the constitution of 1870 sets out a similar plan of organization: "County Medical Associations shall be en-

PAST PRESIDENTS

R. H. HARRISON, 1876   W. D. KELLEY, 1877

JOHN H. POPE, 1879   A. R. KILPATRICK, 1880

PAST PRESIDENTS

ASHBEL SMITH, 1881 S. F. STARLEY, 1882
A. P. BROWN, 1883 H. C. GHENT, 1884

titled to two delegates to the meetings of this Association for every ten members comprising their societies, and one for every additional five members, and shall have two votes upon all questions; and all Medical Colleges in the State, holding charters from the State, with seven professors, shall be entitled to two votes; and no member shall be allowed to vote who is not a delegate of some association or medical college, except such member live in a county where no association exists, said county delegate being entitled to one vote." In 1871, the following was added: "County Medical Associations may be organized under the jurisdiction of this State Association. Each County Association must transmit a copy of its Constitution and By-Laws to the Texas State Medical Association for its approval; which, if approved, said County Association shall have full power to work under the jurisdiction of the State Association."

In the 1870 *Proceedings* is a letter from the publishing committee, announcing the meeting and setting forth the objects and purposes of the Association. The letter closes with this very sensible exhortation: "Commending the above reflections to your calm and thoughtful consideration, let us, in conclusion, gentlemen, urge upon you, if you would preserve the high characteristics of the medical profession, and contribute something to the advancement of science, to form local associations, during the ensuing year, in your respective towns and counties, and to join us, with that harmony and concert of action which springs from unity of purpose, in building up and fixing on a firm and permanent basis a State Medical Association of which we may have reason to be proud."

The 1871 gathering was noteworthy in only one respect: for the first time, formal papers were read and later printed in the *Proceedings*. "A Case of Ataxia Aphasia Resulting from a Blow on the Head" was presented by Dr. H. P. Downman. The patient had been struck in the left parietal region with a loaded quirt handle. Surgical exploration without opening the cranium was resorted to. Gradual recovery ensued. Dr. J. M. Callaway, professor of physiology, Galveston Medical College, read a paper "On Certain Morbid Phenomena Coincident with the Presence of an Excess of Urea in the Urine." The significant thing here is that Dr. Callaway was utilizing a fairly accurate test for urea: nitric acid was added to a measured volume of urine. The urea was thrown down as urea nitrate and could then be weighed. Dr. Callaway also wrote on "Death from Chloroform Inhalation." A man of thirty-five years who had had precordial pain for three months developed a urethral stricture and perineal fistula. After two drams of chloroform had been inhaled, the patient became livid, his breathing became stertorous, and his heart ceased to beat. Callaway, an 1854 graduate of the University of Louisiana, quoted the classical work of John Snow, who had recorded fifty chloroform deaths.[4] Texas doctors apparently were reluctant to give ether serious consideration as an anesthetic agent. While Dr. Callaway opposed the teaching that whenever an operation is justifiable, chloroform is justifiable, he was not "prepared to bring any dogmatical rule against chloroform."

Greensville Dowell, a surgeon of outstanding ability, made a "Report of a Case of Stricture of Urethra." The patient was treated by use of external urethrotomy. Following some rather austere and aggressive after-treatment, it was recorded on the fortieth day that the patient had "continued to improve, until now external opening is completely closed, can make plenty of water, and with a good stream."

In this same year (1871), the publishing committee did less well in financing the *Proceedings* for the previous year. Five thousand copies were printed by the Galveston News Book and Job Printing Establishment for $375.00, but only $260.00 was collected from advertisements. Finances of the Association were rather stagnant. The treasurer started the year with $176.07 and closed with $70.43. To augment the almost depleted treasury, each county society was required to pay twenty-five cents for each of its members, an admission fee of $5.00 was charged new members, and the annual dues were raised to $2.50, payable in advance.

In retrospect, it is interesting to see how these men tackled some of their plaguing problems. "Some time was taken up in discussion, as to the contagion and infection of yellow fever, most of the members agreeing as to its portability." The question of specialization cropped up again. The president, Dr. R. H. Jones, asked that some action be taken on it: "Many vexed questions are likely to arise and engage the attention of this Association in the future, and I know of no single one more likely to present itself than that of

[4] *On Chloroform and Other Anesthetics: Their Action and Administration* (London, 1858).

46

specialties in medicine, and I would be pleased to have you give expression to your opinions upon the subject." As a result, a resolution was introduced and referred to the Committee on Ethics, to the effect "that it is the opinion of this Association that specialists in Medicine and Surgery are to be encouraged by the medical profession as tending to advance the cause and progress of true science. We, however, deem it necessary to say that we only recognize as a specialist one who abandons the general practice of Medicine and Surgery."

Dr. Jones's presidential address maintained the level of excellence set by his predecessors, beginning with Dr. George Cupples in 1853. These men were cultured and well educated. Their addresses reflected the qualities of leadership which the times demanded. The attitude of Dr. Jones is found in this rather laudatory but thought-provoking sentence: "The profession which you represent in the organized capacity of a State Association, has for its object the highest and noblest aims which can possibly engage the thoughts or energies of man; and I hope and believe that you have met with a spirit fully in keeping with the value and nobleness of the ends aimed at, and that your deliberations will be characterized by the utmost decorum and courtesy, having in view the good of the profession and those dependent upon its kind offices."

The question, which had arisen in 1870, of a new charter for the Association, came up again in 1871. It seems that the medical profession of that day had its difficulties with the Legislature. Dr. Jones made this reference to the fate of the charter: "I regret to have to report the failure to obtain the Charter prepared at your last session, and forwarded to the Legislature. I suppose the failure on our part to accompany the application with a sufficient inducement in the way of black mail, accounts for its not receiving attention."

The officers elected for the coming year were D. R. Wallace, of Waco, president; L. Hudspeth, of Hallettsville, first vice-president; J. T. Norris, of Brenham, second vice-president; Alva Connell, Jr., of Houston, recording secretary; D. F. Stuart, of Houston, corresponding secretary; and W. P. Riddell, of Houston, treasurer.

The Association experienced perplexing times in 1872 and 1873. Attendance at the meetings was poor, and the financial situation was shaky. Unpaid dues totaled $170. In 1873, it was decided to assess each member and each county society an amount necessary to pay all indebtedness and to publish the *Proceedings* of 1872 and 1873.

The officers elected in 1872 were R. T. Flewellen, of Washington County, president; J. A. McQueen, of Anderson County, first vice-president; D. F. Stuart, of Houston, second vice-president; Alva Connell, Jr., of Houston, recording secretary; S. O. Young, of Houston, corresponding secretary; and J. Larendon, of Houston, treasurer. The next year the officers were D. F. Stuart, of Houston, president; H. W. Brown, of Waco, first vice-president; J. M. Morrison, of Hearne, second vice-president; S. O. Young, recording secretary; S. B. Hamlett, of Waco, corresponding secretary; and J. Larendon, of Houston, treasurer.

The 1873 meeting, the first of the current series outside of Houston, was held in Waco. S. O. Young reports the reason for the change in meeting place:

After the election Dr. Hudspeth made a strong argument against the policy of holding every meeting in Houston. He pointed out that the Association had had its drag net out over South and Southwest Texas for three years, and that while the result had been quite encouraging, it was evident that all had been accomplished that the Association could hope for. He suggested that it would be well to change the base of operation and hold future meetings at points in West, Central and North Texas. Dr. Hudspeth was followed by Dr. R. D. [*sic*] Wallace, who strongly indorsed the plan and invited the Association to meet the next year in Waco, promising them a warm welcome if they should do so and assuring them a good time.[5]

Following the sequence of the previous *Proceedings*, this meeting was listed as the fifth annual session. In reality it was the seventh, for in the numbering the two 1853 sessions were overlooked. The seven members to answer the first roll call met at the office of Drs. D. R. Wallace and J. H. Sears. Subsequent sessions were held at the Masonic Hall. There was discussion about inadequate care of the insane in the one lunatic asylum at Austin. Many of the mentally afflicted were crowded into jails, while some were permitted to be at large and endanger the lives of children and others. The Association endorsed a bill before the Legislature which aimed at correcting this situation.

There was discussion, too, of a bill under consideration by the Legislature to regulate the practice of medicine. A committee was

[5] *Texas State Journal of Medicine*, V (1909), 121.

48

appointed to confer with the legislators so that the views of the Association might be considered. Resolutions were adopted which expressed regret at the "increasing disposition on the part of the press to indorse in their editorials . . . quack preparations, bitters, etc.—the cards or advertisements of which appear in their columns." "Such indorsements," declared one resolution, "are neither just to their patrons, our fellow-citizens, whose interest we, as conservators of health, should endeavor to protect, nor . . . remunerative to those connected with the press." The members saw with equal regret "the names of prominent clergymen, lending their influence in this direction," and pronounced such action "a perversion of the moral influence which they justly have over a large portion of their fellow-citizens, and a prostitution of their holy office." There was a veiled suggestion that the alcoholic content of the nostrums was an attraction: "We make the declarations contained in the foregoing resolutions, the rather because not infrequently these editorial notices are of such sort as to delude the people into believing that we, the profession, indorse their pretensions, and in order the better to do so they are in the habit of not infrequently quoting the language of our standard, and applying it to nostrums, fixed as specific curative agents, of which alcohol is the base."

The question of publication of a medical journal had been brought up by Dr. T. J. Heard in 1870. Dr. Greensville Dowell had edited and published the *Galveston Medical Journal* with considerable credit from 1866 to 1871, but he abandoned the project because of financial losses. At the 1873 session a careful and sensible report on this subject was made. It is quoted at length because it had much to do with the firm footing on which the *Texas State Journal of Medicine* was established in 1905. It was thought unwise

for an organization such as ours to attempt the establishment of such periodical. In the present case, the project, if otherwise desirable, is placed beyond the limits of practicability, from the fact that we are not a body corporate, and as such could not sue, be sued, or do any of those acts necessary to conduct business.

It is desirable, in the last degree, to have a journal as a means of intercommunication between the profession throughout the State. We have scholarship; we have professional ability; we have peculiarity of local disease and influence, and if we had a journal it would be the means of utilizing this scholarship; of yoking it side by side with the professional ability of the State to the care of professional progress, by which our members would be drawn out and developed; our profession advanced, and the reading public generally, to a considerable degree, reached and influenced for their own and the good of the profession.

We, therefore, pledge the co-operation, moral and material, of this Association to any professional brother who shall supply this so much desired want, to wit: a medical journal, which, while it shall be indorsed and commended by, shall have no pecuniary connection with the Association, as such; provided, always, said journal be representative of the scholarship and professional ability of our State.

The papers presented in 1872 and 1873 were of a varied nature, such as "Report on Haematuria Miasmatica"; "Cerebro-Spinal Meningitis Treated with Bromide of Potassium and Preparations of Ergot"; "Report on Hydrophobia"; "Report of a Case of Femoro Popliteal Aneurism"; "Report on Eclampsia." One patient in the last report was, we must admit, thoroughly treated:

When I saw her she was in a convulsion, pulse about 130 and full; abdomen full and tympanitic; eyes injected and staring; stertorous respiration, and total insensibility. I opened a vein in one arm as soon as possible and bled her freely, so as to reduce and soften the pulse. I also shaved her head in the temples and all the occipital region, and applied cupping glasses, drawing blood freely; then applied collodion cantharida, nearly all around the head; had her feet bathed in hot mustard bath; applied spts. tereb. over the abdomen freely, and laid on it a flannel saturated in the same; gave calomel and comp. ext. colocynth in small doses, repeated every two hours. She had no more convulsions after the bleeding and cupping, and with careful nursing got well without ptyalism, or any unfavorable sequelae.

For the first time the Association in 1873 named accredited delegates to the American Medical Association, which was to meet in St. Louis the following June. They were Greensville S. Dowell, J. F. Matchett, G. C. McGregor, J. A. McQueen, D. R. Wallace, and S. R. Welch. Matchett and Wallace actually attended. While these were the first official delegates from the state association, there had been earlier unofficial attendants: in 1870, T. J. Heard, J. L. Irion, G. C. McGregor, and J. M. Willis, from medical organizations in Galveston, Montgomery, McLennan, and Washington counties; in 1872, Greensville S. Dowell and T. J. Heard, from Galveston.

At the end of the Waco meeting, the usual expressions of gratitude were given to the local profession and to others concerned. In addition, the thanks of the Association were "tendered to the officers of the H. & T. C. R. R. and the G. & H. R. R. for the half fare charged the delegates to the meeting of the Texas State Medical Association." Gratitude was also expressed to Major D. P. Shepherd "for the free use of the telegraph wires during the sitting of this body." [6] It might be recalled that there were only about one thousand miles of railway in the state at the time and that the Houston & Texas Central Railroad had reached Waco just six months before.

The 1874 meeting, held in Dallas with "fully 100 members" present, was a milestone in the career of the Association. Here the four-day session was instituted instead of the three-day, and this schedule has continued to the present time. The attendance and the interest are reflected in the *Proceedings* for the year, which comprise 146 pages, about four times the number in previous years. This same volume, which sold for one dollar, contains 64 pages of the minutes of the two previous meetings. These were included—according to Dr. R. H. Harrison, chairman of the Committee on Publishing—"that the entire work of the Association should be preserved in an easily accessible form."

This Dallas meeting assembled in the Odd Fellows Hall. Subsequent sessions were held in this hall, at Fields Opera House, the Christian Church, and the Hall of the Knights of Pythias. Dr. R. D. Jones "welcomed his professional brethren in a graceful reception speech, which was responded to by Dr. Ashbel Smith, in elegant and eloquent terms." Then, Dr. S. O. Young, chairman of the Reception Committee, pulled out all the oratorical stops:

I am glad to see Dallas not regard doctors as Pliny tells us Rome did, at one period: a sign of intemperate and corrupt commonwealth, and thus banished them for six hundred years. She (Dallas) extends to us a welcome almost as flattering as that which was rendered to Esculapius, when the grateful Greeks built a temple in which to house him. Our meeting, thus auspiciously begun, conducted amid such pleasant surroundings and formed of such material as I see before me, fills my heart with joy, a joy which I see reflected in every face before me. And making myself spokesman for the whole, I will now say, let us at once to work,

---

[6] The telegraph was not new to Texas history. In 1839, S. F. B. Morse "tendered the perpetual use of his Electro Magnetic Telegraph to this Republic."—*Lamar Papers*, II, 546. The significance of this offer was not realized, for it was not until the year 1858 that the first telegraph line was built.—S. C. Reed, *A History of the Texas Railroads* (Houston, 1941), 676.

and make this session a seal that shall stamp all future meetings, and all their acts, with honor, dignity and intelligence; both a blessing to suffering humanity and a blessing to ourselves. Gentlemen, in the name of the Texas State Medical Association, I welcome you.

"The meeting," we are told, "was then opened for business by prayer, by the Reverend Mr. Davenport" of St. Matthew's Episcopal Church. This somewhat irregular order of business may have been arranged with the same thought as that which prompted Dr. Samuel Johnson, on reading some laudatory tombstone inscriptions, to remark that a lapidary never works under oath. A second innovation at Dallas was the invitation to members of the press "to take seats with the Association." Later, proper thanks were expressed to the editors of the *Dallas Herald* and the *Dallas Commercial* for their faithful reporting of the transactions.

In the early years of reorganization, only a few county or local societies were in existence, and—contrary to the original plan of 1853—not all of these were affiliated with the state association. The Waco Medical Association, Harrison County Medical Society, Dallas County Medical Society, Harris County Medical Association, Washington County Medical Association, and probably others were mentioned in the press and *Proceedings* from time to time. At Dallas a closer connection of such groups with the state association was effected, and the following societies, accepting the constitution and bylaws of the parent organization, were admitted: Burleson Medical Association, Coryell County Medical Association, Grayson County Medical Association, Hill County Medical Association, Harrison County Medical Association, Johnson County Medical Association, Jefferson County Medical Association, Lamar County Medical Association, Travis County Medical Association, Washington County Medical Association, and Waco Medical Association. The acceptance of the Williamson County Medical Association was postponed because of a conflict in the bylaws.

It is obvious that there was an early tendency to multiply committees, in part attributable to accepting a committee as a placating expedient or as the simplest temporary solution for a controversial or difficult problem. In the main, however, these committees were created for the definite purpose of solving a problem of the present or of projecting the interests and ambitions of the Association into the future. Some of these committees had no effect and in all likelihood held no discussions. Others realized the importance of their assignments and devoted much time and effort to them. By 1874, the number of committees had increased to sixteen. There were committees on the science and progress of medicine; ethics; diseases of women and children; climatology and epidemics; on indigenous medical resources of Texas; surgery; publishing, finance, and claims; record of cases; grievances and appeals; special legislation; arrangements and invitations; creation of a library; delegates to the American Medical Association; memorializing the Legislature for an appropriation to Galveston Medical College; a state board of health; and psychological medicine.

One committee of unusual importance, that on special legislation, which had been appointed in 1873, reported at the Dallas session. It was made up of Chairman H. W. Brown, Waco; J. B. Robertson, Independence; Ashbel Smith, Bayland, Harris County; and D. R. Wallace, Waco. The year before, the Legislature had passed "An Article to Regulate the Practice of Medicine." This act did not receive complete approval of the state association.

Briefly, Section 1 of the act set down the requirement that a practitioner of medicine must have a degree of doctor of medicine or a certificate of qualification from an authorized board of medical examiners. Section 2 made obligatory the registration of all diplomas and certificates with the clerk of the district court. The clerk was to record all pertinent data in a well-bound book, and for this service he was to receive one dollar for each document. In Section 3 the county courts were instructed to appoint a board of medical examiners of not less than three practicing physicians "of known ability and graduates of some medical college, recognized by the American Medical Association." Each board was entitled to a fee of ten dollars from each applicant.

Section 4 provided for semiannual board meetings, notice to be given in the public press as to time and place. In the interim, any member of the boards was authorized to issue a temporary license after the applicant had passed a satisfactory examination, to be used until the next meeting of the board. Section 5 made violation of the act a misdemeanor, punishable by a fine of not less than fifty dollars or more than five hundred, "one-half of said fine to be paid to the prosecutor, and the other half into the county treasury." It was specifically stated that the provisions of the act were not applicable to men who had been in practice for five consecutive years, "nor to females who follow the practice of midwifery strictly as such." It is worthy of note that Governor Edmund J. Davis, consistently at cross purposes with the Legislature, failed or refused to sign the act, which became a law without his signature.[7]

The Committee on Special Legislation brought in a series of suggested amendments, some amusing, some quite stringent. In the first category, consider this: "Any person who is not a citizen of Texas, entitled to vote, who shall come into the State and advertise to perform surgical operations, or cure diseases, shall, before entering upon such practice, pay into the county treasury the same tax as is paid by persons exhibiting a circus performance or menagerie, and for violating this act, parties guilty of same, shall be subject to the same penalties, to be collected in the same way, as for circus and menagerie exhibitions."

Those government officials of today who would prosecute organized medicine as a monopoly in restraint of trade would have looked with satisfaction on the resolution "That every practicing physician and surgeon, no matter what his education or ——— in the State, shall become a member of one of said Associations, and before the Clerk of the District Court in any county shall register any physician or surgeon, and issue a certificate, as provided for in the first section of this act, there shall be presented to said clerk a certificate, signed by the President and countersigned by the Secretary of the Medical Association of said county, certifying that the physician or surgeon applying for said certificate is a member, in good standing, of the Medical Association of said county."

The Committee on Special Legislation also took up the question of vital statistics, with a recommendation that the "Legislature be memorialized to pass a law requiring a permanent record of all marriages, births and deaths occurring in each county, to be kept in the records of the District Court of said county." The recording of such data was not new in Texas, since in 1828 in Austin's Colony the town council every six months was required to "form a statistical account of the municipality," and every three months to "call on the curate of any parish for a note of those born, married and dead, specifying the sexes, ages," etc.[8] However, this committee in 1874 first brought the subject before the Texas State Medical Association.

The Legislature, however, did not look with favor on the suggested amendments. As a matter of fact, no changes were made in

[7] See Appendix II, where the act is reproduced.
[8] Barker, in *Southwestern Historical Quarterly*, XXI (1919–20), 300.

the act of 1873 until 1876, and then the changes were largely in the direction of clarification and abbreviation. One amendment required holders of medical diplomas to take the examination along with those with certificates. The subjects covered in the examination were named as anatomy, physiology, pathological anatomy and pathology, surgery, obstetrics, and chemistry, "said examination to be thorough"; and the fee was raised to fifteen dollars.

The usual array of resolutions found their way to the floor, some to be given serious consideration, some to lose themselves in a committee appointed on the spur of the moment. Dr. Ashbel Smith asked the Association to use its influence in getting a legislative appropriation for the Galveston Medical College. One resolution deplored the discrimination as to rank and pay which the United States Army practiced against its medical officers. One member wanted the Legislature to make the state medical association a state board of health with authority to create county boards of health. The members of the state association were urged to use their efforts to have the American Medical Association meet in Houston the following year. There was some discussion "on the necessity of securing suitable rooms in advance for the use of the Association and its committees." The first mention of a library was made at this 1874 meeting, when a committee was appointed to inquire into the expediency of creating one.

Yellow fever came in for much discussion, seven papers being offered on this subject. These early doctors were wholly in the dark as to the cause of the disease. As Dr. Greensville S. Dowell put it: "From whence it came, or whither it is going, none of us know." However, he was later to write: "There must be some other condition besides mere personal contagion to produce the disease. . . . This cause is animalcular [objects] . . . too small to be observed with any instruments we now have." [9] In addition, the importance of hygiene and sanitation was mentioned, and the occurrence of cases in proximity to swamps was noted. There were those who thought quarantine was essential. Dr. J. F. Matchett was thinking clearly when he wrote: "I have never known to my own satisfaction a single instance where quarantine ever prevented the prevalence and spread of yellow fever. . . . The time has arrived, or must very soon come, when cities must look to themselves for the cause of yellow fever, and not to distant places, and to the scavenger and

[9] *Yellow Fever and Malarial Diseases* (Philadelphia, 1876), 9, 13.

health officer rather than to quarantine, for exemption. It is not a foreign invader, but a domestic enemy." In Galveston, the Chamber of Commerce appointed five lawyers to investigate and report on the subject of yellow fever; this prompted the suggestion that after consulting his lawyer on this subject a patient should "sleep sounder in his supposed security." All types of remedies were advocated. Calomel, quinine, Dover's powders, and brandy found wide acceptance. During the epidemics, which came practically every year, panic, terror, and confusion caused the towns to be practically deserted. And well might this result ensue, for the mortality rate was very high. Yet the doctors stayed on and did their work with confidence and hope. One man summarized the situation thus: "Give me cases in midsummer, and two good nurses to each case, and I will obligate to cure nine out of ten; but with inexperienced and careless nurses, and cases such as we often have in Texas, late in the fall, after the northers set in, and in open rooms, you might safely reckon your loss nine out of ten, or one half at least."

Some of the other papers presented at this important Dallas meeting were "Atheromatous or Calcareous Degeneration of the Aorta" and "Multilocular Ovarian Tumor," by Thomas D. Wooten; "A Case of Imperforate Anus and Rectum," by J. T. Field; "Stone in the Bladder, of Large Size, Complicated with Urethral Fistules. Lithotomy-Recovery," by L. S. Rayfield; "Report on Strabismus," by John S. Dunn; and "Radical Cure for Hernia," by Greensville S. Dowell. This last paper, which was in advance of the surgical thought of that day, was expanded two years later into a book.[10]

One rather odd report was sent in by Dr. A. R. Kilpatrick, of Navasota. After mentioning certain factual data about the annual rainfall for several years and warning that a return of a cholera epidemic could be predicted that year, the report continued with a description of the autopsy findings on the celebrated Siamese twins: "The umbilicus is on the band—same on either abdomen, therein resembling Adam and Eve more than any other of their descendants. The ensiform cartilages joined across the band; so do the livers and the peritoneum; many blood vessels and nerves. Eng's liver is on the left side, so as to unite with Chang's." The Siamese twins, after a rather tumultuous domestic life, had died in North Carolina two months before, and an autopsy had been per-

[10] *A Treatise on Hernia* (Philadelphia, 1876).

56

formed by a committee of surgeons from the College of Physicians of Philadelphia. The post-mortem findings were almost exactly those reported by Dr. Kilpatrick, who doubtless got his information from the lay press.

Dr. B. E. Hadra,[11] of San Antonio, reported six cases of trichiniasis in which a microscope was used to identify the "threadlike, spiral and rounded worms" in the uncooked pork which the patients had eaten. This 1874 report is one of the early references to the use of the microscope in Texas.

President D. F. Stuart in his address made the customary remarks about medical ethics, legislation for the control of medical practice, the creation of a satisfactory board of health, medical education, and the publication of a medical journal. He devoted considerable space to the question of treatment of disease. He felt that many theories of disease, "most of them the productions of Northern writers," were vague and unsettled. He thought that the remedies for Texas ailments would be found in the vegetable and mineral kingdom of Texas and that research would reveal them. In support of his belief, he quoted Henry Ward Beecher as saying "that among the roots and herbs to be found in nearly every grave-yard, there is a remedy, if only ascertained, which would have relieved over half the victims who were laid to rest in death's embrace beneath its green sod."

The new officers were A. G. Clopton, Jefferson, president; T. D. Wooten, Paris, first vice-president; M. H. Oliver, Dallas, second vice-president; W. A. East, Austin, recording secretary; J. E. Lay, Hallettsville, corresponding secretary; and J. Larendon, Houston, treasurer. The new president adjourned the meeting with "a few farewell sentiments, which in their entirety constituted a rhetorical gem of rare beauty and polish," to meet in Austin the following year.

[11] Hadra will long be remembered in gynecological circles. In 1888 he published, at Philadelphia, one of his two books, *Lesions of the Vaginal and Pelvic Floor*, a signpost in the history of American gynecology. "While Emmet had recognized the importance of the fascia of the anterior vaginal wall, no great progress was made until Hadra of Texas, in 1888, first used the method of flap-splitting and of elevating the bladder. . . . Hadra (1888) and Sanger in Germany and later Watkins in America did pioneer work in the field of plastic surgery of the anterial vaginal wall."—Richard A. Leonardo, *History of Gynecology* (New York, 1944), 324, 391. The work of Hadra was "the beginning of modern operations for prolapse," says Howard C. Taylor, Jr. ("Notes on Fifty Years of Progress in Gynecology," *American Journal of Surgery*, LI [1941], 106).

VIII

Slow Progress, 1875–79

THE 1875 MEETING, at Austin, continued the momentum which the Association had gained at Dallas. The sessions were held in the Chamber of the House of Representatives, use of the hall having been granted by an act of the Legislature. This was in the old capitol, which was burned six years later. Much of medical importance had happened since that band of pioneers had organized the Association in Austin twenty-two years before.

President A. G. Clopton called the meeting to order, and after prayer by the Rev. Thomas B. Lee of St. David's Episcopal Church, Dr. W. A. Morris of the Committee on Arrangements gave the welcoming address. He said he had "no elaborate speech" but proceeded to unburden himself of more than two thousand apt words. He closed his address with an oratorical flourish which is worth repeating: "When your friends are falling around you like autumn leaves, and the bravest hearts quail and flee from the carnival of death, duty and your love for humanity will keep you at your post. To the hero of the battle-field, poetry and oratory make their richest offerings, and columns point to the clouds of Heaven, on which are inscribed their grandest triumphs. The hero of the pestilence finds his reward in the consciousness of a noble discharge of duty, and in the heartfelt tribute of his patients—the rich and the poor— by whose bedside, in the lone vigils of the night, the silent victory has been fought and won."

The treasurer presented an itemized report showing a deficit of $4.35, which he himself had paid to keep the finances of the organization clear. The principal item of expenditure, $435.00, was for printing the *Proceedings* of the Association; all other expenditures amounted to only $14.75. Making this sacrifice year after year in order that the *Proceedings* might be published, these men left a historical and scientific heritage of great value.

For the first time the secretary made a formal report on the problems of the Association, some of which have continued into more modern days. Naturally, all his records had to be kept in longhand. He took care of the correspondence and made two copies of the minutes, which had grown to an annual thirty-five or forty pages, one for his records and one for the printer. For all this work, it had been the custom in previous years to award the secretary an honorarium of $50.00 or $100.00. At the Austin meeting the bylaws were amended so that he would be paid $200.00 at each annual session.

The Committee on Publishing also had its trials. Copies of some papers could not be obtained. One paper by a Galveston doctor was not legible because it was "badly damaged by the great storm." But the main complaint of the committee had to do with calligraphy:

The Committee desires to call the special attention of the members to a very prevalent and a very bad habit amongst them: negligence in composition. We are aware that this is a common, and to some extent, an excusable fault in medical men, whose attention is constantly distracted by the multitude and diversity of claims upon it: but there is, nevertheless, a limit beyond which indulgence to delinquencies of this class ought not to extend; and some of our contributors have, at least, attained that limit. Defects resulting from inattention in this respect, and a penmanship that would defy the skill of an expert in cryptography, have added greatly to the labors of the Committee, and will doubtless be found to be the source of most of its errors.[1]

At the Austin session, rather extensive entertainment was afforded. Governor Richard Coke gave a reception at the Mansion on the second night for members of the Association and for "citizens and strangers." The Travis County Medical Society gave a banquet

[1] Some years before, Oliver Wendell Holmes was bringing similar complaints before the American Medical Association: "It is by indirect means, rather than by direct contrivances, that this desirable object [the improvement of our medical literature] is to be promoted; by elevating the standard of education; by the stern exclusion of unworthy articles from medical journals; by the substitution of original for parasitical authorship; and by introducing such a tone of general scholarship and scientific cultivation that the finer class of intellects may be drawn towards the ranks of the medical profession."—Davis, *History of the A.M.A.*, 61.

at the Raymond House on the third night, and a ball was held on the final night. Dr. M. A. Taylor and Mr. G. B. Zimpleman also entertained for the visiting doctors.

It had become the custom to invite to the annual sessions several nationally eminent physicians. This year Dr. J. Marion Sims, of Alabama and New York, was invited; but he declined in these intimate words: "I thank you very much for your kind invitation to your next annual meeting, to be held at Austin, on the sixth of April. Nothing could give me more pleasure than to be with you then, but unfortunately, it is impossible. I am bound to your State by many ties of kindred and friendship; Walker County contains the remains of my honored father, and the cemetery at Galveston those of my son. One of my sisters, and her children and grandchildren lie amongst you, and I have many friends throughout the State. But my greatest happiness in visiting you—were it possible—would consist in meeting the Texas State Medical Association." [2]

Numerous memorials to the Legislature were adopted at the 1875 meeting. Some of them dealt with the sale of poisons, the levying of a heavy occupation tax on all venders of patent medicines, the establishment of a state university with a medical department, and proper qualifications of druggists. Discussions on sundry subjects arose. One man raised the question whether emasculation as a treatment of insanity could be recommended. Greater discussion followed the report of Dr. J. H. Sears on "Psychological Medicine." This paper was discussed by fifteen doctors, among whom was little agreement. Dr. Ashbel Smith said that psychology is "the doctrine of the soul, and as medical men, we have but little to do with it." Dr. L. Hudspeth thought that "somebody was suffering with inflammation of the imagination, superinduced by the electric fluids operating on the cerebro-spinal-axis."

The presidential address of Dr. A. G. Clopton followed the pattern and upheld the standard of his predecessors. He made a short but adequate survey of the history of medicine, with apt references to Homer, Hippocrates, Socrates, Galen, Newton, and Franklin. He knew the contributions of Michael Servetus to our knowledge of the circulation of the blood. He realized that he was living in

[2] Granville S. Sims was in Paris with his father during the Civil War. There he was most unhappy. "All he seemed to desire was to get over to Texas to help the cause" of the Confederacy. He contracted yellow fever in Havana and died twenty-four hours after he arrived in Galveston.—Seale Harris, *Woman's Surgeon: The Life Story of J. Marion Sims* (New York, 1950), 243.

an age of comparatively rapid progress: "Now, brought closer together by the progress of the age, every avenue of instruction and association is open to us. Medical literature is conveniently accessible, and interchange of medical experience and observation enjoyed. . . . We contemplate with pride the rapid advance of the medical and every other science, during this enlightened age, for which all former ages have come and gone, when national intercourse has become almost universal." On the history of medicine he spoke philosophically:

In the onward march of humanity it has advanced, "pari passu," with the other departments of knowledge. It has had its periods of advance and decline; of light and darkness; of shadow and sunshine; of calm and storm, in common with every department of human progress. When we turn our eyes over the course of the human race, we observe it marked by various fortunes. Nations have risen, acted their part and fallen; freedom has had brief triumphs and retired; kings have feasted at regal and sumptuous tables and fed upon grass as an ox. Epochs of light and darkness have succeeded each other, and through all the intermediate stages of intelligence and civilization, medicine has shared the fate of all things connected with humanity, and depended upon human labor and research for its progress and development.

And Dr. Clopton knew that medicine must continue its progress: "The facilities for diagnosing disease will be further extended; every department of medical science will continue to advance, and above all, the cause of disease, now so veiled in mystery, will be well understood by a future age as the treatment to be pursued." There was much of idealism in the address. Great sacrifice, high estimation of ethics, self-respect, retiring modesty, sympathy with humanity, discipline to duty, dignity of character, a heart to love—these, said Dr. Clopton, are the qualities that characterize the true physician.

Set apart from those who were much in the public eye or who held important office were many obscure doctors in Texas, who, in their limited spheres, held high the ideals of medicine. One of these was Dr. Sherman Goodwin, of Victoria (1814–81), who confided to his journal the innermost thoughts of his heart, not dreaming that they would ever find their way to the printed page. In summarizing the obligations and rewards of the physician, he had this to say:

In time he must rise up to enlistment against powers of evil, the defeating forces which make men go slowly, stumble, think unsurely, stop their thinking, lie down dead. Then we join the powers that cleanse and build; and though man cannot here be perfectly cleansed or his building last beyond his season, it is something to have labored for the betterment of life.

Finally, through the very pursuit of science, the doctor comes into the service of God. In every place where his step is uncertain and his way darkened, he must be with God or there is no going.[3]

Some of the papers presented at this 1875 meeting were "Report on the Science and Progress of Medicine," by D. R. Wallace, Waco; "Climatology and Epidemics," by John H. Pope, Marshall; "Malarial Haematuria," by T. J. Heard, Galveston; "Tetanus Treated with Chloral Hydrate," by O. H. Seeds, Columbia; "Hydrophobia," by W. J. Burt, Austin; "Report on Surgery," by Thomas D. Wooten, Austin; "Esmarch's Bloodless Operation," by M. A. Taylor, Austin; "Skin-Grafting and Transplantation of Skin, for the Relief of Scars Following Burns, Etc.," by C. W. Trueheart, Galveston; "Carcinoma and Stricture of the Rectum," by Hillary Ryan, Galveston; "Lithotomy, Operation under Extraordinary Disadvantages," by H. Ryan, Galveston; and "State Board of Health," by R. H. Harrison, Columbus.

The "Report on Surgery," by Thomas D. Wooten, was most scholarly. His language was clear and his approach was forward-looking. In great detail he outlined the known facts about the histological changes that take place in inflammation, quoting Cohnheim, Billroth, and Burton Sanderson.

The essence of inflammation, therefore, is not to be ascribed to the action of the vaso-motor nerves, dilatation of vessels, rapid flow of blood, or subsequent contraction of the vessels; but is due to some unknown change or alteration in the walls of the capillaries of the affected part. . . . The exuded *liquor sanguinis* that occurs in the reparative process contains the fibrin-producing elements of the blood; certain conditions determine the coagulation, upon which depends the subsequent capillary and granulation tissue formation. In a stratum of this coagulated fibrin, capillaries and granulating tissue cells form, the latter spring up around the newly formed capillaries, and by the coalescence of capillaries, through the medium of these granulating cells wounds are closed and parts healed.

[3] Quoted by Harry Ransom, in "Sherman Goodwin, Texas Physician, 1814–1881," *Southwestern Historical Quarterly*, LV (1952), 339–40.

This is not the full story as we know it today, but it is certainly a long scientific step forward.

Although Lord Lister had published his paper "On the Antiseptic Principle in the Practice of Surgery" eight years before, little or nothing had been written on it in Texas. Dr. Wooten was thoroughly familiar with the cleansing of wounds and the use of carbolic acid dressings as advocated by Lister. By way of emphasizing the new information about inflammation and the new methods of combating it, he has this to say: "Revolutions never go backward. I, for one, do not expect old hoary headed Time ever to wave back upon posterity the old antiphlogistic regime. It is a historical page in medicine, and belongs to the archives of a period more benighted than the present."

In his report, Dr. Wooten considered many aspects of surgery in more or less detail: diseases of the joints, club foot, aneurism, lithotomy, ovariotomy, surgery of the rectum, and anesthesia. He advocated introduction of the whole hand into the rectum as an aid to diagnosis. He appreciated that ether was a safer anesthetic than chloroform, although he felt that chloroform was safe in capable hands, such as his. The intravenous injection of chloral hydrate to produce anesthesia was reported to be satisfactory. Drowsiness of two days' duration was noted in some cases.

Dr. Ryan's lithotomy was most unusual. Some months before, the patient had passed a squirrel tail into his urethra, and a large stone had formed around it in the bladder. Two operations were performed. The first was done at midnight with the assistance of three boys, and an ordinary pocketknife was used to incise the perineum. A finger was introduced into the bladder and a stone about one inch in diameter was removed. A larger stone was left in the bladder because the amateur anesthetist thought the patient was dying. Greater preparation was made for the second operation: "We passed the director into the bladder and made an incision into the urethra, passed a probe bistoury in, as before, and made the cut in the same direction, to the left of the rectum. As soon as the cut would permit the finger to pass into the bladder, the director was withdrawn and the finger used. The opening was enlarged very slowly and carefully until we had extended it for about two inches and a half; we then, with some difficulty, drew out a stone one inch and a half thick by three and a half long, and *in it the squirrel's tail,* of about five inches in length, one inch and a half bent back on itself. It was in a good state of preservation and looked very much like salted meat." The patient was not seen for ten days. Then he was found up and around, "passing his water the natural way." [4]

Dr. R. H. Harrison's report on a state board of health was made as chairman of the committee appointed at the preceding meeting to consider the possibility of having the Legislature pass an act giving the state medical association the powers of a state board of health. The proposed bill submitted by the committee was very inclusive; it provided for the incorporation of the Association, the investing of the Association with all the rights and duties of a board of health, and the appointment of all subordinate boards of health. The subject was brought before a special committee from both legislative bodies, of which Dr. C. B. Stewart, of Montgomery County, was secretary. The bill passed the House of Representatives, but no action was taken by the Senate. Some thought the bill failed because too much power in the hands of "visionary, impracticable members of the medical profession might prove troublesome or aggressive." "A self-constituted committee of three Homeopaths, alone assailed the policy with about as much vigor and as little discretion as the distinguished bovine did the locomotive, when he undertook to butt it off the bridge." It may be that with the Senate "moneyed considerations were evidently considered superior to the protection of life or the preservation of health." But Dr. Harrison was not discouraged. The state association would continue to be interested in the mental and bodily infirmities of the people of Texas, "and it is the province of State Medicine to lay the foundation for their cure." This is an early use of the term "state medicine," though of course in a different sense from that which it has today.

In 1874, fourteen delegates to the American Medical Association were elected. Of these, five attended: Drs. Richard W. Allen, Thomas J. Heard, James W. McLaughlin, J. M. Morrison, and M. A. Taylor. Dr. E. T. Easley represented the Dallas City Medical

---

[4] Some years later, Dr. Frank Paschal had a similar experience while he was practicing in Mexico. A man inserted a piece of chewing gum into his urethra as a contraceptive device. Later on when he looked for the gum, it was not to be found. His first thought was to consult a doctor, and the doctor's first thought was to pass a sound. The gum was not recovered. A year later, Dr. Paschal removed a large stone from the man's bladder, and at its center was the much-sought piece of chewing gum.

Society, and Dr. H. W. Brown, the Waco Medical Association. The next year the number of delegates to the national association was twenty-one, nearly half the number in attendance at the annual state session; and seven of these attended: Drs. J. M. Callaway, J. M. Fort, S. G. Haynie, J. Larendon, G. C. McGregor, W. H. Park, and J. W. Stalnaker. Dr. Easley again represented Dallas. Dr. W. E. Saunders was a delegate from the Grayson County Medical Society, and Dr. J. M. Willis, from the Waco Medical Association. In 1876, delegates were assigned to state associations of Alabama, Arkansas, and Virginia, and to the International Medical Congress. Apparently, very few of these delegates fulfilled their assignments. Of the fourteen delegates to the American Medical Association in 1876, only two attended: Drs. Greensville Dowell and L. E. Locke. Presenting a paper on hernia, Dr. Dowell exhibited the instruments which he had devised and reported ninety-six operations and eighty cures.[5] In 1877 and 1878, times were hard in Texas. Railroad fare to Chicago and Buffalo must have been generally prohibitive, for only one delegate was present each year: Drs. A. E. Carothers and James S. Bailey, respectively. By 1879, the state association was well represented by Drs. James B. Adair, H. W. Brown, J. M. Willis, and Greensville Dowell. At this meeting, his third, Dr. Dowell was listed as a permanent member. Nowhere is there a record of any of these delegates bringing back reports of the meetings of the national organization.

The officers elected for the coming year were H. W. Brown, Waco, president; L. S. Rayfield, Jefferson, first vice-president; M. A. Taylor, Austin, second vice-president; R. H. Harrison, Columbus, third vice-president; J. Larendon, Houston, treasurer; and W. A. East, Austin, secretary. Marshall was selected as the place of the next meeting, to be held on the first Tuesday in April, 1876.

The tenth annual session convened in the Opera House at Marshall on April 4. Marshall at the time had a population of about five thousand. Four years before, a traveler had given this description of the town: "Almost every house is surrounded by a lot adorned with trees and flowers. The streets are broad and spacious and the population somewhat exclusive. The public men are known for their talents and culture."[6]

[5] *Transactions of the A.M.A.*, 1876, p. 506.
[6] John W. Forney, *What I Saw in Texas* (Philadelphia, 1872), 7.

In his welcoming address, Dr. E. P. M. Johnson indicated that East Texas was still recovering from the Civil War and Reconstruction: "We present you with the freedom of our city. You have the privilege of walking our streets, entering our homes, and sharing at our hands such fare as misfortune has left us. Welcome, thrice welcome to Marshall." Dr. D. W. Yandell, a prominent visitor from Louisville, was introduced.[7] He replied happily thus: "You are the most liberal people I ever met. You offer your hearts, your hands, your halls and your streets. When I received your letter inviting me to your Association, my wife was not willing for me to come, fearing I would not return." Dr. Yandell later addressed the Association on "The Present Mode of Treating Syphilis." Unfortunately, the paper was not published in the *Proceedings*. He praised the other papers and was granted an abstract of them for his journal.

Telegrams greeting their brethren of the Lone Star State were received from the state medical associations of Kentucky and Tennessee, both in session at the time, and reciprocal messages were sent to these two organizations. Telegrams or letters were read from Drs. J. Marion Sims; Paul Eve, of Tennessee; Hunter McGuire, of Virginia; Samuel D. Gross, of Pennsylvania; and ten others.

The treasurer made his report, with the usual close call in making ends meet. This time there was a positive balance of $21.90. The Committee on Publishing precariously but persistently continued to come out with the *Proceedings* of the preceding year. The cost was $639.32, and only $504.75 was available. Even this latter sum

---

[7] A teacher of the first rank, Yandell was president of the American Medical Association in 1871 and medical director on the staff of General Albert Sidney Johnston.—Kenneth W. Rawlings, *Medicine and Its Development in Kentucky* (Louisville, 1940), 107. Yandell attended General Johnston at the Battle of Shiloh when the General's right popliteal artery was torn by a Minié ball. "Dr. Yandell, his surgeon, had attended his person during most of the morning; but, finding a large number of wounded men, including many Federals, at one point, General Johnston ordered Yandell to stop there, establish a hospital, and give them his services. He said to Yandell: 'These men were our enemies a moment ago, they are prisoners now; take care of them.' Yandell remonstrated against leaving him, but he was peremptory, and the doctor began his work. He saw General Johnston no more. Had Yandell remained with him, he would have had little difficulty with the wound. It was this act of unselfish charity which cost him his life."—William Preston Johnston, *The Life of General Albert Sidney Johnston* (New York, 1880), 615.

was made possible only after five members had advanced $10.00 each to insure publication.

The following local medical associations became affiliated with the state organization at the 1876 meeting: Dallas County Medical Association, Ellis County Medical Society, Gregg County Medical Society, Guadalupe County Medical Association, Hays County Medical Association, Jasper County Medical Association, Limestone County Medical Association, Medical Association of the City of Dallas, Nacogdoches County Medical Association, Newton County Medical Association, Panola County Medical Society, Texarkana Medical Society, and Titus County Medical Society.

In the 1876 *Proceedings*, for the first time, an alphabetical list of members was published, giving the post office and county of residence. There were 147 names on this list, these having paid their dues. However, on the treasurer's books there were 186 names and 20 county and city societies.

The only legislative matter to come up at the Marshall meeting was a further report on the board of health problem by Dr. R. H. Harrison, who had done much previous work on the subject. He advised the Association to await a more propitious moment. "The time has been," he said, "when our law-makers were expected to be possessed of some of the elements of statesmanship; to be able to discriminate as to measures necessary or likely to confer benefits upon their constituency; but that time is passed, and the average legislator now waits as long as possible 'to see which way the cat will jump' before he ventures 'to make up his mind' upon the merits of any question whatever."

A marked innovation in 1876 was the presentation of cases for operation. "Dr. T. D. Wooten, of Austin, assisted by Dr. A. E. Carothers of Austin, removed a part of the upper maxillary bone from a boy sixteen years of age, in presence of the Association." Dr. T. D. Manning "operated for cataract of left eye, linear incision, upon a negro."

It has been repeatedly emphasized that these doctors of the past century were men of education and culture. To them the Bible and Shakespeare and the classics were as real as Gray's *Anatomy* and Gross's *Pathological Anatomy* and Flint's *Practice*. Little short of startling was some of the material that was offered. For instance, at this 1876 meeting Dr. A. R. Kilpatrick, of Navasota, presented the

Cherokee alphabet, systematically arranged, demonstrating the sounds and showing upper- and lower-case characters. In addition, he gave "a brief description of the oldest medical work in the world, written by Hermes Trismegistus, 1500 years before Christ; procured at Thebes in Egypt in 1872, by George Moritz Ebers, the distinguished Archaeologist of Berlin, Prussia; with a brief sketch of William Caxton, the printer."

Each year a committee was appointed to select a prize essay on an assigned subject. This year the subject was the *Eucalyptus globulus,* and the winner was Dr. R. L. H. Bibb. The eucalyptus was known as "the fever-destroying tree." Although cinchona bark and its derivatives had long been available, there was a desire to eradicate malaria and kindred diseases by rendering inert "the miasmatic agency supposed to be the cause of fevers in low, wet and marshy districts." The eucalyptus tree was reputed to accomplish this purpose in two ways: "First, by the far spreading roots of this gigantic tree acting like a sponge, as it were, and thus pumping up water and draining the ground; and, secondly, by emitting odorous antiseptic emanations from its leaves." The thirty-two pages of this presentation, after a lapse of seventy-four years, may at first glance appear futile. Yet this paper is evidence that these men were seriously concerned with the problem and were giving their best efforts to its solution. This theory, moreover, was a step in the direction of drainage, screens, and insecticides.

Other papers on a wide range of subjects were read. Dr. W. J. Burt reported on the difference in resistance to disease between the white and Negro races. He felt that the explanation was to be found in lack of vital power and nervous endurance, in less lung capacity, and in the smaller brain of the Negro. Dr. A. R. Kilpatrick had some suggestions about the medicinal value of certain Texas plants. Among others, he recommended the common cocklebur as a vesicant, as an antidote for snakebite, and as a remedy in all urinary affections. Dr. B. F. Eads made a report on three cases of diphtheria which required tracheotomy. Dr. G. W. Holcom discussed two cases of resection of the head of the femur. Other papers had to do with imperforate hymen, retention of dead fetus in the uterus, difficult labor in a woman with double vagina, and lithotomy.

Dr. John H. Pope gave an estimable report "On the Science and Progress of Medicine." He was interested in the cause and treat-

68

ment of infectious diseases. "The theory of a *contagium vivum* as the cause of the acute Infectious Diseases," he said, "is constantly gaining favor. This doctrine has risen and sunk and risen again, in the sea of medical opinion, bringing, each time that it comes to the surface, new facts to buoy it up. Some observers claim to have found certain low organisms in the blood of patients suffering with certain of the infectious diseases. Others acknowledge their presence, but deny their significance and say they are accidental. But, if we remember, the itch mite, when first discovered, was said to be an accidental accompaniment of scabies; now it is acknowledged to be the sole and sufficient cause of this disease." As to specific therapy, he might have been hopeful, but he retained his doubts. He quoted Sir William Jenner [8] to the effect that "there will never be such a discovery as a cure for an acute infectious disease, after its action is once established in the system. That is, no remedy will ever be able to shorten the natural duration of such a disease as Typhoid Fever."

Dr. Pope called attention to the growing popularity of hypodermic medication, predicting that "the time is not far distant when no physician's armamentarium will be considered complete without the *Hypodermic Syringe*. The most recent application of this instrument is for the purpose of giving nutritious substances. Some of the experiments recently published are interesting on this point. Cod Liver oil is considered the substance best adapted to this plan. Considerable quantities of it can be inserted into the connective tissue, without evil consequences; and the biliary constituents of the oil are an advantage toward its assimilation. The demonstration of the feasibility of this means of nourishing the body would create quite a sensation in the medical world." [9]

The importance of accurate records was a matter of concern to Dr. Pope. "Every lover of the profession of medicine," he advised, "should be a careful observer and an accurate recorder of his observations. The blanks, now published for this purpose, render this duty light, compared with what it used to be. Yet, most of us are derelict in this very important matter; and we can hardly compute

[8] Not to be confused with Edward Jenner.

[9] Francis Rynd, of Great Britain, first employed hypodermic injections in 1845. The hypodermic syringe was introduced into the United States in 1856 by Fordyce Barker.

how much such neglect, on the part of the mass of medical men, contributes to the struggle medicine has to make in her efforts to advance."

In his presidential address, Dr. H. W. Brown paid high tribute to his predecessors:

The prime movers in state organization felt, evidently, as we must today, that nothing of which we have a right to expect great results, can be accomplished short of labor, self-sacrifice and constant vigilance. We note, with interest, their stirring appeal to the laborers in this common field to come up to the work, to fall into line at roll call, standing shoulder to shoulder to give aid in the great battle for truth and right. We must continue the bugle note till the scattered forces of our order are marshaled under the catholic banner of true scientific medicine. . . . Have they failed in their purpose? Have these good seed been cast upon barren soil? or been trodden under foot by an unappreciating profession? Not entirely, we feel sure. The rewards have not been equal to our wishes—have not fully met the expectations of the more sanguine, perhaps. But see, in the growth of this body, the increasing interest in its action—the swelling numbers of county associations—the better working of its committees, the number of interesting reports, able, exhaustive, voluminous.

After mentioning the great need for a state university with an adequate medical department and for a state medical journal, he continued: "There are other obligations upon us, such as spring from a love of truth and science, devotion to the sacred principles of our calling; those which are born of common effort to the same great end, reflecting mainly upon the credit, character and status of the profession itself; and those which are evolved by professional attainment, and called into exercise by due sense of obligation to our race, the dictates of humanity, as taught of God and illustrated by the life and example of the Great Physician, the Son of Righteousness, the brightness of whose example continues to illuminate the pathway of the true physician with lines of never fading light."

The type of advertisements carried in the *Proceedings* is of interest. In 1875, Reed & Carnick were the only advertisers. One and one-half pages were devoted to Lactopeptine as an aid to digestion. The next year twenty-five advertisements were carried on nine pages. A variety of business enterprises was represented: banks, drugstores, insurance agencies, restaurants, a bookstore, a livery stable, an insurance agency, and a land agency. Sharp & Dohme had a full page, with aromatic cod liver oil as the most promising item. Fluid extract of damiana was offered as a new aphrodisiac. The Baltimore College of Dental Surgery was reminding the readers that it was the oldest dental college in the world. Aloe & Hernstein, of St. Louis, were advertising Tiemann's "celebrated surgical instruments" and Carpenter's improved saddlebags.

Officers elected for the coming year were R. H. Harrison, Columbus, president; John H. Pope, Marshall, first vice-president; Thomas W. Wiley, Dallas, second vice-president; and W. H. Park, Tyler, third vice-president. W. A. East was continued as secretary and J. Larendon as treasurer. Galveston was chosen as the next meeting place.

At the 1877 meeting of the Association, in Artillery Hall at Galveston, Dr. Greensville Dowell delivered the address of welcome. He spoke of medical conditions in Galveston and then enlarged on the prospects of his city and his state. "It is no stretch of the imagination to say the State of Texas will hold and support 40,000,000 people and not be as thickly inhabited as France or Belgium. That Galveston will be as large as New York is now, and railroads will carry coffee and sugar from here to Alaska by our projected railroads, almost on a straight line, and bring gold and silver from those distant regions. We will have others going to the City of Mexico and the Pacific ocean. We certainly have a bright future before us."

This meeting was notable for the controversies that flared up. When the chairman of the Board of Censors reported favorably on the application for membership of Dr. W. H. Dial, of Marshall, Dr. J. H. Pope, of that city, registered vigorous objection. After discussion by six members, the application was recommitted to the Board of Censors, where the matter was apparently dropped. Dial's name does not appear on subsequent rosters of the Association.

A more serious difference of opinion sprang up over some developments regarding boards of medical examiners. The new state constitution (Art. XVI, sec. 31) made this reference to the practice of medicine: "The Legislature may pass laws prescribing the qualifications of practitioners of medicine in this State, and to punish persons for malpractice, but no preference shall ever be given by law to any schools of medicine." The amendments which the Legislature had added to the Medical Practice Act in 1876 were in reality not serious: applicants with diplomas had to take the examinations along with other applicants, and power to appoint the examining boards was shifted from county to district judges. But two judges had appointed "irregular practitioners" to serve on the boards in their district. One of the appointees lived at Austin, and the Travis County Medical Society brought in this resolution: "*Resolved,* That the State Medical Association approve of the action of the Travis County Medical Society, in refusing to co-operate, in any professional manner whatever with irregular practitioners in establishing a mixed Board of Medical Examiners to regulate the practice of medicine and surgery in the State."

Heated discussion of the resolution was continued through seven pages of the *Proceedings* and was participated in by twelve members, six on each side of the argument.[10] Dr. J. H. Sears argued that failure to pass the resolution would besmirch the honor of the medical profession and result in disintegration of the Association. "The light of truth and irresistible principles, that govern the regular practice," declared Dr. George Cupples, "could never be eclipsed by the energies and efforts of all its enemies combined." He could "see no excuse now for the Convention, in the shape the question had taken, to evade its adjudication, and concluded by saying that if the relationship with the American Medical Association was to be kept up, the Convention was bound to sustain the resolution." Dr. R. M. Swearingen was equally emphatic. He "could not rejoice when such men as Dr. Ross [of the Travis County Board], upon whose head the wings of time had already begun to scatter its silver dust, and around whose brow honor had entwined its wreaths, went into the midst of the enemies of truth and aided them in carrying on a warfare with virtue."

Dr. J. B. Robertson felt that passage of the resolution would array the Association against the constitution and laws of the state. He rather wisely observed that "whenever and wherever attempts were made to suppress irregulars, they had been strengthened in their claims for support." Dr. J. H. Pope reminded the gathering that the present law had been drawn up by the Travis County Medical Society, and, to be consistent, the Association should reject the

---

[10] It is worth noting that two Confederate officers on one side of this controversy, Drs. Cupples and Sears, were arrayed against two on the other, Generals Smith and Robertson.

resolution. Dr. Ashbel Smith, small in stature, dignified, and high-tempered, then arose and made this contribution:

The doctors of Texas would not permit a little, insignificant judge at Austin to drive them away from the benefits of a law that sought to protect them. He would have the gentlemen of the Convention to imitate Governor Hampton.[11] If they cannot get all they are entitled to, take what they can get, and get it in installments. Said there was no professional ethics involved in the question before the Convention. The duties of the board were simply ministerial. Liberty had been defined by old Prof. Gregory to be the right to go to hell in any way the traveler in that direction might elect, and so all the people of Texas, in the exercise of their sovereign rights, might patronize, and would patronize, medicine or homoeopathy, just as they might choose to select, and this Convention was powerless to remedy the evil.

The upshot of the matter was a resolution by Dr. Smith to postpone action for six months, the resolution carrying by a vote of 39 to 35. But this resolution was only temporary. The question flared up the next day more violently than ever. When the heated discussion produced a threat to form a rival association, the original resolution upholding the action of the Travis County Medical Society was "carried amid applause." And then Dr. Cupples, Chesterfield-ian gentleman that he was, offered a resolution which absolved Dr. Ross or any other member from censure and smoothed the ruffled feelings of all concerned. The resolution carried by unanimous vote.

In the way of entertainment, the members of the Association attended St. Patrick's Bazaar, a banquet at Turner Hall tendered by the ladies of the Baptist Church, and a picnic given by the Military Battalion "on the narrow gauge railroad."

The secretary's report indicated progress. His roster showed a membership of 262, a gain of 122 over the preceding year. The following local societies were accepted: Smith County Medical Society, Limestone County Medical Society, Western Texas Medical Association, and the Southwestern Texas Medical Association. The secretary announced that he had received *Transactions* from ten state and local associations. The treasurer's report also showed improvement, receipts being $746.10 and expenditures $669.32, leaving a balance of $76.78.

The papers presented brought up several new subjects: preven-

[11] Wade Hampton, governor of South Carolina, 1876-79.

tive medicine, myocarditis, essential paralysis, cerebral injury, congenital umbilical hernia, uterine fibroid, and Texas as a health resort. A "Report on Ophthalmology and Otology," by Dr. T. D. Manning, shows that diseases of the eye and ear were being segregated as a specialty. Yellow oxide of mercury ointment was justly praised for use in eye infections. Dr. W. J. Burt told how he had reduced the size of a large uterine fibroid by daily injections of three grains of ergotine "over and around the tumor." Over a period of about six months, four hundred grains of ergotine was used, with marked symptomatic improvement. "What more can we expect from treatment than was accomplished in this extreme case?"

Under the heading of "Conservative Surgery," Drs. J. W. Fennell and J. M. McKnight reported on their management of a severe injury.

We were telegraphed for on the night of the 24th of December last to attend the wounded from a railroad accident five miles west of the Guadalupe river. Found one man, Henry Miller, aged twenty years, terribly mutilated, but the weather being bitter cold, and the shock very profound, we could only make a superficial examination, stimulate, watch for hemorrhage and for daylight. On Christmas morning, found our patient had rallied pretty well, so we proceeded to the examination, and found the left arm completely crushed at the elbow, and laid open for several inches, with the ends of all the bones smashed. Found also a compound fracture of the left tibia, a little below its middle, with great laceration of the soft parts. Injury seemed to have been done by a bolt driven through the leg, there being open wounds on either side. There was also a compound fracture of the metatarsal bone of the left great toe. The case seemed almost hopeless. The arm, of course, had to come off immediately, and with the kind assistance of Drs. Crawford and Graves we amputated as low down as possible. Notwithstanding the deplorable condition of the leg, we decided to make an attempt to save it, and if it failed we would fall back on our forlorn hope—secondary amputation. The fractures were reduced, and the leg placed on a double-inclined-plane splint. The after treatment consisted in the free use of opiates, moderate stimulation, and good nourishment, with local use of carbolic acid and water dressings thoroughly carried out.

A trying convalescence ensued, but the man "made a good recovery."

Most of the committees, which by now had become rather numerous, made no report at many of the annual meetings. But one com-

74

mittee—that on necrology—reported regularly, for the Grim
Reaper was unceasingly busy. This year Dr. Pinckney, U.S.N.,
gave a eulogy on the life and sacrificial death of Dr. George W.
Peete. After a review of Dr. Peete's life of service, Dr. Pinckney
concluded:

The heroic death was worthy of the life. At a point a little distant from
Galveston, on that fearful night, September 16th, 1875, while the tidal
wave of the gulf stream was pouring its surging billows in relentless fury,
there stood a noble and manly figure, and by its side a bright and lovely
boy of scarce fourteen summers. It was Dr. Peete and his little grandson,
Willie. He had sent his wife to the city, and the boat had returned for
him. As he was about to leave, a man approached and asked the doctor
for his boat to rescue his wife, who was in a dangerous situation. The
doctor knew his own peril, but he said "take it." The man and his wife
were saved, but in the fury of the tempest, rising higher and higher, this
brave health officer, with his devoted grandson, met the fiat of Provi-
dence.

Dr. R. H. L. Bibb gave a twenty-page report on "Preventive Medicine." The burden of his paper was philosophical and speculative;
but, like some of his predecessors, he toyed with the idea that infectious diseases were due to "living germs." "A disease germ," he
ventured, "is a living, solid, insoluble, indiffusible colloidal particle, the smallest quantity of which, when supplied with its proper
pabulum, will grow and multiply, giving rise to millions of little
particles like itself, each particle capable of being transmitted
through certain media to human organisms, and there inducing
the violent perturbation of its specific disease." And then he added:
"There is, therefore, always danger lurking in water liable to con-
tamination from animal matter, and more especially when such
matter contains evacuations from patients suffering from certain
specific diseases, such as cholera or enteric fever."

Very wisely Dr. Bibb realized that in matters of public health,
education is more effective than legislation: "It must ever be borne
in mind that enactment of laws, with penalties prescribed for their
infringement, looking to the protection of the public health, has no
more effect in abolishing the causes of disease than enactment of
penal laws has in suppression of crime. The people cannot be
dragooned into cleanliness, or be made virtuous by police regulations, and hence it is that the most thoughtful among practical re-

formers of the present day base their hopes of sanitary progress on the education of the masses as the real groundwork of national health."

The theme of the presidential address by Dr. R. H. Harrison was medical education. Public confidence in the profession was declining. The cause, he maintained, was to be found in a breakdown of the educational system. The average medical student, after a short course of lectures, enters his name in some reputable physician's office, whereupon he "reads a little, hunts and fishes a good deal, attends a course of lectures and returns to his preceptor with a wise look and assumption of dignity that entitles him to additional professional courtesies." A second course of lectures, duplicate of the first, wins for him his diploma. Can the public be blamed, asked Dr. Harrison, for confusing doctors with charlatans? Those who love the profession for its own sake and who venerate it for its antiquity must insist on premedical preparation and medical facilities commensurate with the lofty aims of the profession. Then the student can take his degree "with credit to himself, honor to the profession and benefit to humanity."

On recommendation of the Committee on Nominations, W. D. Kelly, Galveston, was elected president; George Cupples, San Antonio, first vice-president; R. M. Swearingen, Austin, second vice-president; and J. H. Sears, Waco, third vice-president. The meeting was then adjourned, to meet in San Antonio the first Tuesday in April, 1878.

Economic conditions, which had been bad ever since the Civil War, became worse in the late 1870's. Hard times came to all, including the doctors. The fact that the population of the state doubled between 1870 and 1880 did not alter the situation. The state government met the problem in the only logical way: it reduced expenditures, even in appropriations for public schools.

The Association likewise reduced expenditures because of curtailed income. Membership did not change very much, the roster showing 264 in 1878 and 251 in 1879. But the collected dues decreased markedly: $629.75 in 1878 and $532.63 in 1879. Since the dues were $2.50, it is obvious that an increasing number were delinquent. In the matter of expenditures, the main saving was effected in publishing the *Proceedings*. In 1878, only five hundred copies were published, and in 1879 the prepared papers, the consti-

PAST PRESIDENTS

E. P. Becton, 1885   T. N. Nott, 1886

Sam R. Burroughs, 1887   J. F. Y. Paine, 1888

PAST PRESIDENTS

R. M. Swearingen, 1889   W. P. Burts, 1890

W. H. Wilkes, 1891   J. D. Osborn, 1892

tution and bylaws, and the code of ethics were omitted. Thus the number of pages was reduced from about 240 to 50. In this period of financial stress, advertisements as a source of revenue may have been neglected, since none were carried for several years. Dr. Austin Flint, Jr., of New York, seems to have considered the *Proceedings* a worthy advertising medium; in 1878 he inquired about inserting a notice concerning Bellevue Medical College.

The 1878 meeting assembled at Wolfram's Garden in San Antonio on April 2. From the time thirty-three members answered the initial roll call to the final session, there was nothing to reflect difficult times except the treasurer's report. Dr. Ferdinand Herff welcomed the assemblage with words of pride in the accomplishments of the medical profession of Texas:

The sacred fire of science, which we light today in the backwoods of Texas, will perhaps not dazzle their [distinguished guests'] eyes with its brilliancy, but will certainly warm their hearts and leave a favorable impression of the zeal and harmony pervading this assembly. . . . Good physicians are now counted by the hundreds, and they form a strong body, well able and always ready to fight the good battle of science against quackery and superstition. . . . Many members of this Association have distinguished themselves in practice, and many have written creditable treatises on different subjects. It is true we cannot boast of great medical discoveries or meteor-like theories advanced by members of this Association. But let us have all the advantages which our more fortunate brethren in the older States possess. Let us have hospitals, libraries, laboratories, and museums, and it will not be long before we may enter the arena and win the prize. One thing is certain, we have attempted and achieved, in Texas, everything that was attempted and achieved by others before us. Our reports show that there is no difficult case in medicine, no capital operation, no feat in obstetrics and gynaecology, which has not been successfully mastered by one or another of this Association. Texas is inferior to none in scientific zeal, and superior to many in brotherly feeling existing between its members.

Sixteen new members were admitted, among them a man who was to mean much to organized medicine in Texas: Dr. Frank Paschal, then of Chihuahua, Mexico.

The usual number of resolutions, on various subjects and of varying importance, were passed: that the dues of Dr. R. B. Thomas, of Flatonia, be remitted because of severe injury; that county societies be requested to furnish a list of all practitioners of medicine in their respective counties, classifying them as regular physicians, notorious quacks, or in a doubtful category; that a committee be appointed to consider the propriety of establishing an Association journal; that the Legislature be urged to found a hospital "for the care and treatment of confirmed inebriates"; that members refuse to sign certificates of death until a post-mortem examination had been requested and permitted; and "that the Association express its admiration of Dr. Russell's gallant fight in defending the freedom of thought and speech against the brutal efforts of intolerance." [12]

The custom of inviting guest speakers had not been established, but this year (1878) Dr. S. E. Chaillé, of New Orleans, was present as a delegate from the recently organized Louisiana State Medical Association. He addressed the Association "on many interesting and important subjects." His address was not recorded. Letters and telegrams from eminent doctors in other states were read. Copies of many papers presented or published elsewhere were sent in.

As the *Proceedings* from year to year are studied, it is easily apparent that the papers presented were improving in content. Some of the older concepts were being abandoned, and a more rational approach was being made to the solution of the cause of diseases, notably infectious diseases. Another striking change was in the length of papers; fewer and fewer presentations of twenty and thirty pages were being offered. But at least another generation had to pass before medical speakers were to be convinced of the wisdom of the trite saying that few sinners are converted after the first twenty minutes.

Dr. J. H. Sears, one of the dependable stalwarts of the Association, in his "Report of Committee on Climatology and Epidemics," gave this very sensible summary:

Could we get the State to drain our large swamps, and our land owners generally to adopt a thorough system of drainage; all our citizens to filter their drinking water and pay more attention to cleanliness of homes and persons, and use only wholesome food and drink in moderation; and with better ventilation of their dwellings, we would establish for our State a norm of sanitation, and probably reduce the death rate from 12 or 14 to 2 or 3 per thousand, thus saving to the people the great loss of time, the suffering and the costly expenditures of sickness, and to

[12] Dr. T. S. Russell had come as a delegate from the recently organized Bell County Medical Association. Dr. Russell had been attacked by a mob back in his home county and had been asked to give a statement of his experience.

the State and society the services of many valuable lives. . . . In the name of humanity, we should make constant and loud appeals to our law makers in behalf of the best interests of the people, until our cry is heard and our influence felt and duly acknowledged.

Dr. T. J. Heard, reporting before the Section on Practical Medicine, Materia Medica, and Pathology, called attention to the danger of transmitting "certain taints, syphilis, scrofula, etc." when cowpox vaccination was done from arm to arm. In treating "varicose and chronic ulcers of the leg," he recommended firm application of a strong, elastic bandage. Dr. S. Weir Mitchell only a few months earlier had published his *Fat and Blood, and How to Make Them;* and Dr. Heard was able to bring this book to the attention of the Association.

In his forty-eight-page "Report of Section on State Medicine and Public Hygiene," Dr. A. R. Kilpatrick deplored the nonexistence of a board of health and named those states that had such boards: Alabama, California, Colorado, Georgia, Illinois, Kentucky, Louisiana, Maryland, Massachusetts, Minnesota, Michigan, Mississippi, New Jersey, North Carolina, Tennessee, Virginia, and Wisconsin. He strongly advocated compulsory vaccination, which "protects all alike from pestilence, suffering and death," and "is truly a democratic measure, designed to bestow the greatest freedom and the greatest happiness upon all alike, regardless of place, or position, or race."

Dr. J. T. Field reported having amputated both legs and one arm of a man who had been struck by a railway engine. He had no difficulty with the legs, but massive hemorrhage from the axillary artery during the operation practically exsanguinated the patient. Artificial respiration and alertness, however, saved the man's life. After three attempts to ligate the vessel by means of an aneurism needle, said Dr. Field, "I now requested Dr. Field [erroneous for Dr. S. W. Fields, who assisted] to put a tenaculum between my teeth, my hands being occupied in holding the vessel. I let go, and fortunately succeeded in gigging the vessel with the tenaculum at the first spurt of blood, and Dr. F. secured it by a ligature at the lower border of the first rib." Despite sloughing of all the flaps and a generally turbulent convalescence, the man got well. After three months it was reported that the "wounds all healed. He was getting fat and crawling around first rate."

Dr. T. D. Wooten made a report on two cases in which he ligated the subclavian artery. In one case, disarticulation at the shoulder joint was done. The second case required amputation two days later. Both recovered. Dr. Wooten concluded that "if there is disease or injury in the axillary region necessitating ligation of the subclavian artery, disarticulation at the shoulder is necessitated also, for the safety of the patient." Accompanying his article was a table which records 504 similar cases from five reports, two each from the United States and Germany and one from England, with a mortality of nearly 50 per cent.

Dr. B. E. Hadra advocated diagnostic aspiration and surgical drainage of liver abscess. More radical was his recommendation of aspiration of distended intestines. "From my limited experience," he reported, "a quick relief, without the least harm, is derived from a frequent puncture of the bowels, this giving the gases a free chance of escape."

Dr. W. D. Kelly's presidential address, according to the secretary's report, was "eminently practical, manfully outspoken, and attracted profound attention." Speaking in the shadow of the Alamo, he paid eloquent tribute to the heroes who fell there. "They died for liberty and country," he said, "and strange though it be, no surgeon was there to bind one mortal wound." [13]

Dr. Kelly was the first official to emphasize brevity in the presentation of papers. He set a good example by limiting his address to twelve pages as printed in the *Proceedings,* about half of the previous average. With a subtle blending of apology and diplomacy, he said: "I hope you do not understand me as wishing to clip the wings of young ambition, ready to soar into the giddy and dangerous heights of official recognition, but rather a desire to repress that *cacoethes scribendi,* of which so many perish."

New, too, was his vehement condemnation of the flood of patent-medicine advertisements. The mails groaned under the weight of circulars, and doctors' offices were invaded by annoyingly persistent agents. "We have chemicals showered upon us in resistless fury; are pelted with pills, and carried over the cataract by an overwhelming torrent of liquors, elixirs and fluid extracts, to flounder in a seething and boiling whirlpool more dangerous than the cauldron stirred by the witches in Macbeth. From this dire dilemma we can

[13] This is an error. Dr. Amos Pollard and two or three other doctors made the supreme sacrifice at the Alamo.

be extricated only by the most skillful selection of all that is good, and the sternest rejection of that which should be condemned."

Dr. Kelly made short shrift of Darwin and his theory of evolution: "A Christian, actuated by a sense of true piety and scriptural teaching, stands aghast at so monstrous a doctrine." And yet he upheld the lability of medicine and science. The contributions of each doctor and each generation of doctors, he said, would bring about the eventual triumph of truth. "Restless as the waves of the sea, we beat upon the shores of the unknown, perhaps not the unattainable, and if attrition may wear away the mystic veil that separates from us the undiscovered, we shall be the first at the goal."

Sentiment and eloquence may be out of style in these modern days. May it not be that herein we are the losers? Can it be that our composite soul is so dead that we fail to thrill when we read Dr. Kelly's peroration?

Gentlemen, our profession has had in its ranks orators as accomplished as Walpole, and as passionate as Mirabeau; authors as classic and graceful as Addison; thinkers as profound as Newton; men whose daring skill has been the admiration of mankind. I need not have paused to make this defense of Medicine as a science or an art; in the broad light of its unsurpassed achievements is to be found its amplest vindication. The illustrious names I have cited need no champion; they shrink from no comparison; they demand honor, for it is due. They have won it, and not they alone, when pestilence covered the land, and men and women fled as from the face of death; when cities and empires stood appalled before the avenger; in the palace, in the lazar-house, and the crowded hospital; on the field of carnage, amid the roar of musketry and the thunder of artillery, and the rush of armed men to death; by a bravery and single-hearted devotion to duty, a skill and intelligence so rare as to place them above praise. With a patience unsurpassed, a devotion unequaled, an ardor that would brook no opposition, a Christian philanthropy never excelled, a consecration of the highest intellectual powers to the noblest purposes, they have made Medicine a leading science, and adorned it with the most splendid triumphs.

Some changes in the constitution and bylaws, most of them made at the Galveston meeting in 1877, should here be reviewed. The objects of the Association were enlarged to include proficient organization of the medical profession, the promotion of good relations in the Association, and the encouragement of high standards in every phase of medical endeavor. Membership was opened to "every regularly educated man within the limits of the State, who is a graduate of a regular Medical College in good standing, and who adopts and conforms to the Code of Ethics of the American Medical Association." The time of meeting in the early years had been that of the Grand Lodge of Texas. The change in the bylaws left the time and place of meeting to the annual decision of the Association. Annual dues had been increased from $1.00 to $2.50. The Committee on Nominations was now composed of one member from each county represented. The most important advance was the creation of a Judicial Council of twenty-one members, to be appointed by the Nominating Committee for terms of one, two, and three years. All questions of an ethical or judicial character and all complaints and protests were to be handled by this council, whose decisions were to be final.

The formation of sections of the Association indicated definite progress. Morning sessions were of a general nature. Afternoon meetings were devoted to reports and papers in the separate sections, which were as follows: Practical Medicine, Materia Medica, and Pathology; Obstetrics and Diseases of Women and Children; Surgery and Anatomy; Medical Jurisprudence, Chemistry, and Psychology; State Medicine and Public Hygiene.

This San Antonio session seems to have been most businesslike. The only reference to entertainment was a decision to continue with the business of the Association rather than visit "the [San Pedro] Springs in response to an invitation." The Committee on Nominations brought in three names for each office. Drs. T. D. Wooten and M. A. Taylor withdrew their names as nominees for president, and Dr. George Cupples was elected. It will be recalled that he had served as president in 1853. A similar sequence of events led to the election of R. W. White as first vice-president, W. E. Saunders as second vice-president, and J. T. Field as third vice-president. The efficient services of W. A. East as secretary and J. Larendon as treasurer were acknowledged by their retention in office without a vote's being taken. On written invitation of the Grayson County Medical Society, Sherman was named as the place for the 1879 meeting.

As the decade of the seventies was passing, the effects of the panic of 1873 were being felt less and less in Texas. But business stagnation had not cleared completely, and the physician, then as now, recovered more slowly than the average man of business. The Sherman meeting was rather poorly attended. The exact number present is not recorded, but from the balloting it seems to have been about twenty-five. Very likely the factors of time and distance played their part. Five hundred miles in modern Texas may not seem very far, but in 1879 it meant several days of travel. This decrease in attendance was partly attributable also to stringent economic conditions.

The meeting was presided over by second vice-president W. E. Sanders, the president and first vice-president being unable to attend because of severe illness. Dr. George Cupples, the president, wrote a long letter of regret. He expressed his deep concern about the welfare of the people and the good of the profession. He reminded the Association that funds were lacking to meet publication cost of the *Proceedings* and that it had become "necessary to supply the deficiency from private sources," which no doubt meant that he, Dr. Ferdinand Herff, and a few other members had paid the bill.

Fifteen new members were accepted. Among them, special note should be made of a graduate of the University of Kentucky in 1877: Bacon Saunders, then of Bonham but later of Fort Worth. Three new county societies were admitted: Fayette, Navarro, and Tarrant.

The records are not clear as to what medical subjects were discussed. A report was made on surgery and obstetrics. Two papers were presented on "Sayre's Plaster Cast," one on "Post Partum Hemorrhage," and one on "Intestinal Obstruction." Much of the four days was devoted to discussion of resolutions, communications, and various subjects of general medical interest. Dr. T. C. Richardson, a visitor from New Orleans, proposed a four-state medical association to comprise the states of Louisiana, Mississippi, Arkansas, and Texas. This proposal, on recommendation of a committee, was acted on favorably.

A resolution that a Texas state medical journal be established under the auspices and patronage of the Association and that $300 be set aside each year for this purpose was rejected. No one should have doubted the wisdom of this decision when the income of the Association for that year was only $532. One outraged individual wanted to rebuke the Houston and Texas Central Railroad for its attitude on fees. He felt that "it is unprofessional to allow corporations to dictate to medical men a fee bill." The Judicial Council ruled that all matters pertaining to fees should be handled by the county societies.

One anonymous member, obviously disturbed in conscience or eager to get home, put through a resolution "That this Association regard with disfavor, the custom of physicians, societies or people at our annual meetings, giving expensive entertainments, and we would respectfully request that hereafter no banquet, excursion, or entertainment whatever be extended to the members of the Association." If any particular entertainment provoked such a resolution, it must have been one not on the record. Certainly the complimentary dinner given at this meeting by the Grayson County Medical Society or the proposed trip to "the Springs" at San Antonio could hardly be calculated to raise any serious objection.

The establishment of a medical college in Texas, this time under the auspices of the Texas State Medical Association, came up again. Discussion led to appointment of a committee of six. The following year (1880), the committee asked for further time. While the Association was in session, the Legislature passed an amended medical practice act which found little favor with the medical profession. The secretary was instructed to telegraph Governor O. M. Roberts, urging him to veto the bill. This bill, originally framed by a committee from the Association, had been so changed as to rob it of its efficiency. In his report for the Committee on State Board of Health and Legislation, Dr. T. D. Wooten permitted his disappointment to get the better of him and made some disparaging remarks about the doctors in the Legislature. He spoke of their "short sighted policy and ignorance of the public wants." He referred to them as "hindrances and stumbling blocks to all proper advancement." Dr. J. A. Allen moved that, since Dr. Wooten had cast reflections on physicians in the Legislature, the report be consigned to the wastebasket. The situation was quieted by passage of an amendment to the motion, that the report be returned to Dr. Wooten for revision.

Officers elected for the ensuing year were John H. Pope, Marshall, president; J. F. Matchett, Brenham, first vice-president; S. F. Starley, Corsicana, second vice-president; and S. Eagan, Sherman, third vice-president. Brenham was picked as the place of the next meeting.

IX

Unexampled Prosperity, 1880–84

THE BUSINESS DEPRESSION, which had hung like a pall over the state of Texas since the Civil War, cleared with the coming of the early 1880's, and the state experienced the most prosperous era it had ever known. At the close of the administration of Governor Oran M. Roberts in 1883, the Old Alcalde could report a reduction in the public debt of more than a million dollars, a marked reduction in the annual interest, and the accumulation of a substantial surplus in the treasury. This had been accomplished by the application of economy and good business practices. John Ireland, who succeeded Roberts in the governor's chair, continued the policy of thrift in government.[1] Thus, good government at Austin encouraged and supplemented the general prosperity of the state. Marked expansion of cotton production, remarkable development of the cattle industry, the rapid influx of people, the phenomenal growth of railroads and other businesses—all these combined to bring to Texas an era of unprecedented prosperity.

The smiles of good fortune, however, were slow to reach the medical profession of Texas. But prosperity, once it did come to the medical association, grew rather rapidly. In 1880, from a membership of 269, only $305 was collected; this meant that about half of the members failed to pay their dues. By 1884, $906 was collected from 369 members; nearly all the members paid their dues.

[1] These words of Governor Ireland have a modern flavor: "Our fathers were happier and freer and more prosperous with oxcarts and living in the log cabins of pioneer days than their children are in these days of steam and electricity and universal avarice."—*San Antonio Express Magazine,* March 23, 1952.

85

The 1880 session at Brenham, in Washington County, was well attended. It will be recalled that the Washington County Medical Society had issued the initial call for the reorganizational meeting in 1869. The 1880 meetings were held in the Opera House and Armory Hall. The exact attendance is not recorded, though fifty-six doctors are mentioned in the *Proceedings* as having participated. After the meeting was called to order by President John H. Pope, the scientific portion of the program was taken up under the Section on Obstetrics. The bylaws had set aside the afternoons for the sectional sessions, but this change was apparently logical and temporary for this meeting.

The chairman of the section, Dr. L. L. P. Russell, provoked a four-page controversy when he "read an elaborate article setting forth advantages to be derived from discarding the use of the bandage and ligature in treating the cord." It was his idea that, by pressing the gelatinous material from the umbilical cord and then ligating, one could greatly decrease the likelihood of hernia, tetanus, or other infections. Although Dr. Russell was able to report successful use of the method over a ten-year period, the idea of leaving the cord untied, even temporarily, received only faint acceptance from the five or six men who took part in the discussion.

Dr. A. R. Kilpatrick read a report of a case of extrauterine fetation. Three years previously, a woman had been pregnant, and the "child had died in her." She continued in good health, however, and menstruated regularly. Then an abscess formed, which was treated by puncture, presumably through the cul-de-sac. The true nature of the situation was revealed when fetal bones began to pass per rectum. The patient came to autopsy. Absence of the right Fallopian tube indicated the initial location of the pregnancy, which had later become abdominal.

Dr. R. H. L. Bibb presented a committee report in a paper entitled "Medical Jurisprudence, State Medicine and Toxicology." The term "state medicine," as here used, referred to preventive measures which the state could well be expected to carry out. Several recommendations along public health lines were made, such as examination of locomotive engineers and steamboat pilots for color blindness, restrictions on the sale of narcotic and anesthetic drugs, penalties for adulteration of foodstuffs, and the provision of better accommodations for the insane. In support of adequate laws to protect the people against quackery, the report cited the

86

case of "one John Brooks, a graduate of pharmacy, but not in medicine, who had acquired considerable reputation as an obstetrician, having tied the penis instead of the cord, resulting in loss of that organ, a suit for damages in the sum of ten thousand, with an award of five thousand dollars."

Electricity, which was to play a dubious role in therapeutics for two or three generations, appeared in a paper read by Dr. M. A. Taylor under the title "Galvanism in the Treatment of Puerperal Convulsions, the Relief of Pain in Traumatic Injuries, and Other Painful Conditions." "For the relief of pain or spasm, almost regardless of their cause," it was asserted, "the constant galvanic current has no equal."

Dr. J. B. Adair read an article on "The Discovery of Anaesthesia." Dr. Adair practiced at Cedar Creek, in Bastrop County. It is heartening to be reminded that this country doctor, doubtless doing a big practice on horseback, had the time, the inclination, and the ability to write this scholarly paper. His summary should be reprinted:

First, That since 1800 the inhalation of nitrous oxide gas has been known to produce a peculiar intoxication, and allay headache and other minor pains.

Second, That Sir Humphry Davy proposed it as an anaesthetic in surgical operations.

Third, That for more than fifty years, ether inhalation has been practiced in New England Colleges, as an excitant.

Fourth, That the inhalation of ether as an excitant was common in Georgia forty years ago, but not practiced in the Colleges.

Fifth, That Dr. Long was the first man to intentionally produce anaesthesia for surgical operations, and that he did it in 1842.

Sixth, That Dr. Long did not accomplish it by accident, but reasoned it out in a logical and philosophical manner.

Seventh, That Wells, without knowledge of Long's labors, demonstrated, in like manner, the principle of anaesthesia by using nitrous oxide gas in 1844.

Eighth, That Morton, intending to follow Wells by using the gas in dentistry, asked Wells to show him how to make it in 1846.

Ninth, That Wells referred Morton to Jackson as a scientist, and that Jackson advised Morton to use ether as it possessed the same properties as the gas, and was safer, and easier to get.

Tenth, That Morton, acting on Jackson's suggestion, used ether in 1846, for painless extraction of teeth.

Eleventh, That Warren, Haywood and Bigelow performed important Surgical operations in the Massachusetts General Hospital, in 1846, on patients etherized by Morton, and thus popularized the practice throughout the world.

Other papers presented were "Report of a Case of Popliteal Aneurism Successfully Treated by Esmarch's Bandages, Genu, Digital and Hammer Handle Compression," "Placenta Previa," "Post-mortem Evidences of Virginity," "The Causal Relation Nerve Stimulants Sustain to Insanity," "The Treatment of Crime," and "A Peculiar Case of Cyanosis."

Sending of questionnaires to collect data for papers on the program was sometimes resorted to. Here is an illustration:

OFFICE OF J. K. DAVIDSON, M.D.
    PHYSICIAN AND SURGEON,
        GRAHAM, TEXAS, NOV. 10, 1879

DEAR SIR:

About what is the population of your city? What is its altitude? What is your mean temperature? What is your average rain-fall? What is your annual death rate? What per cent. of that number die with phthisis, and what number of the deaths from phthisis originated in this State?

By answering the above questions at your earliest convenience, you will greatly oblige,

        Yours, truly,
        J. K. DAVIDSON, M.D.

The presidential address of Dr. John H. Pope bore the rather dramatic title "The Struggle for Existence, or the Love of Life and Pleasure and the Dread of Pain and Death." Dr. Pope went into a long and abstruse discussion of his subject, and then he expressed some very practical ideas about sanitation and preventable disease:

There is a law-breaker that hides in your damp cellars and closets, that works in the night and is more to be feared than the burglar. There is an enemy in ill-constructed school houses, more stealthy than the pickpocket, that would rob you of a treasure more precious than gold. There is a highwayman that waits for you where the narrow alleys cross your streets, to demand "your money or your life." It is not less necessary to have policemen of a kind that can protect you against these enemies. I think it is at least an open question whether preventable diseases do not cause more injury to a city than would be suffered from outlaws were there no police. . . . There should be a county health office in every county. . . . I have not traveled all over the State, and yet I have seen enough to assure me that our cities and towns are far from being in good sanitary condition. There are many existing local causes of disease that should be remedied. God grant the purification may come without the fire of an epidemic.

In closing, Dr. Pope quoted Dr. Samuel D. Gross: "Oh! for a glance at the profession a half a century hence, when man enlightened and refined by education and redeemed from the thraldom of ignorance and superstition, shall reflect more perfectly the image of his maker." Then he paraphrased these words and applied them to the future of the Texas State Medical Association: "Oh! for a glance at this association in the years to come. Will it be truly the exponent of the medical talent of this State? Will its influence be always toward advancing medical science, elevating the profession, and encouraging good-will amongst its members? Will it be such a body that the people of the State can look to it as authority, and for advice and guidance in matters of public health? Will its annual sessions be such occasions as that its members eagerly flock to them in search of new discoveries and scientific truths, and return home better physicians and better men? Will it be such a body that we shall all be proud to call ourselves members of it? I believe the heart of every one of us fondly wishes it may be all these."

The business sessions of the Brenham meeting were rather active and not entirely harmonious. The perennial problem of a state board of health came up for its usual consideration. This time it was suggested that the medical association submit twenty-one names to the governor and that he appoint a board of seven, six to be physicians and one a civil engineer. Dr. J. W. McLaughlin, of Austin, introduced a resolution in favor of holding the meetings of the Association at the same place every year. Then, he argued, a library and museum could be established. As it was, books, records, and anatomical specimens were scattered all over the state, "especially at places where ex-presidents and secretaries lived." Dr. Greensville Dowell stated that such a plan would lead to disruption of the Association and that the plan had already been tried and abandoned. Apparently, he was referring to the four meetings held in Houston from 1869 to 1872. At any rate, his opinion prevailed and the resolution was tabled.

Dr. D. R. Wallace, by request, offered a resolution to the effect "that members of this Association will not receive students in medicine, not possessed of good English education and sufficient knowledge of Latin to write and translate prescriptions correctly." Dr. Dowell argued for this resolution, believing that a higher type of medical student would thus be offered to the medical schools. And then, strangely, Dr. Wallace caused his own resolution to fail when he said he would vote against it because he felt that this subject should be left to the medical schools of the country.

Dr. R. H. Harrison, a strong states'-righter, introduced this far-sighted resolution: "That this Association looks, with grave apprehensions, of disastrous consequences to our section of the Country, upon any extension of the powers of the National Board of Health." When his resolution was tabled, Dr. Harrison seemed to interpret the action as a personal affront. He took it so seriously that he "said when he ceased to be of any service to his fellow man, he hoped God would, in his goodness and mercy, sever his earthly connections therewith, and, being convinced that he was no longer of use to this Association, he desired to sever his connection therewith, and and asked permission to withdraw therefrom." In spite of the fact that he was a well respected past president, his request was granted. A member goaded Dr. Harrison a bit by saying "he had oft times heard, that so soon as a member of this Association becomes an ex-president thereof his interest therein abates." Dr. Harrison replied that such was not the case. On motion, he was elected an honorary member. Then he withdrew his original request for permission to retire from membership.

A disturbing note of disharmony was sounded over the subject of contract practice. Dr. B. Powell, of Houston, in a resolution charged Dr. D. F. Stuart, also of Houston, with making a contract with the Texas Central Railroad Company and with signing agreements with subcontracting physicians along the line "at such contemptible and ruinous fees, as to work serious injury to brother physicians, and to the degradation of the honor and integrity of the profession." The resolution was ruled out of order on the basis of a decision made at the last meeting by the Judicial Council that matters pertaining to fees should be decided by the subordinate societies. The next day, however, a more scathing resolution, signed by nine influential physicians, was introduced. The resolution pointed out that at the previous meeting the presiding officer, Dr. W. E. Saunders, and the chairman of the Judicial Council, Dr. Alex W. Acheson, were both subcontractors under Dr. Stuart, as was

President A. R. Kilpatrick, who had ruled on the resolution the day before. Then these nine doctors served notice that appeal to the American Medical Association would be made. Drs. D. R. Wallace and Greensville Dowell were appointed to represent the state association in the appeal. By the time of the next meeting tempers had cooled, and the appellants were ready to let the matter drop.

The new officers were A. R. Kilpatrick, of Navasota, president; R. M. Swearingen, of Austin, first vice-president; E. J. Beall, of Fort Worth, second vice-president; O. H. Seeds, of Columbia, third vice-president; J. Larendon, of Houston, treasurer, and R. H. L. Bibb, of Austin, secretary. Dr. Bibb replaced Dr. W. A. East, who had served since 1874. There is no record to indicate whether Dr. East's replacement was related to his being one of the dissenters who wished to appeal the contract-practice decision to the American Medical Association. Certainly he had served the state association well during six crucial years. No official notice was taken of his long service, but Dr. Bibb, in his speech of acceptance, paid special tribute to the proficiency of his "distinguished predecessor." After the usual expressions of thanks to the physicians, the press, and the people of Brenham, the Association adjourned, to meet the next year in Waco.

On the first Tuesday in April, 1881, the Association came to Waco for the second time. The 1873 session had been held in that city, and now the Association was in Waco for its fifteenth annual meeting. Dr. D. R. Wallace, one of the founders of the organization and its fifth president, gave a warm welcoming address. President A. R. Kilpatrick called attention to the growth of Waco since its origin twenty-six years before:

It seems but a re-enactment of one of those tales of enchantment in the Arabian nights! Waco in 1855 and Waco in 1881! Then but a rude border town, with humble shanties and humble dwellings; now you have palaces worthy of princes. Then a few stores, poorly supplied with staple goods, to sell to frontiersmen or the Indians; now bazaars and marts blazing and overflowing with the riches of "Ormus and of Ind!" Then a rude flat to transport travelers across the Brazos river; now that stream is spanned by a grand suspension bridge, such as Xerxes and Alexander never saw. Then probably a plain building served as a school-house during the week, and as the temple of God on Sunday; now your colleges adorn your streets, and your churches add glory to your corporation. Education and religion go hand in hand, and have made Waco the boast of Texas.

According to an editorial in the *Texas Medical and Surgical Record,* a new venture in medical journalism, the attendance was 140, although only 26 answered the initial roll call. There were 318 names on the roster of members, of whom 25 were new members. Since the dues had been raised to $5.00, the faithful treasurer, J. Larendon, could not have been proud of the $497.50 which he reported as collections for the year. Even so, since a new arrangement had been made for publishing the *Proceedings* of the Association, he was able to show a favorable balance of $203.07.

At this Waco meeting, Parke, Davis & Company had on exhibit "a supply of their beautiful Pharmaceutical preparations" and thus became the first exhibitor at a meeting of the Texas State Medical Association. "The profession took great interest in viewing and tasting them, and many supplied themselves with samples, in order to test them," the *Record* commented editorially.

Good as the scientific sessions were, they were overshadowed by several important discussions and decisions. Discontinuance of the *Proceedings* was a marked departure. Over a period of years, the subject of a medical journal sponsored by the Association had been discussed, but the proposal had regularly been rejected. In the discussion, from time to time, it had been suggested that the Association might utilize some privately owned medical journal without accepting any financial obligation. At the Brenham meeting of 1880, Dr. C. H. Wilkinson, who had served as chairman of the Committee on Publishing for two years, reported that he had arranged for the publication of original papers in the *Galveston Medical Journal.* This periodical, owned and edited by Dr. Greensville Dowell, had ceased publication in 1871, but its revival may have been contemplated. In the same report, Dr. Wilkinson recommended that, because of scarcity of funds, "arrangements be made with some home journalist for publication of the minutes, and if possible, of the original matter of your annual convocations." There must have been a good deal of correspondence on the subject during the following year or active discussion at Waco, for the following resolution, introduced by Dr. J. H. Sears, was adopted, apparently without opposition: "That the Texas State Medical Association adopt the *Texas Medical and Surgical Record,* published at Galveston, as the official organ of this body; that the proprietors of said Journal, be requested to publish the Proceedings of the Texas State Medical Association, together with all the original papers turned over to them by the Publishing Committee, as worthy of publication, and that a copy of said publication be mailed, free of charge, to every contributing member, and in consideration of which, the Treasurer is hereby authorized to pay said proprietors, the sum of Two Dollars per capita, for each of such contributing members of this Association."

A word of explanation should be given about the *Texas Medical and Surgical Record*. A group of physicians, calling themselves the Texas Medical Publishing Company, controlled the publication. They were R. H. L. Bibb, of Austin; F. Herff, of San Antonio; T. J. Heard, J. F. Y. Paine, and C. H. Wilkinson, of Galveston; E. J. Beall, of Fort Worth; John H. Pope, of Marshall; and S. Eagan, of Sherman. Paine was president, Beall vice-president, and Wilkinson secretary and editor of the company. The first issue appeared in January, 1881. It was a small octavo, resembling in appearance such publications as Fenner's *Southern Medical Reports* and the *Eclectic Repository*. Each issue, of about forty pages, contained an editorial written by Dr. Wilkinson, professor of clinical surgery in the Texas Medical College and Hospital; several original articles; and a department called "Gleanings," which contained abstracts from other journals and items of general interest. The outlook for the owners seemed promising the first year: a dividend of $22.05 (35 per cent) was declared. At the end of the second year, however, when Dr. E. J. Beall was president and Dr. William Penny vice-president, there was no mention of a dividend. The agreement with the Association lasted for two years. The *Record* then came rather quickly to the end of its way. During its three years of life, it was a credit to medical journalism and made a definite contribution to the cause of organized medicine in Texas.

One of the most heated debates that had ever come before the Association concerned the location of a medical college under the auspices of the Association. A committee brought in a recommendation that Galveston be the site. The discussion consumed three hours, thirteen pages in the minutes, and was participated in by fourteen doctors. The deliberations were expanded to include the recent action of the Legislature authorizing the establishment of a state university with a medical department, its location to be de-

termined by a vote of the people. Separation of the medical department from the main university came in for vigorous argument on
both sides. Eager proponents of Galveston, Waco, Austin, and
Dallas presented the advantages of their respective cities. It was
debated whether Galveston Island was "in constant danger of in-
undation from the gulf storms." The discussion was strangely and
abruptly halted, and then indefinitely postponed, when three announcements were made: an invitation "to witness the workings
of the Celebrated Rotary Plow," an invitation by the Central Railroad "to take an excursion up that road to Morgan," and an invitation to attend a complimentary ball at Curtis' Hall that night, when
"all were given an opportunity to gaze upon and silently admire the
beauty and fashion of Waco."

About this time, mutual-aid societies were becoming quite popular in Texas. In line with this trend, it was recommended by a committee that a life insurance department of the Association be organized. An admission fee of five dollars and an assessment of one dollar on the death of each participating member were recommended.
The wide divergence of opinion in this matter is illustrated by the
positions taken by Dr. T. J. Heard, who "regarded the scheme as
the best and most important ever inaugurated by the State Medical
Association," and Dr. W. H. Wilkes, who "expressed doubts concerning propriety of scientific bodies embarking in life insurance
business at all, certainly if not based upon sound business principles." The recommendations of the committee were finally adopted,
and Dr. D. R. Wallace was elected general director, with instructions to proceed with the organization of the life insurance department. The next meeting in 1882 saw the end of this proposed in-
vasion of the field of business by the doctors of Texas. Dr. Wallace
admitted that this idea which he had nurtured was beset with pitfalls. So the matter was tabled, and all those who were interested
in cheap insurance protection were referred to the Texas Benevolent Association.

This and other controversial problems were not in keeping with
the hope devoutly expressed editorially in the *Record:* "that the
proceedings of the next Association may be devoid of all personalities, all class legislation, and particularly of all long-winded, tedious
and irrelevant discussions, the slightest approach to which, should
be discountenanced by the better thinking members of the Association."

94

At this Waco session, Secretary Bibb made his first report. It was confined chiefly to an assignment given at the previous meeting. By use of the mails, he had obtained the names, addresses, and place and date of graduation of more than eight hundred physicians outside the Association. The newspapers of the state carried notices of the next annual meeting. The object of Dr. Bibb's activities had been to increase interest and hence membership in the Association. Certainly the results were more than enough to justify the expenditure of the modest sum of $33.35 for stamps and stationery.

The expected run of reports and resolutions was presented. Dr. J. Larendon was given $150.00 "as a slight token of appreciation for his long, faithful, and gratuitous services as its Treasurer." The committee appointed to consider the four-state medical association asked to be discharged, since it "had done nothing and was not likely to do anything." The gathering went on record as opposing that part of the Medical Practice Act which permitted "ignorant and irresponsible females, without any evidence of qualification, to practice midwifery." One important resolution, introduced by Dr. John H. Pope and passed, provided "that the Secretary be instructed to collect 'The Transactions' of every meeting of this Association, from the time of its organization to, and including the present meeting, and have them strongly and neatly bound in one volume, and indexed for every reference; the collection not to include papers, addresses or cases reported, but the minutes, resolutions, by-laws, constitution and ordinances." It was further provided "that it be the duty of the Secretary, to have said volume at every future meeting of this body." If this motion was ever carried out, the volume is not known.

Several new committees appeared in the *Proceedings* of 1881: a committee on necrology, a committee to consider the propriety of the Association's holding its every third annual meeting at Austin, a committee to secure a room in the new Capitol Building for the archives and library of the Association, a committee to revise the list of members, and a committee to memorialize the Legislature on the subject of fees for expert testimony and post-mortem examinations.

Papers read at the Waco meeting included: "Epidemic Cerebrospinal Meningitis," "Double Amputation of the Feet," "Hydrocephalus," "After Perineorrhaphy," and "Hypodermic Administration of Carbolic Acid." This last paper was presented by Dr. N. B.

Kennedy. Carbolic acid, rightly considered an antiseptic and anesthetic, was injected into carbuncles, hemorrhoids, and tumors. The drug in its pure state was applied to the skin before incising abscesses. It was hailed as "an antiseptic and anesthetic disinfectant *facile princeps* in surgical cases."

The title of the article on perineorrhaphy is unclear. It was intended to convey the idea of a delayed operation. A woman had been delivered by two midwives with a resulting laceration extending through the anal sphincter and two inches up the recto-vaginal septum. Dr. T. H. Nott, of Goliad, was the surgeon. He had waited eight weeks. Then, one Sunday morning, he and his four assistants went ten miles out in the country for the operation. When ether had been administered, he "closed the sphincter after Emmet's method, and the perineum after Sims' method, using eleven sutures —interrupted silver wire—did the paring with Emmet's angular scissors, and used Sims' needle holder, with straight round needles." The sutures were removed on the eighth day, and the knees were kept securely tied together for two weeks. On the fifteenth day, a fecal impaction was discovered. Dr. Nott used an apparently new method for dealing with this complication. With two fingers in the vagina, he broke up the fecal mass by pressing it against the sacrum, so that the fragments could be washed out without exerting undue strain on the repaired sphincter. In belittling the possibility that this procedure might be new, he said: "I am satisfied that some charitable professional brother, in a spirit of justice and courtesy to some old Greek or Roman, will find where this was done centuries gone by."

A study of the papers on this and on previous programs reveals that surgery was making more definite progress than medicine, as emphasized in a case report by Dr. B. E. Hadra, of San Antonio. A large uterine tumor, removed *per vaginam,* was examined microscopically. The examination "showed very large granular cells, partly caudate with many nuclei—in short, sarcomatous cells." Dr. Hadra had studied in Berlin, and if he did not have Virchow as a teacher, he no doubt was familiar with the work on cellular pathology which that great investigator had published about twenty years earlier.

As the subject for his presidential address, Dr. A. R. Kilpatrick chose "Foods and Drugs and Their Adulteration." In that day, no legal protection was afforded. The president described the various

96

methods of adulteration and suggested remedies. He put in a good word for oleomargarine and condemned "ready ground coffee" as "unhealthy and deleterious." After twenty-seven pages, he explained that he had intended to take up several other subjects: the establishment of a school for women nurses, since "some male nurses are nuisances, and drink up all the wine and stimulants furnished for the sick"; the proper location of cemeteries in relation to towns, advising that they be placed on low ground with a stream intervening; and arguments in favor of cremation. "I also desired to say something against vulgar, coarse, trashy reading by the young," he added, "and to denounce dime and nickel novels, as injurious to the manners and morals of the young, leading them into vicious practices, and consequently bad health, crime and death!"

After hearing the president, "the Association was invited to a banquet, given at the McClelland House, and here the profession demonstrated the fact that they knew how to enjoy themselves when given the opportunity to do so. About 250 members and invited guests sat down at 10 P.M., to enjoy the rare wines and other delicacies then and there provided. Toasting and speaking continued until a late hour, and it was nearly midnight when an informal adjournment was held, so as to allow participants to recuperate their waning powers for the last day's deliberation."

For the following year venerable Ashbel Smith, of Cedar Bayou, was elected president; S. F. Starley, of Corsicana, first vice-president; J. W. McLaughlin, of Austin, second vice-president; J. A. Summers, of Sherman, third vice-president; J. Larendon, of Houston, treasurer; and R. H. L. Bibb, of Austin, secretary. The selection of seventy-six-year-old Ashbel Smith as president was worthy but long delayed. From the year 1837, he had served well his state and his profession in many capacities. The *Record* devoted an editorial of six pages to the life of Dr. Smith, "the finished scholar and chivalrous gentleman." And he was more than this: physician, patriot, soldier, diplomat, and educator. The editorial concludes thus: "Although in the evening of life, he may well be considered an intellectual giant, and as a parliamentarian Dr. Smith has no superior in Texas."

The next meeting was assigned to Fort Worth, on the last Tuesday in April instead of the first, the bylaws having been changed to that effect. Dr. J. T. Field, of Fort Worth, "invited every member of the medical profession present, as well as those throughout the State, to attend, assuring them that the citizens of the city of heights, artesian wells, the Queen City of the prairie, would extend them a most hearty welcome, and leave no effort untried to render the meeting a pleasant and profitable one." The editor of the *Texas Medical and Surgical Record,* too, urged physicians to attend the Fort Worth session. He argued that "the only way to drive ignorance, quackery and fogyism out of Texas is to organize against it; and the very first step toward such organization is to ally with one of the highest and most responsible bodies of physicians in the State—the Texas State Medical Association. . . . The ride, the reunion and recreation will amply compensate the doctor for the time lost and money spent in the trip."

The 1882 session of the Association was welcomed by Dr. Will B. Davis, of Grapevine, to the "city of artesian wells and of windmills—the Queen of the Prairies, and the future Atlanta of Texas." Meetings were held in the district courtroom, and the *Record* stated that rarely had there been so full an attendance. The exact number present is not on record, but on one rather controversial resolution 58 votes were cast. There were 218 names on the rolls, a rather small fraction of the estimated 3,000 physicians in the state. One noticeably absent member was Dr. Greensville S. Dowell. This prominent surgeon, editor, and author had died June 9, 1881. In recognition of what he had meant to the medical profession of Texas, the *Record* devoted two pages to his accomplishments. Dr. Dowell will perhaps be best remembered as the first to suggest the mosquito as the carrier of yellow fever. This was in 1876.[2] Years later, before the Association, Dr. James Carroll, one of Walter Reed's associates in Cuba, gave full credit to Dowell.[3]

The Committee on Arrangements announced that a grand ball at Godman's Hall was being tendered to the Association by the citizens of Fort Worth on Wednesday night, following the address of President Smith. On Thursday night, the citizens gave a banquet at the El Paso Hotel.

Treasurer Larendon gave a favorable report, showing a balance of $344.92. Dr. Bibb reported in detail the activities of the secre-

[2] *Yellow Fever and Malarial Diseases,* 13.
[3] "Yellow Fever—A Popular Lecture," *Texas State Journal of Medicine,* I (1905), 71.

98

tary's office. He also resigned his office at this meeting because of his intention of moving to Saltillo, Mexico. A resolution of thanks was tendered him by the Association "for his gentlemanly deportment as one of its members, and for the able, efficient and faithful manner he has discharged the various duties it has assigned him." The *Texas Medical and Surgical Record* gave his departure a page-long notice, offering this summary of his work in Texas: "Dr. Bibb, though young in the practice, has earned an enviable reputation in all the professional duties he has undertaken in our State. For four years he served as assistant superintendent of the State Lunatic Asylum at Austin; for four years he was city physician, as well as president of the Board of Health at Austin; was president of the Travis County Medical Society, and was a member of the Board of Medical Examiners for the Sixteenth Judicial District. As secretary of the Texas Medical Association he won for himself golden encomiums, and his resignation was deplored as a loss to that society."

While secretary, Dr. Bibb had served as reporter for the *Texas Medical and Surgical Record* in connection with a famous discussion which took place before the Travis County Medical Society. Adjutant-General John B. Jones, noted as the commander of the Frontier Battalion of the Texas Rangers, had become severely ill with what may have been an amebic abscess of the liver, which subsequently ruptured into the right pleural cavity. He was treated by Drs. J. E. Morris, R. M. Swearingen, J. W. McLaughlin, and E. G. Nicholson. Over a period of four months, he gradually lost ground. A trip was made to San Antonio, where Dr. Ferdinand Herff failed to find pus by aspiration. When the patient was *in extremis*, Dr. T. D. Wooten was called in consultation. He found evidence of fluid in the right pleural cavity and advised aspiration. Forty ounces of pus was withdrawn. The patient died the next day. Because of the prominence of General Jones, the prolonged nature of his illness, and the number of physicians involved, the case attracted widespread interest. Unfortunately, a bitter controversy arose between Dr. Wooten and the other four physicians. So heated was the dispute that six months later the matter was brought before the Travis County Medical Society, where Dr. Bibb set down forty-five pages for the *Record*. Dr. Wooten contended that the condition was empyema of the pleural cavity from the beginning, whereas his opponents held that a liver abscess had ruptured into the chest cavity. And there was bitter discussion as to who first detected the presence of pus in the pleural cavity. Dozens of pages of quotations from medical authorities were paraded in defense of both sides.

Not satisfied with the report in the *Record*, Dr. Wooten furnished fifty-two more pages on the subject, for the next issue of the journal. He concluded his defense with this barbed paragraph:

In taking leave of the "attending physicians," I may be permitted to compliment their zeal at the eleventh hour, and to hope, that, when next again they come to treat a similar case, they may display the same ingenuity and research *before* the fatal crisis, that they have, in this instance evinced, in their endeavor to justify their unfortunate error, *after* Nature had closed the scene. And I would further suggest, that in future, when they would seek to disparage the professional skill, and to even impugn the veracity of a brother physician, by a fabrication built to suit the emergency, they should call to mind the advice of the French philosopher, that, "he who would deface the temple of truth and justice— must have not only *sharp nails,* but *clean hands.*"

The whole affair was most unfortunate. The sole results were personal animosity, professional jealousy, and unfavorable publicity. It could not fail to discourage medical harmony in Travis County and in all Texas. Realizing these facts, the editor of the *Record* wisely closed the unhappy chapter with this remark: "Hereafter articles containing anything of a personal nature, or consuming more than half the available space of the *Record,* must seek some other journal for publication." A few months later, doubtless recalling the ugliness of this controversy, the editor wrote on "Professional Vices" and had this to say about jealousy: "It is, moreover, the embodiment of foolishness, since what portends to the downfall or injury of one physician, tends to the downfall of the entire profession. . . . Let us then eradicate this cankerous vice. Let us frown down everything that tends to belittle the individual members of the profession, in the hope that we may thereby add dignity and strength to the body of physicians at large, and to ourselves in particular."

If Dr. Ashbel Smith, who presided at the Fort Worth session, gave an address, it has not been preserved. Apparently he made a few informal remarks and then asked Vice-President Starley to deliver the chief message. The *Record* indicates that Dr. Starley's "theme was well taken upon the vast changes that had occurred in our State as likewise in our profession, during the past half century."

The papers presented dealt with such subjects as sympathetic ophthalmia, middle-ear infections, rheumatism and its treatment by veratrum viride, phlegmasia dolens, treatment of strangulated hernia, puerperal convulsions and treatment by venesection, surgery of the pancreas, and reports on surgery and gynecology. The paper on eclampsia, by Dr. George S. Sykes, provoked free discussion. Most of the participants agreed with the author that venesection was the principal mode of treatment, and that if the patient with eclampsia did not recover, then venesection was resorted to too late or too timidly. Dr. D. R. Wallace, however, dissented: "The indications point to it, but believing as I do, that the indications in this or any other affection in modern times seldom call for it, I think it but seldom this remedial principle of the past should be resorted to. I am one of those who believe in a change of type, as it is called." Dr. F. M. Hall, of Bryan, was slightly misquoted when the reporter recorded him as saying that he had treated six or seven cases successfully by "vivisection."

Dr. W. J. Burt, in his report on gynecology, aroused considerable interest. He held the "fashionable" obstetrician responsible for many lacerations of the perineum and cervix because of his eagerness to "rupture the membranes in the early stages of labor; to give ergot before complete dilatation of the cervix; to push up the thin cervix over the presenting part of the child, and to resort to the forceps before nature has prepared the way for the descent of the child." He felt that "every laceration, with ectropium of the cervical mucous-membrane, should receive surgical attention—removing one of the main conditions favoring cancerous development in the cervix." This report led to some discussion on cancer of the cervix. Then as now, the statistics on cancer were fearful to contemplate. Then as now, women were asking, "Have I cancer, or will my disease run into cancer?" Local irritation was stressed as a causative factor. Three physicians testified that they had never seen a cancer of the cervix in a Negro woman.

Matters of business brought before the Association at the Fort Worth session were not of utmost importance. One had to do with the appeal made to the American Medical Association in regard to railroad practice. Dr. D. R. Wallace reported that, having been appointed a member of the Judicial Council of the American Medical Association, he had brought the matter before that body, which had ruled that no transgression of the code of ethics was involved. The appellants then dropped the subject. There was also some discussion about publication of the *Proceedings* of the Association. The decision for continuing the arrangement with the *Record* for another year prevailed.

It is surprising to note that an act of the New York State Medical Society should arouse the indignation of Texas doctors. The New York society had passed this resolution: "Members of the Medical Society of the State of New York, and of medical societies in affiliation therewith, *may meet* in consultation any legally qualified practitioner of medicine." An effort was being made to take the subject before the American Medical Association. It had the support of several illustrious names: Agnew, Sayre, Jacobi, Barker, and Squibb. The New York resolution carried with it the suggestion of consultation with irregulars, and Texas doctors were prepared to "fight to the hilt every effort to degrade the emblems and erase the landmarks of regular medicine, by inviting into the sacred precincts of our councils, the 'kith and kin,' and advocates of all who claim to be doctors." By unanimous vote, delegates to the American Medical Association were instructed to vote against the resolution. On hand two months later, when the American Medical Association convened at St. Paul, to assist in the successful effort to expel the New York society from the national association were H. C. Ghent, W. H. Park, J. H. Sears, and T. D. Wooten.

Several minor resolutions were passed at Fort Worth. One dealt with claims of the curative powers of medicinal wells and springs, and the association of physicians with such claims. Others concerned "underbidding by physicians for practice, public or private" and the payment by the state of adequate fees for serving as expert witnesses and performing autopsies. On motion of Dr. E. J. Beall, Dr. C. B. Raines, of Gordon, was elected to honorary membership. Attention was called to "the first cousin of our profession, and one essential to our success, therapeutics, and particularly to Mr. F. M. Odena, now in the hall, with some of these preparations on exhibition. Mr. Odena represents that wide awake and enterprising firm, Parke, Davis & Co., Detroit, Mich."

As the 1882 meeting came to a close, an affecting incident took place. Dr. D. R. Wallace rose to his feet and, with mingled pride and nostalgia, addressed the gathering. If his words sound like the final admonition of a medical patriarch, they were not so intended. Dr. Wallace was only fifty-seven years old. He had a long life of usefulness before him, extending as far as 1908, when, as the oldest living graduate, he spoke at Wake Forest College. He greeted his audience as "Mr. President and Brethren of the Texas State Medical Association," and then continued:

The scene through which we have just passed, calls up memories connected with the original organization of this association in a small room at the Hutchins House, in Houston, fourteen years ago. I know not that there is a single individual present, except myself, who was there, when six or eight of us (for there was never more than this present at any one time during [the] first meeting), went through with the farce of organizing the Texas State Medical Association; if so, he will recall with me most vividly the contrast between the association then and now. Then it was thought necessary, in order to secure a meeting at all, to assemble in connection, or rather, at same time with the Grand Lodge of Masons. Truly was it the day of small things. But a few of us were hopeful, we kept at work, and kept up the meetings, until today we may challenge a comparison in point of numbers and ability with any body of men meeting within the broad limits of Texas. This, most certainly, is matter of gratulation to all. As for myself, with my soul bound up in the enterprise from the first, having labored for years to get on a stable basis, I look over this large and talented assemblage—representative of the medical intelligence of the State, I am inspired with the utterance of Simeon of old, "Now Lord, lettest these thy servants depart in peace, for my eyes have beheld thy salvation." [4] Gentlemen will excuse these remarks; my emotion will not permit me to say more; the reminiscences that cluster about this occasion as I call up the incidents of the past, forbid me to say less.

Tyler was decided on as the place for the 1883 meeting, and the following officers were elected: S. F. Starley, Corsicana, president; W. P. Burts, Fort Worth, first vice-president; W. A. Adams, Fort Worth, second vice-president; Joe S. Willis, Waco, third vice-president; W. J. Burt, Austin, secretary; and J. Larendon, Houston, treasurer. The editor of the *Record* thought that "the crowning event of the occasion was the banquet given Thursday night by the committee, to their visiting guests. Wine mingled with wit, and joy with fleeting hours. The work was over, and a volume of sentiment had to be expressed before the rush for home occurred."

Some evidence of the growth of organized medicine in Texas was reflected in activities of the subordinate societies. The *Record* for 1882 carried reports of semiannual meetings of the Northwest

[4] Dr. Wallace or the reporter quoted fellow-physician St. Luke incorrectly (Luke 2:29).

Texas Medical and Surgical Association and the North Texas Medical Association. The latter organization created a Committee on Library and Museum to "take charge of all specimens and anomalies that may be contributed to the Association, as well as all books, journals and other literary matter that may be placed in their hands." Dr. J. B. Stinson, of Sherman, presented a case of elephantiasis of the scrotum, weighing seventy-five pounds and of twelve years' duration. Since the patient could not be brought before the meeting, the doctors were taken to the patient's home. Surgical removal was advised; but it is very doubtful whether this advice was taken, since the patient was an Indian. Every Indian looks forward to his entry into the Happy Hunting Grounds with his anatomy intact.

Albertson's Opera House, in Tyler, was the meeting place of the 1883 session. One of the welcoming addresses was by former Governor R. B. Hubbard. Oblivious of thyroid extract of the future, Hubbard announced that he "was not a candidate for their pills and mixtures, as his two hundred and forty pounds of avoirdupois would certainly demonstrate." His accuracy as a prophet was not strengthened when he added that "the time for quackery was about at an end in this State, and the people were sufficiently enlightened to demand a high order of medical talent, that would carry with it the elevating influence of the noble calling."

Chairman W. H. Park of the Committee on Arrangements announced that Professor John A. Wyeth, of New York, would address the Association Tuesday night on "Higher Medical Education." On Wednesday night the president gave his address, after which the "doctors and their wives and sweethearts, and as many others as would do so, visited the Ferguson House and pleased the physical man, by using the delicious viands, that lay in profusion on the tables." Then followed a ball at the Opera House, given by "the young gentlemen of Tyler." The banquet, which along with the ball had become an established feature of the program, was held Thursday night.

The scientific part of the program showed evidences of gradual improvement. Subjects discussed included Caesarian section, treatment of internal hemorrhoids by injection of carbolic acid, antiseptic surgery, anesthesia in obstetrics, summer complaint of children, vesico-vaginal fistula, and malarial hematuria.

104

The Caesarian section reported was performed by Dr. J. J. Burroughs, of Houston, on a woman who had died of eclampsia.[5] The child was alive and, thanks to goat's milk and Miller's infant food, after six months was well nourished and thriving. Dr. Hillary Ryan told how he had cured a case of vesico-vaginal fistula by utilizing the knee-chest position and silver wire sutures. The wires were fastened together "with a piece of dressed buckskin."

Dr. S. W. Johnson, of Ennis, in his paper on "Summer Complaint of Children," emphasized the seriousness of infant diarrhea. He felt that teething played no part in its causation and as a preventive measure recommended that children should wear flannel underwear, summer and winter. As to treatment, he relied on hygienic measures, laudanum, and Borden's Eagle Brand condensed milk.[6]

In the annual report on surgery, it was stated that "preparatory treatment in surgical cases is very essential prior to operative interference. Strict hygienic attention and all the essential requisites of what is termed listerism should be observed." The work of Lister referred to here, coupled with the experiments of Pasteur, was making abdominal surgery more safe. Three papers on ovariotomy were read in 1883, reporting five successful operations for ovarian cysts. These operations were so rare that eight or ten visiting doctors were present as observers. Three of the cysts weighed forty-four, sixty-five, and seventy-six pounds. The largest was removed by Dr. J. J. Burroughs. He was exploring the terra incognita of surgery in Texas as he "extended the incision in the medium line, both upward and downward, until it was about nine inches long, while the wall of the abdomen was so tightly upon the large tumor within, frequently rinsing or washing his own hands and requiring all assistants to do the same in carbolized water, sometimes in a five per cent. solution, and sometimes in a two and one-half per cent. solution." The operation required two hours and forty-five minutes for its completion, one hour of which was consumed in soaking the silk-ligated stump in 5 per cent carbolic acid solution before drop-

[5] This procedure was not new in Texas. As early as 1802, a royal decree had been sent out from Spain requiring the doctor or the priest to do a Caesarian section on all women dying in childbirth.—Bexar Archives, September 21, 1804.

[6] Thirty years before, working in his crude laboratory at Galveston, Gail Borden had established the principles of evaporating milk *in vacuo*.—Clarence B. Wharton, *Gail Borden, Pioneer* (San Antonio, 1941), 181–99.

ping it back into the peritoneal cavity. The wound was closed, without drainage, with interrupted silk sutures.

Drs. E. J. Beall and W. A. Adams reported on the use of sponge-grafting. A man with a seriously damaged foot and much loss of tissue was treated by placing thin strips of sea sponge over the granulating area. The sole of the foot was thus built up so that a normal weight-bearing surface was obtained. The sponge acted as a framework on which the granulations could grow. With this success in mind, they speculated: "It may not be considered far-fetched for the imagination to wander into the future and returning to the present, be laden with impressions that surgeons often build up lost parts by sponge grafting, and introducing into such parts periosteum and marrow, have bone produced as well."

Dr. T. H. Nott, an influential member who was to become president of the Association in 1886, put some very thorny ideas into his paper on "The Embryo Physician as a Specialist." To orient himself, he began by saying that he was "an isolated member of this honorable body, there being no other member in less than seventy-five or one hundred miles of me, and no medical organization nearer than that, while I am without railroad or telegraphic communication with the rest of the State or world." He continued with these pointed observations:

In the good old times gone by a specialist was a physician and something more. . . . [Today he is,] as our late retiring President of the American Medical Association happily expresses it, something less than a physician. A sort of one-horse doctor. . . . He sits back on his dignity and grows rich and famous, while we struggle for a living and a small reputation and drum for him. . . . Now, gentlemen, I would ask, can practice, pathology, or therapeutics be advanced by such men? What are their fine spun theories worth? Is it not lowering the standard of medical education? Are such men entitled to an M.D. after their names? . . . Is it possible to divide up so complex a machinery as the human system and understand one part *ab initio?* . . . Let us put in a plea to keep our people out of the hands of the born specialist, by inserting a clause in the article regulating the practice of medicine, which shall forbid any person to practice a specialty in this State who has not done a general practice for at least ten years.

In a different vein, but none the less seriously, Dr. W. J. Burt talked on the "Decadence of the Family and Forced Abortion as a Cause of Disease in Females." After emphasizing the basic impor-

106

tance of the family as an institution and pointing out the fate that befell nations in which family life became decadent, he bemoaned the tendency of his own day:

Today, free-thinking, frivolousness, fashion, Frenchy ideas and customs, nervousness, weakness and sterility of the American women take the place, largely, of the plain salutary home life of the Puritan families of one hundred years ago. . . . Too much brain work and too little body work, is one of the crying evils of the present system of female education. . . . The result of this high pressure system of education fills our towns and cities with pale-faced and flat-chested girls, who often seem to have no other hold upon life than a capacity for momentary enthusiasm, and no other aim in life than to cultivate small hands, small waists and small feet. . . . Released from the school-room desk this weary, wornout, rest-needing-girl launches into the dissipations of society, petted, praised and pushed along by the proud doting mother. . . . Of all the causes of diseases among females, I believe prevention of conception and forced abortion, the most disastrous. These are two sins which defile every class of society. Sins, which like the plague of the frogs, "creep into our houses and bedchambers and beds." . . . Why is it that the waiting-rooms of the gynaecologists are crowded with so many querulous and complaining women? women with headaches and spine-aches—women without sexual feeling or too weak to indulge them—women with a drawer full of the implements of the brothel.

And then, after reminding his listeners that in many states there was one divorce to twelve marriages and that large families were becoming fewer, he inveighed against the evils of abortions: "So it will be seen that abortion strikes a blow at the very foundation of society itself. And its enormity from this stand-point can be readily understood when the fact is announced that there are more abortions than confinements at the full term of gestation, or, in other words, that one-half the fertile pregnancies are cut short and their fruits blasted."

Dr. Starley, by then of Tyler, chose "The History and Mission of the Profession of Medicine" as the subject for his presidential address, and a very scholarly address it was. He traced the history of medicine from its early beginnings. His choice of words and his clarity of style are well illustrated by a few brief quotations. The era following Galen, he said, "was characterized by that long and dark night of superstition and barbarism which threatened the total overthrow of all literature and all science. The frail bark of humanity, with all that remained of human knowledge and of human hope lay sluggish and rotting upon a seemingly interminable ocean of darkness and despair." [7] As to the outlook for medicine of his day, he felt that

the physiologist must extend his researches further. Upon him devolves the task of exploring the entire field of organic life, and he must cease not his labors until he is able to understand the mutual relations and dependencies which link together by one common chain the entire realm of animated nature.

In this pursuit of knowledge the true votaries of our profession are not lagging in the rear. They have thrown off the shackles of preconceived theories and of formerly recognized authority, and have entered upon open fields of investigation. By the aid of that most wonderful instrument, the microscope, the student of nature is enabled to extend his researches into the minutest atoms of created matter.

After urging his hearers to forswear all relations with quacks of every kind "as you would shun personal contact with the victims of leprosy or the plague," he set down the true mission of the physician as he saw it: "If you are to be useful and honored members of your profession, you must lay upon its altars the free will offering of a life-long servitude. Self-sacrificing devotion to the cause of humanity, and profound sympathy with the sufferings of our race constitute the crowning excellencies of the true physician, and in this he approximates more closely than any other the character of the great Physician who continually went about healing the sick and relieving distress, and finally yielded up his life upon the cross for the race that it was his mission to save." [8]

Prior to 1883, a few prominent visitors had attended the meetings of the Association. This year, Dr. John A. Wyeth, of New York, was the guest speaker, and a synopsis of what he had to say on "A Plan of Medical Education, Embracing Four Years of Study" has been preserved in the *Proceedings*. He began by picturing the qualities to be desired in a medical student: "The student-life of a medical man should begin before he has seen the walls of a medical school, and should end, if he is true to his trust, only when death closes

[7] Sir William Osler expressed the same idea more briefly but no more aptly: "The dead hand of the great Pergamite [Galen] lay heavy on all thought" for a thousand years.—"Harvey and His Discovery," in *An Alabama Student and Other Biographical Essays* (London, 1908), 307.

[8] In 1952, the original handwritten address of President Starley was presented to the Association by his grandson, Dr. W. F. Starley, of Galveston.

PAST PRESIDENTS

J. H. SEARS, 1893   J. W. McLAUGHLIN, 1894
P. C. COLEMAN, 1895   J. C. LOGGINS, 1896

PAST PRESIDENTS

Bacon Saunders, 1897   J. T. Wilson, 1898
A. B. Gardner, 1899   B. E. Hadra, 1900

the door to his library. Every individual who is to study to become a practitioner of medicine, should be an educated gentleman, above suspicion and without reproach. He should possess those qualities of character which make a man, a man. Gentle and tender, yet courageous; refined and polished in manner, yet unassuming; neat in person and appearance, yet without display; at the bed-side of the pauper or under the roof of the millionaire, he should be the same; careful, considerate and dignified."

A good, well-rounded education with emphasis on Latin and Greek languages was the prerequisite recommended by Dr. Wyeth for admission to medical schools. He advocated a course of four years of eight months each. Anatomy, chemistry, botany, and physics should be studied the first year. "Anatomy should never be taught but in the dissecting room." In the second year, anatomy, histology, physiology, materia medica, pathology, and chemistry, "by recitations and laboratory exercises," should be studied. The third year "should be devoted to anatomy, pathology, therapeutics in laboratory work, and to the lectures and recitations in surgery, medicine and obstetrics and their various subdivisions." The fourth year should be limited "entirely to practical and clinical study under experienced teachers."

Very little business was transacted at the Tyler meeting. Thirty-five new members were accepted, including such men as F. M. Hicks and G. G. Watts. It was agreed to discontinue the contract with the *Texas Medical and Surgical Record* and to publish the *Proceedings* separately. Somewhere along the line, the bylaws had been amended to this effect: "No paper shall be read before either of the sections, the reading of which occupies more than twenty minutes." The *Proceedings* recorded this change, which was probably not enforced. The *Proceedings* also contained a useful table listing the officers from 1869 to 1883 and the places of meeting. C. W. Alban, of Memphis, had surgical instruments on exhibit. J. E. Anderson, representing Chamberlain & Company, of St. Louis, showed a number of medical books.

Dr. Larendon revealed that the treasury had a pleasing balance of $1,340.71, with all bills paid. Secretary Burt reported that "in addition to the usual correspondence he has revised a list of about 1200 physicians in the State; has given liberal notification of this present meeting, has distributed 500 memorials on fees in expert testimony; has mailed 500 addresses of the President of this Association; has mailed 50 copies of the proceedings of the last annual meeting to the Secretaries and members of other State Medical societies, and has written over 300 letters to various persons in the United States in answer to queries about this State and her medical and civic interests."

Elected as new officers for 1884 were A. P. Brown, Jefferson, president; T. H. Nott, Goliad, first vice-president; J. D. Osborn, Cleburne, second vice-president; and Frank Allen, Lexington, third vice-president. Burt and Larendon were retained in their respective places as secretary and treasurer. When Dr. Osborn was presented, he "made a brilliant response, and gave evidence of a talent for the rostrum not often accorded to Doctors." Belton was decided on as the place for the next meeting.

The eighteenth annual session of the Association convened at the Opera House in Belton on April 22, 1884. In his introductory remarks, President Brown spoke thus of the papers to be read: "While it is a lamentable fact that some men write too much, it is equally true that there are those who do not write enough, and by such neglect of real duty lock up many valuable facts which are often too dearly obtained to be lost, and should not perish with their possessors." Dr. Brown touched on the subject of a library and museum: "Nothing gives more pleasure than a well selected library and attractive museum." He felt that the state should give assistance in this project and that space should be provided at the University of Texas. Another recommendation had to do with the training of nurses. "Judicious nursing by trained hands," he said, "often determines the result of disease." He advocated the establishment of a school for nurses in the medical department of the University of Texas.[9] Later on in the program, a resolution requesting information about the establishment of the medical department was passed. This request was pertinent in that two members of the university Board of Regents were present.[10] Dr. Ashbel Smith, president of the board, had no difficulty in furnishing the desired in-

[9] In 1881, Austin had been selected by popular vote over Tyler as the location of the main university, and the first class entered in 1883. By a vote of 29,741 to 12,586, Galveston was chosen over Houston as the site for the Medical Department, which was not to open until 1891.—Lane, *History of the University of Texas*, 250.

[10] Of the eight regents, three were physicians: Ashbel Smith, B. E. Hadra, and T. D. Wooten.

formation: the Legislature had not appropriated funds for establishing the medical department.

Of the 369 members of the Association at this time, 88 were admitted at the Belton session. The names of two of these new members were to be appearing regularly in the *Transactions* (which had replaced the *Proceedings*) for many years: E. P. Becton and J. E. Gilchrist.[11] This large number of accessions made it possible for Treasurer Larendon to report that his cash on hand had increased to $1,748.01. Dr. Burt reported both as secretary of the Association and as chairman of the Committee on Publishing. Four hundred copies of the 1883 *Proceedings* were printed and mailed at a cost of $343.40. Each member of the Association received a copy, thirty-six copies went to medical journals, and several to other state associations and leading Texas newspapers. Dr. Burt's committee realized that the *Transactions*, with its three to five hundred pages, was becoming cumbersome and, as a remedy, recommended that no paper be considered for publication unless it presented "new facts, new modes of practice, principles of real value, original experimental researches, or so complete a statement of facts as to enable the writer to deduce therefrom legitimate conclusions of importance to the profession."

The Judicial Council recognized the following regional organizations: Bell County Medical Association, Dallas County Medical Society, Ellis County Medical Society, Fayette County Medical Association, Fort Worth and Tarrant County Medical and Surgical Society, Hill County Medical Society, Johnson County Medical Society, Lampasas County Medical Society, Leon County Medical Society, Long Medical Society, Southeast Texas Medical Society, Travis County Medical Society, Waco Medical Society, and West Texas Medical Association. This list is obviously far from complete, for several active societies are not included. In fact, up to this time no complete list of subordinate societies had been included in the *Transactions*.

A resolution, based on services rendered nearly fifty years before, was passed unanimously and by a rising vote. To the Texas Veteran Association, then meeting in Paris, Texas, this resolution was telegraphed: "The Texas Medical Association, in convocation assembled, sends greetings and respects to the Texas Veteran Association. May your days be long in the land you freed. May the blessings

[11] Spelled also Gilcriest and Gilcreest.

of millions yet to come cling around the memory of your noble band." The following day this reply was received: "The Texas Veteran Association reciprocates your courtesy, and invokes God's blessings on your labors for the relief of suffering humanity."

There was discussion concerning treatment of the "unfortunate poor and criminals." The methods in use by city and county authorities tended rather to "encourage ignorance and quacks than to encourage and uphold intelligence." It was suggested in a resolution that one member of the Association in each area be designated by the local authorities to take care of these individuals at an agreed price.

Recommendations and resolutions were forthcoming about changes in the Medical Practice Act, about the creation of a state board of health, and about incorporating the Association. The last item was dismissed without discussion because it was "not thought necessary to procure a charter." And this situation was to prevail until 1889. One resolution received easy approval. This concerned the status of the New York State Medical Society, whose behavior had not been forgotten, and gave approval to a group of New York physicians who had withdrawn from this banished society.[12]

A new journalistic venture appeared about this time: the *Texas Courier-Record of Medicine,* edited and published by Drs. F. E. Daniel, of Austin, and W. B. Brooks, of Fort Worth. In a resolution before the state association, it was hailed as "a medical organ of a high order of merit, a fit representative and exponent of rational medicine . . . whose teachings, based on an acceptance of, and a profound reverence for, the National Code of Ethics, advocate a higher code of morals, a higher standard of education, and unity, harmony and concord in professional ranks."

The scientific part of the Belton meeting showed evidence of original thinking. Dr. H. W. Dudley, in his paper "Animal Ligatures and Sutures," reported on the suture of wounds by use of tendons from mule-eared rabbits. At that time, the following suture material had been employed: "hemp, twine, cotton, etc. of the vegetable kingdom, and shreds of leather, silk, catgut, nerve and nerve sheaths, horse-hair and tendons of the curous [waterbuck] of the animal kingdom, and gold, silver and platinum of the mineral kingdom." One day Dr. Dudley had been following his greyhounds

[12] The New York association was not readmitted to the American Medical Association until 1905.

112

as they chased a jack rabbit. Just as they caught it, one of the dogs was badly cut by barbed wire. Not having any suture material with him, Dr. Dudley hit upon the thought that he might use tendons from the rabbit's leg. This he did, and the wound healed *per primam*.[13] Following this experience, Dudley used the material in twelve accident cases with good results. These included ligation of the anterior tibial and brachial arteries by use of these tendons. The separated tendons were preserved in a 5 per cent solution of carbolic acid and glycerine, and thus were kept soft and pliable for an indefinite length of time.

Dr. C. W. Trueheart reported on the use of "Periosteum Grafting." A young man had received the full blast of a shotgun in his left shoulder at short range. The wound was cleaned up; gun wadding, fragments of clothing, and sixty-four shot were removed; and skin grafts were later applied. The wound healed, except for the clavicular region, but there was marked drooping of the shoulder because of a three-inch defect in the clavicle. Nine weeks later the granulation tissue was removed, and the space between the ends of the bone was lined with small periosteum and bone grafts taken from "healthy dogs, chloroformed or killed for the purpose." "The grafted surface was covered with perforated oil silk; a compress of picked lint, moistened in a 2 per cent carbolized water, put on, the whole being held in place by adhesive strips." Eight out of ten of the grafts "took," "a better result than with human skin-grafts." As granulation tissue covered the grafts, other grafts were inserted to a total of three layers. After two months, the space had filled in and the two clavicles were of equal length. In discussing his results, Dr. Trueheart was frank in admitting that bone proliferation may have resulted from fragments of clavicular bone and periosteum. He was firm in his conviction, however, that the canine grafts were the responsible factor. Certainly, his operation was a forerunner of the bone chips which are extensively used today.

Under the title "Continued Fevers," Dr. S. H. Stout, of Cisco, discussed the several febrile conditions about which there was continuing confusion. Although Dr. W. W. Gerhard, of Philadelphia, had differentiated typhoid and typhus fever in 1837, and although Dr. Stout stated that he had "walked the wards of the Pennsylvania Hospital for a year" with Gerhard, the distinction between these

[13] This is an excellent example of serendipity. See Walter Bradford Cannon, *The Way of an Investigator* (New York, 1945), 69–78.

two diseases was far from clear. Stout felt that the prevailing prolonged fevers of Texas were typhoid fever. Typhus, he thought, was "a blood poisoning provoked in jails, in filthy hovels, and other localities by the putrid effluvia of decaying organic matter." He was less correct when he recorded that paroxysmal fevers, of malarial origin, are "generally conceded to be idiopathic, and are properly classed by pathologists among the neuroses." The disease called "typhoid malaria" was dismissed as a "fashionable pathological heresy."

Another paper of importance was presented by Dr. R. P. Talley, of Belton, on the hypodermic use of quinine. It was realized that quinine in pill or capsule was only partly absorbed and might pass through the intestinal canal unchanged. Hypodermic use of this drug was of recent origin. Dr. Talley found it especially useful in "pernicious malarial fever." He used 15 grains of bimuriate of quinine, along with morphine grain $\frac{1}{3}$ and atropine grain $\frac{1}{60}$, dissolved in 20 minims of water.

Later it will be seen that the programs of the Association came in for criticism, the claim being made that the papers were presented on a volunteer basis after the Association had assembled; unannounced, a member would show up with a paper and be permitted to read it. On several occasions, physicians from out of state sent in papers for presentation or publication; one of these was Dr. R. R. Madden, of Ireland.[14] There is evidence, however, that some papers were solicited. The following letter is one of several which confirm this fact.

WACO, TEXAS, Jan. 1st, 1884.

DEAR DOCTOR,

Contributions from you to the Section on Medical Jurisprudence, Chemistry and Psychology, to be presented at the April meeting of the Texas State Medical Association, at Belton, are respectfully solicited. Please send papers to the Secretary by April 10th.

Respectfully,

J. S. WILLIS, M.D.
Chairman

Asa W. Pope, M.D.
Sec., Marshall, Tex.

An unusual feature of the 1884 meeting was the memorial tribute paid to Dr. T. D. Manning by Dr. R. M. Swearingen, both of Aus-

[14] Irish patriot, surgeon, traveler, and author of *The Infirmities of Genius.*

114

tin. A severe epidemic of yellow fever had broken out in Memphis, Tennessee. Dr. Manning had felt impelled to go to the stricken city and to lend himself and his profession in any possible way. When the epidemic was under control, he proceeded to Holly Springs, Mississippi, which was also hard hit by yellow fever. There he contracted the disease and died.[15] This sacrificial devotion to duty moved Dr. Swearingen deeply. "No sentinels with measured tread," he declared, "no bugle's blare nor cannon's roar was there. A more terrible enemy than man environed the doomed places and moved his noiseless battalions along the desolate streets, and through the poisoned air. Many of the inhabitants were prostrated by sickness, and many others appalled in the presence of the great unseen, unknown destroyer, while a gallant band, worn out, but never resting, grief-stricken, but unbending, were falling, one by one, like true knights, at the post of duty. Conspicuous among that gallant few, faithful, hopeful, daring, a pillar of strength for the weak, a light of guidance for the strong, moved that princely leader, the gifted, fearless, undaunted Manning."

Dr. Swearingen, too, had been a volunteer physician at Holly Springs, along with twelve sisters from nearby Bethlehem Academy. Of the twelve, seven had died of yellow fever. On the wall of the courthouse, which had doubled as a hospital, as late as 1896 could be read the following tribute which Dr. Swearingen paid to one of these courageous women: "Within this room, September, 1878, Sister Corintha sank into the sleep eternal. Among the first to enter this realm of death, she was the last, save one, to leave. The writer of this humble notice saw her in health, gentle but strong as she moved with noiseless step and serene smile through the crowded ward. He saw her when the yellow plumed angel threw his golden shadows over the last sad scene, and eyes unused to weeping paid the tribute of tears to the brave and beautiful 'Spirit of Mercy.' "[16]

The number of exhibitors at the annual meetings was increasing: in 1884, Parke, Davis & Company, of Detroit, William S. Merrell Chemical Company, of Cincinnati, and W. H. Schieffelin & Company, of New York, showed their drugs; Dr. George T. Atkins, of Dallas, and J. B. Alban & Company, of Memphis, displayed surgical

[15] This is not an isolated example of a physician's loyalty. A similar experience in Florida, under similar conditions, is reported by Webster Merritt, *A Century of Medicine in Jacksonville and Duval County* (Gainesville, Florida, 1949), 105.

[16] *Memphis Commercial-Appeal*, March 21, 1896.

instruments; J. H. Chambers & Company, of St. Louis and Atlanta, exhibited medical books; and Dr. W. S. Richey, of Chicago, showed a "full line of artificial dentures."

In the annual elections H. C. Ghent, of Belton, became the new president; E. P. Becton, of Sulphur Springs, first vice-president; H. H. Darr, of Caldwell, second vice-president; and M. Matkin, of Hearne, third vice-president. Drs. Burt and Larendon were continued in their positions. After thanking "the good people of the loveliest village of the plain" for their indefatigable efforts in supplying perfect ease and comfort to members of the Association, the eighteenth annual session adjourned, to meet in Houston on the third Tuesday in April, 1885.

X

Steady Growth, 1885–89

THE STEADY COMMERCIAL and agricultural development of Texas continued. The production of cotton, the chief money crop, increased from 696,000 bales in 1876 to 1,514,000 bales in 1886. Railroad mileage advanced from 2,000 miles in 1876 to 8,000 miles in 1887. The assessed valuation of property increased from $257,632,000 in 1876 to $630,525,123 in 1886. The greatest increase, however, was in population: from 1,591,749 in 1880 to 2,235,527 in 1890.

This continuing prosperity, of course, meant the coming of more doctors to Texas. It meant steady growth for the Texas State Medical Association. It meant improvement in medical methods and techniques. Great impetus was given to medical progress in Texas during this period by the opening of the Medical Department of the University of Texas in 1891.

For its nineteenth annual session, in 1885, the state association came back to Houston after an interval of thirteen years. The City Council Chamber was used for the meetings. Sixty-two members answered to roll call on the first day. Congressman Charles Stewart gave a long address of welcome. He asserted, incorrectly, that the Association had returned to its birthplace, stating that its organization had been effected in Houston in 1869. Stewart was overlooking a fact remembered by only a few: the Austin meeting in 1853. Of this few, President H. C. Ghent was one, but he was too polite to correct his guest speaker. However, in his presidential address he made reference to the correct place of origin of the Association.

Since the day was April 21, Stewart proudly and rightfully referred to the decisive battle which had been fought a few miles away forty-nine years before. He spoke of those doctors who had made contributions to the independence of Texas: Charles B. Stewart, James B. Miller, John S. ("Rip") Ford, Branch T. Archer, N. D. Labadie, Alexander W. Ewing, William M. Carper, and Ashbel Smith.

In reality, Dr. Smith played no part in establishing the independence of Texas, since he did not arrive until 1837; but during his long years of public service, he did much to confirm and maintain it. He was not present at this meeting. Indeed, he was at the time suffering from a severe illness, from which he was never fully to recover. A resolution, appropriately introduced by Dr. George Cupples, expressed a "heartfelt hope that he may soon be restored to health and usefulness." The resolution spoke of Dr. Smith with high regard and affection as "the Nestor of the profession, the advocate of all wise measures in the bright and shining world of the good physician."

The poor attendance must have occasioned much disappointment. Those 62 members at the initial session were a good approximation of the total attendance at this meeting. On one important matter only 46 votes were cast. At this time the total membership of the Association was 332.[1] The Judicial Council recognized thirteen lesser societies. This list, very similar to the one submitted in 1884 and again not complete, included the following organizations: Association of Physicians of Washington County, Colorado County Medical Society, Comanche Medical Society, Dallas County Medical Association, East Line Medical Association, Ellis County Medical Society, Fayette County Medical Society, Hill County Medical Society, Johnson County Medical Society, Long Medical Association, North Texas Medical Association, Travis County Medical Society, and West Texas Medical Association.

As annual meetings came and went, there developed a growing attitude of impatience and dissatisfaction at the indifference and inactivity of the Legislature in matters of medicine and public health. Time after time, the Association had made recommendations, only to have them ignored or rejected. This time Dr. Cupples, chairman of the Committee on Legislation, reported on a bill to

[1] The American Medical Association had 3,887 members in 1885. The income of the Texas association for that year was $1,552.50; that of the American Medical Association, $18,117.25.

118

regulate the practice of medicine: "It was brought up on its second reading and was most ruthlessly strangled by the majority." The *Galveston News* and other papers opposed the bill, and this opposition inspired in some legislators a feeling of "selfish fear and honest timidity." Dr. A. G. Clopton, in discussing Dr. Cupples' report, was convinced that the doctors themselves had an important part to play in instructing the public. "Let the profession do their duty between now and the next election," he said, "and all will be well. Our next Legislature will be virtually instructed, and will act *fearlessly*, for no danger will confront them." Dr. F. E. Daniel, of Austin, who was in close contact with the Legislature, reminded the Association that a legislative committee had given its approval to the desired legislation and yet it "was thrust into a roughly hewn grave." "Before I would again sacrifice my self-respect by appealing to such a Legislature," he cried, "withered be this right arm."

The same subject came up for vigorous discussion before the Section on State Medicine and Public Hygiene when Dr. Q. C. Smith, of Austin, read his paper "Lycurgus and Hippocrates—Can Quackery, in or Out of Our Profession, Be Suppressed by Legislative Enactments?" "Lycurgus would have us believe," Smith said in justifying his title, "that legislators and other civil law-makers were little less than gods, while the balance of mankind were at best mere imbeciles, hence he would enslave all other classes of citizens to politicians,—as a class, the most venal and corrupt in all ages and countries." Hippocrates, on the other hand, "taught that science, in any and all its branches, flourished only when left untrammelled by legal hamperings, free to work out its own grand mission of ever increasing beneficence, doing good for all, working harm to none. And the beautiful teachings of the wise Coan sage, are as true and applicable today, as when our noble exemplar laid deep and wide the enduring principles of free scientific medicine."

And then Dr. Smith proceeded to belabor the politician with much enthusiasm and no little conviction on the part of his audience. What can we expect, he asked, "when the mercenary harlot, politics, with bayonet power, captured white-robed science and forced her into most unholy prostitution, for the sensual gratification of her avaricious, dissolute masters?" In emphasizing his theme, he called in the great Dr. Daniel Drake, who had said that "more than half the States of the Union have laws to regulate the practice of medicine; but I am by no means convinced that they have ever done any real good to the profession or society." He quoted the editor of the *Pacific Medical and Surgical Journal,* who had spoken contemptuously of "the hundreds of unlicensed and incompetent pretenders who are dealing death and destruction among the sick of this city. And yet it is a notorious fact that juries will not convict such offenders, even though they be the lowest Chinese charlatans." "No, my friends," he argued, "you cannot suppress the quack, or elevate the practitioner that needs elevating, by legislative enactments; for they find place and favor in all professions and avocations, and are simply an outgrowth of human corruption, and doubtless will be found in all human institutions this side of the millennium."

The regulation of the practice of medicine, Smith was sure, could not be accomplished by legislation. It must come from the doctor himself. "For it is only the live, intelligent, working, honorable, devoted physician, whose greatest pleasure consists in perfecting himself in the various resources of the healing art, who scorns vile tricks of venal impostors of every shade and class, who lives, morally, above all written 'ethical codes' and legal chains, whose chiefest delight is found in ceaseless effort to relieve or prevent the greatest possible amount of human suffering. Such a physician is the only true faithful representative of free honorable scientific medicine, or worthy of the confidence and esteem of his fellow-citizens."

The reactions to this appeal were mixed. The feeling of the leaders was that, in spite of disappointments, the Association must continue in its efforts to influence desirable legislation. Dr. E. P. Becton, of Sulphur Springs, spoke with emphasis the views of many of those present: "The medical fraternity needed no protection at the hands of the State government. It was able to protect itself. That it was the protection of the people of Texas, the women and children of this fair land against murderous quacks and impostors that the Association asked, through its regularly constituted committee, and the act of the Texas Senate in ruthlessly disregarding such appeal stamped that body as no friend to the people of Texas, or of progress in useful science. What have these Senators done? Have they made records of which they or their constituency can feel proud?"

With this vexing problem temporarily out of the way, only to recur each year up to the present, there remained but a few items of business, other than routine reports of the officers. It was brought to the attention of the Association that the State Electro-Therapeutical Association was disbanding and had asked that a section on electrotherapeutics be established by the Texas State Medical Association. This was done. Dr. J. D. Osborn, of Cleburne, always practical and always loyal, made a motion that in the future no balls or banquets be given as entertainment. A substitute by Dr. W. J. Burt to the effect that "the citizens and physicians do as they please" in this matter was accepted. There is no mention of banquet or ball at this Houston meeting, but a grand sight-seeing tour included visits to the Houston Infirmary, Electric Light and Power Company, Glenwood Cemetery, the New Cotton Exchange, and the Cotton Compress and Oil Mills.

Some new subjects were discussed in the scientific sessions: "On the Use of Salix Nigra (Aments), a New Sexual Sedative, in the Treatment of Masturbation, Excessive Venery, Spermatorrhoea, and Ovarian Disease," by F. T. Paine; "Some of the Causes of Heart Disease," by Edmund Goldmann; "Iodide of Potassium in Typho-Malarial Fever," by O. L. Williams; "Dementia and Hemiplegia, Resulting from Cerebral Compression, Relieved by Trephining," by H. W. Moore; "Report of a Case of Incised Wound of the Abdominal Walls and Intestines," by John C. Jones; and "A Report on Forty Operations under Cocaine," by G. P. Hall. Dr. Goldmann gave three principal causes of heart disease: pregnancy, cold baths, and syphilis. Dr. Moore's report was the first on trephining of the skull to be made before the Association, although the remarkable report of Dr. Cupples the following year cited thirty-six somewhat similar cases. The use of cocaine as a local anesthetic had been introduced by Carl Koller in 1884. In another paper read at this meeting, the introduction of cocaine was hailed as the most notable advance in surgery during the year, and the drug was being advertised in the *Transactions* by Parke, Davis & Company. The following year a Texas doctor was using it in eye, nose, and throat surgery. He used it in 4 to 8 per cent solution and of course knew nothing about the hazard to life and the danger of habit formation.

The report on surgery was made by E. J. Beall. The scope and the grasp of the report cannot adequately be presented in a brief space. Antiseptic surgery had come into its own, and Dr. Beall was fully conscious of its possibilities. He referred to the International Medical Congress, which had met in Copenhagen in 1884, and spoke as though he may have been there. His conception of the

121

various racial characteristics added up to the universality of medicine: "Our daring, quick, inventive American brethren clashed in mental conflict with the German brother and his tenacity and transcendentalism; as well, the slow, plodding, but sure Englishman, and the irrepressible, imitative Frenchman. At this great international convocation, race was unthought of, politics and religion left for other minds, theirs being wholly engrossed for the good and advancement of a noble profession, having for its end the common good of mankind."

Dr. Beall applauded the brilliant operations of Czerny, Billroth, Bergmann, and Kocher on the stomach and intestinal tract. In connection with malignancy of these organs, however, he thought that "these bold and dangerous procedures can only, at best, protract the life of the sufferer from the malignant distempers for which they were devised; and, I think, should be reserved for execution only by the steadiest hands and coolest heads known to the profession." He reminded his audience that radical cure of inguinal hernia was being revived by excision and ligation of the neck of the sac. He believed that the operation was "justifiable under the new surgery, and will, in the near future, become well and permanently established and recognized." One surgeon was advocating removal of the testicle as an extra safeguard for the closure. This idea prompted Dr. Beall to say that "it is particularly easy to estimate lightly the importance of another man's testicle."

Perhaps the most significant part of Dr. Beall's report dealt with carcinoma of the breast. He had removed the breast and the axillary glands in five cases. To emphasize the importance of a lump in the breast, he repeated what he had heard Dr. Gaillard Thomas, of New York, say at one of his clinics: " 'Whenever you find a tumour of the female breast, strike! remove it as quickly as you get the opportunity; it matters little what may be its exact nature. Remove it first, and make the diagnosis afterwards, for,' continued he, 'a woman with a tumour of the breast is a disturbed, an uneasy woman; she is constantly feeling the growth; she is displaying it upon all occasions to her relatives and all the women of the neighborhood; her mind is very much exercised as to its nature and consequences, and to that degree that digestive and neurasthenic manifestations will ensue; and, furthermore, a growth which to-day might be determined benign confers an uncertain immunity that it may not become malignant in the future.' " Beall described a very creditable operative technique. In one case, the closed incision was fourteen inches long. The pectoral muscles were not removed. This and other improvements were not added until the operation by Halsted was reported in 1888.

The presidential address of Dr. H. C. Ghent in its early paragraphs summarized the history of the Association. Dr. Ghent was among the few present who knew of the first meeting, in January, 1853. He gave the Washington County Medical Association proper credit for issuing the call for reorganization in 1869. He paid tribute to the small but determined group of men who laid the foundation for permanent organization: "Thus, twenty-eight medical gentlemen, sixteen years ago, by mutual concessions, united and harmonious efforts, organized the Medical Association, of which every true physician in the State feels justly proud. All honor to the noble band who had the moral courage to undertake the difficult, yet laudable, enterprise of giving form and life, and may we not hope immortality, to the Texas State Medical Association." The purposes and hopes of the Association were then presented. He quoted the four qualities which Hippocrates considered indispensable to a good physician: learning, sagacity, humanity, and probity. He regretted that the Legislature had treated all the suggestions of the Association with ridicule and contempt. He paid tribute to the country doctor and used Edward Jenner and J. Marion Sims as illustrations of what men in isolated areas could accomplish.

Although the Civil War was just twenty years in the past, as proof that internecine hate heals more rapidly in a scientific atmosphere, this Confederate soldier allowed himself, in closing, to use language reminiscent of Lincoln's Gettysburg Address: "Let each one of us here and now resolve, by the hallowed recollections of the past, by the splendid achievements of the present, by the grand and glorious possibilities of the future, to reconsecrate himself in the great work before him."

The Nominating Committee brought in the following names as officers of the Association for 1886, and they were elected: for president, E. P. Becton, Sulphur Springs; first vice-president, R. Rutherford, Houston; second vice-president, John C. Jones, Gonzales; and third vice-president, Sam R. Burroughs, Guy's Store. As usual, the secretary and treasurer were re-elected. What a heritage to posterity it would have been if a picture could have been made of Drs. Cupples and Osborn, both worthy and dignified, as they escorted the newly elected officers to the platform!

Before Dallas was chosen to entertain the 1886 meeting of the Association, the usual vote of thanks was given the people of Houston, the local physicians, and the press. Somewhat unusual was the motion by Dr. R. P. Talley that "the Association compliment the Houston Post with $50, for its fair and full reports of the sessions." The motion was adopted, and the treasurer's report for the following year shows that the money was accepted by the *Post*.

It will be recalled that the 1874 meeting, held in Dallas, had been the most successful thus far. Again in 1886 Dallas was the scene of a meeting that proved to be a high point in the history of the Association. The sessions were held in the Merchants' Exchange Building. The *Dallas Morning News* of April 27, after speaking of the assemblage as a most "intelligent looking body," gave this description of the assembly hall: "Above the speaker's table appears the word 'welcome' in floral letters very artistically arranged, and in front of it stand two floral stars, the scintillations from which are represented by very delicate festoons. Under the gallery extending around three sides of the large hall flowerpots containing the rarest exotics are placed close together with very beautiful effect."

The Association found itself in a truly expansive mood; veritably, it had come of age. The opening session, with 350 of 449 members present, 85 of them new, had an air of formality not often in evidence before. Dr. R. H. Chilton, chairman of the Committee on Arrangements, called the meeting to order and asked Bishop A. S. Garrett to open the meeting with prayer.[2] Mayor John Henry Brown made an official address of welcome on behalf of the city. After offering "a sincere tender of salutations and hospitalities . . . to the representatives of a profession which comes nearer home to our firesides, our sorrows, and our inner life than any other," Brown, himself a historian, fittingly paid tribute to those doctors

---

[2] Two years before, a resolution was introduced in the House of Delegates of the American Medical Association which would have abolished the custom of opening sessions of that body with prayer. The resolution set forth that the association was made up of members from many denominations, sects, and creeds, and that some were agnostics and materialists. This resolution, which probably reflected the influence of Robert G. Ingersoll, then in his heyday, was unanimously rejected.—Fishbein, *History of the A.M.A.*, 116.

who had helped to make the history of early Texas: Branch T. Archer, Anson Jones, T. J. Gazley, B. B. Goodrich, George W. Barnett, and Ashbel Smith. The mayor, however, abandoned history when he said of Dr. Goodrich: "In my youth it was currently understood that he had been cured of consumption in Vicksburg, Mississippi, by having the tubercle cut from his lungs by a leaden ball fired in a duel. I do not vouch for the fact, but have no reason to doubt it, as I was personally cognizant of a similar fact in Gonzales, Texas."

Dr. S. D. Thurston welcomed the Association on behalf of the Dallas County Medical Association. The Hon. Seth Shepard gave a "rousing welcome" from the citizens, and, finally, Dr. E. L. Thompson, of Dallas, introduced President E. P. Becton. It had become the custom for the president, early in each session, to survey the general situation and to make what recommendations he saw fit. This year Becton proposed that members of the Association whose names had been dropped for nonpayment of dues be reinstated on liberal terms. He urged that the state association use its influence against those minority groups which would disrupt the American Medical Association. Then he emphasized the opinions which he had expressed at the last meeting:

I am now, and have ever been, opposed to asking for any legislation in behalf of the medical profession. In this I am aware of the fact that I differ from a majority of this Association. . . . But, as President of this Association, I feel it my duty to recommend that no action be had at this meeting looking to asking the Legislature to pass any law to "regulate the practice of medicine." . . . The educated physician needs no protection, except such as the law gives every good citizen. Quacks cannot be suppressed by legal enactments. . . . Vile impostors and pretenders are found in the pulpit, at the bar, in politics—everywhere; and every effort to rid our profession of them and to elevate the standard of honorable medicine by legislative enactments will prove abortive. Let our annual meetings be gatherings of educated gentlemen, for the purpose, as is so happily stated in our Constitution, "of organizing the medical profession of the State in the most efficient manner possible; to encourage a high standard of professional qualifications and ethics, and to promote professional brotherhood." If the people want protection from quacks, pretenders and irregular practitioners, let them ask for it; let them invoke the aid of this Association, and it will be cheerfully accorded. Any effort that we might make in their behalf would, as has been done, be misconstrued and treated with contempt. This Association cannot afford to knock at the door of the Texas Legislature until that body has learned to appreciate the honor, dignity and purity of the medical profession and the value of human life. Let us elevate the profession, asking no favor of any earthly tribunal.

For the first time, printed programs were available, and thus "the work of the Association was greatly promoted." Because of the large number of new members, including Dr. Edward Randall, of Galveston, the treasurer was able to report increased income. But because of increasing expenses, a cash balance of $1,045.06 was reduced to $45.52 during the year. The Committee on Publishing made a flattering report. Seven hundred copies of the 1885 *Transactions* were printed, at a cost of $698.35. A desire had been expressed to have a handsome and attractive volume, "the equal of the transactions of any other State," and the committee seems to have gratified it. Complimentary letters were quoted from the *New England Medical Monthly,* the *North-western Lancet,* and the *Florida Medical and Surgical Journal.* "This," said the last-named journal, "is the chastest volume of Transactions we have ever seen. It is bound in black muslin, heavy and bevelled, with red edges, and the Lone Star on the cover in gold. It is rich in literature and matchless in execution." The report was so impressive that, on motion of Dr. J. D. Osborn, the Committee on Publishing was voted $200.00 in gold "as a slight token" of appreciation. This honorarium, well earned though it may have been, was a good illustration of the feeling of growth and expansiveness which had come over the Association. It was one of the things which was to cause financial embarrassment in the future.

An unusually disagreeable experience in the life of the Association of this period was the expulsion of Dr. M. Salm, of Austin. This is the record in the *Transactions:*

Dr. M. Salm Expelled.

We charge M. Salm with conduct unbecoming a gentleman and physician.

First Specification—In that he has been guilty of gross plagiarism.

Second Specification—In that he was guilty of seducing a young lady under the most grave and heinous circumstances, and is now, on this account, a fugitive from justice, and cannot be found to serve a citation upon him for trial.

J. B. ROBERTSON, M.D
E. P. BECTON, M.D.

We, the Judicial Council, having had the above charges and specifications brought before us, and having had overwhelming evidence of the truth of the charges presented to us, we do hereby present the name of Dr. M. Salm as that of a man expelled from the Texas State Medical Association.

M. H. OLIVER,
President Judicial Council.

W. A. ARCHER,
Secretary Judicial Council.

That much importance was attributed to this case is seen from the fact that the charges were brought by the president of the Association and by a former Confederate general. Dr. Salm had been an active member of the Association for five years, had presented several papers, and at the time of his expulsion was a member of the Judicial Council. The only available suggestive background is found in two papers read by Salm in 1881: "Tobacco and Alcohol, and Their Effect upon the Eyesight" and "A Few Cases of Cysticercus." These papers were published in the *Texas Medical and Surgical Record* for August, 1881.

In the November issue, Dr. A. N. Denton, of San Marcos, took violent exception: "It may be taken for granted that no medical practitioner will attempt to report his professional experience for publication, unless he has sufficient medical information to save him from serious blunders, and sufficient knowledge of the language in which he writes to use it accurately and intelligibly." The presence of cysticercus in the eye, as seen by "M. Salm, M.D., Oculist and Aurist," was exceedingly rare, contended Dr. Denton, and yet "Dr. Salm is a fortunate observer, having had two cases of this rare affection at the very threshold of his professional career."

There is no recorded discussion about the case, or any statement about the relative seriousness of the two specifications. The charges were brought in and action taken.

Dr. J. D. Osborn, chairman of the Committee on Prize Essay, reported that members of his committee "after a fair ballot, have decided to award the prize of $100 to the essay entitled, 'Reflections on Physical and Mental Culture, in Reference to Hereditary Predispositions, Action and Reaction of Mind and Body, Habit, Normal Automatic Mind Action, Automatic Mental Action, Resulting from Stimulants and Narcotics, Clinical Aspects and Suggestions for Physiological and Psychological Advancement,' from the pen of J. R. Briggs, of Fort Worth."

This eighty-five-page essay does not lend itself to analysis. Its theme, "physical, mental and moral diseases thrive and multiply by concealment," hardly gives the clue. It is a well-written dissertation on disease, crime, poverty, climate, heredity, education, man's relation to his environment, relation of mind and body, automatic mental action, with firm emphasis on physiology, psychology, and philosophy. The essay was a compliment to the intelligence as well as the patience of the Texas doctors of 1886.

Some of the many subjects discussed at Dallas were "Texas Quackery," "Early Blistering in Pneumonia," "The Teeth in Congenital Syphilis," "Prophylaxis in Smallpox," "Antiseptics and Antiseptic Surgery," "Glaucoma," "Interstitial Keratitis," and "Ophthalmia Neonatorum."

Dr. Edmond Souchon, professor of anatomy and clinical surgery at Tulane University, and Dr. Thomas A. Foster, former president of the Maine Medical Association, were guests of the Association. Dr. Souchon, in a paper entitled "Recapitulation of Surgical Cases," gave in more or less detail the history and treatment of forty-eight surgical cases. These ranged all the way from eye enucleation to cancer of the rectum. And then, for good measure, he gave a detailed description of an operation in which he had resected the superior maxilla for cancer. As an assistant he had had young Dr. Rudolph Matas, his "chief of clinic." The dissection was extensive, bloody, and prolonged. Twice the operation was halted so that the patient could be revived. "The cavity of the wound was packed with sponges, the head was hung down, whisky was injected freely into his limbs, the right side of his face and the pericordial region were slapped hard with the end of a wet towel, and his weak respiration was assisted by artificial means." Two things, said Dr. Souchon, can be learned from this case: "first, how much human nature can stand; second, that, if the patient had applied sooner, all the disease could have been eradicated, thus increasing very much the chances of cure." [3]

But despite the fine impression which Professor Souchon must

[3] The description of this operation, with all its bloody details and technical difficulties, was published in the *Dallas Morning News,* April 30, 1886. In fact, the paper carried the full proceedings of the Association, with name and address of those in attendance.

have made, the climax of this meeting was the report of the Special Committee on Surgery. This committee was made up of Drs. E. J. Beall, A. G. Clopton, George Cupples, B. F. Eads, J. M. Pace, and D. F. Stuart. Dr. Cupples was chairman and reporter, and as such was the author of the report. "The whole report was written and every entry made by the same hand." Justification for devoting the prodigious amount of work the report required is offered in a foreword: "It will not be denied that in whatever walk or vocation of life an individual may be placed, it is good for him to pause from time to time, and to review his work in the past; how advantageous must it then be for the Surgeons of Texas, scattered over a vast territory, frequently isolated from professional intercourse with their brethren, in innumerable instances compelled to rely on their own resources, where delay or hesitation would entail the loss of human life; how advantageous it must be for each one of them to review his individual labors, and by recording them, to furnish data for a general review, the value of which will increase in the ratio of the number and of the experience of the reporters."

Dr. Cupples was proud of his accomplishment and proud of his fellow-surgeons. "If the whole truth must be told," he wrote, "the writer of this Report remembers to have read in the London Lancet some years ago—'What good (professionally, that is) can come out of Texas?' and he has it very much at heart to answer the sneer of the great London journal by proving, from a survey of their work, that the surgeons of Texas, country doctors though they be, though no long string of academic honors illustrate their names, are second to those of no country in the variety, the boldness and the success of their operations, in practical skill, in fertility of resources, and in that self-reliance founded on knowledge, without which no man can be a successful surgeon."

As a means of collecting material for the report, more than 6,000 questionnaires were mailed, asking for information on the reason for operation, whether injury or disease; age of patient, sex, color; nature, mode and site of operation; name of operator and assistant; anesthetics and antiseptics used; and the result of the operation. In addition, 1,500 postal cards and more than 700 letters were sent out. One hundred thirty-eight Texas surgeons responded, beginning with Dr. Alex. W. Acheson, of Denison, and ending with Dr. T. D. Wooten, of Austin. The report can best be summarized in Dr. Cupples' words:

The condensed report, from those furnished your committee, covers 4,293 operations, and is contained in seventy-four folio sheets exhibited for inspection in the hall, and the result will be found in the summary of operations in each class, with the deaths and recoveries and ratio of each; in a table of major and minor operations, with deaths and recoveries, and in a third table setting forth the number of cases of Secondary Hemorrhage, Tetanus, Pyaemia, Septicaemia, Erysipelas and Gangrene, occurring after operations, with the mortality; also a tabular view of anaesthetics and antiseptics employed and their effects. There are further tables of the more important operations. There is also a list of gentlemen who have furnished reports, from which it is to be regretted that the names of so many well-known surgeons are absent.

The report is presented under the following headings: "Amputations and Dislocations"; "Resections of Bone in Continuity"; "Ligation of Arteries"; "Tumors, Noteworthy for Size, Site, Character, etc."; "Operations Involving the Head and Neck"; "Operations Involving the Thorax"; "Operations Involving the Abdomen"; "Operations Involving the Rectum and Anus"; "Operations Involving the Male Genital and Urinary Organs"; "Operations Involving the Female Urinary Organs"; "Divers Operations Involving Bone"; "Plastic Operations"; "Operations on Organs of Special Sense"; and "Miscellaneous Operations." And then there is finally an "Abstract of Operations, Recoveries, and Deaths in Each Class."

It need not be stated that the surgeons performed most of these operations, not in hospitals, "but under the most difficult circumstances, deprived even of necessary instruments, and, as has fallen to the lot of some of our number, compelled to amputate a limb in a negro cabin with a bowie knife and a carpenter's saw." Chloroform was chosen over ether in the proportion of about 35 to 1. Carbolic acid was practically the only antiseptic used, with occasional mention of iodoform and mercuric chloride. It took skill to remove a sixty-five-pound ovarian cyst with "extensive adhesions" or to do a splenectomy. Indeed, it took courage to do surgery at all when faced with mortality rates like these: trephining, 15 per cent; splenectomy, 100 per cent; herniotomy, 26 per cent; abdominal hysterectomy, 92 per cent; transfusion, 75 per cent; all major operations (2,080), 16 per cent. Many of these operations were done in pre-Listerian times; naturally the later results were much better. But there was no juggling of statistics here: the bad went in with the good. This report on surgery, submitted to the Dallas meeting in 1886, is a signpost in the advance of surgery in Texas. Its scope and its significance can be appreciated only after it has been carefully studied.

President Becton addressed the Association on "American Medicine." He found in Sydney Smith's impertinent questions, "What does the world owe to American physicians or surgeons? What new substances have their chemists discovered, or what old one have they analyzed?" ample provocation to defend American medicine. After eulogizing McDowell, Long, and Sims, he continued:

I pass the names of Rush, Physic, Warren, Jackson, Chapman, and a host of others, eminent for their learning in the profession, and come at once to the name of William Gibson, who was the first to tie the common iliac artery; Roger, of New York, the first to tie the common carotid; Mott, the first to tie the arteria innominata; Post, the first to successfully tie the subclavian, for the cure of aneurism, after Sir Astley Cooper and Abernethy had failed; John Rhea Barton was the originator of a most valuable operation for the relief of anchylosis; Knight was the first to successfully apply digital compression for the cure of aneurism; metallic and animal ligatures were first employed by American physicians and surgeons; Dugas, of Georgia, was the discoverer of that valuable diagnostic sign in dislocation of the shoulder joint; Deadrick, of Tennessee, was the first to excise the lower jaw; Jameson, of Baltimore, the first to excise the upper jaw; Nott, of Mobile, the first to operate for coccygeal neuralgia.

Dr. Becton spoke out in defense of animal experimentation, dismissed the teachings of Darwin and Huxley as doctrines which wither and blight like the winter's frost, and then launched into a vigorous championing of the American Medical Association against that small group which would bring about a schism in the national organization. The Texas State Medical Association was represented in St. Louis the following week with these words inscribed in letters of living light on the glittering folds of its banner: "The perpetuity of the American Medical Association. The honor, dignity and purity of American Medicine. For these we live; for these we labor." Thirteen Texas delegates were present: W. H. Calfee, George Cupples, O. Eastland, J. D. Jordan, B. F. Kingsley, C. W. LeGrand, J. W. McLaughlin, J. F. Y. Paine, R. W. Park, J. C. B. Renfro, Bacon Saunders, Frederick Terrell, and T. J. Tyner. The effort to disrupt the national association was a complete failure. The *Philadelphia Medical and Surgical Reporter* was able to say that "the main body of the American Medical Association is today more united than it ever was, and it has lost the allegiance only of those who got mad because they could not control."

All in all, the Dallas session was most successful. The *News* reported that the meetings were reeled off with "dispatch and good digestion." The exhibitors had increased to six, including four newcomers: Sharp & Dohme, Mellin's Food, A. S. Aloe & Company, and Stearns & Company. The *Transactions* for this year had seven hundred pages, whereas the preceding and the following volumes had only four hundred each. Its reputed value as an advertising medium is suggested by the presence of full-page notices from Tulane, Jefferson, Bellevue, University of Nashville, and St. Louis Medical College. A "professors' general ticket" at these institutions cost $140, $140, $140, $75, and $90, respectively.

The new officers elected for 1887 were T. H. Nott, Goliad, president; R. H. Chilton, Dallas, first vice-president; J. C. Loggins, Ennis, second vice-president; and H. L. Parsons, Kaufman, third vice-president. Drs. Burt and Larendon were re-elected, but at Burt's death a few months later his place was taken by Dr. F. E. Daniel, of Austin, where the next meeting was to convene.

The 1887 meeting was called to order in the Chamber of the House of Representatives in Austin by Dr. J. W. McLaughlin, chairman of the Committee on Arrangements. As he had done in 1875, the Rev. Thomas B. Lee, of St. David's Episcopal Church, opened the exercises with a prayer. The reporter rightly spoke of it as "beautiful and impressive":

> Thou from whom each good gift cometh,
>   Holy Father, Thee we pray,
> Behold Thy servants gathered,
>   In our city on this day.
>
> For the gracious gift of healing,
>   Which Thou hast on them outpoured,
> From the fullness of Thy spirit,
>   Thee, we praise, and thank, O, Lord.
>
> Let not even pride of knowledge
>   Hold them back from knowing Thee,

Rather, let each science triumph;
Deepen their humility.

Thou, Thyself the Great Physician,
Let Thine Image in them shine.
So their minds and wills shall daily
More conformed be to Thine.

Prosper Thou their work upon them,
May they be in blessing blest,
Till at length both healed and healers
Enter Thine eternal rest.

Many changes had taken place in Austin and in the Association since the first meeting thirty-four years before. From "a frontier village of a few hundred people," Austin had grown to be, according to Mayor J. W. Robertson, one of six Texas cities with population over twenty thousand. The Mayor reminded the assembled physicians that the capital city had grown in beauty as well as in size. "The people who dwell on these surrounding hills are vain enough to claim that this is the most beautiful and desirable city in the State, and I trust that the gentlemen composing this most honorable and distinguished assembly will take occasion, during their stay in our midst, to satisfy themselves of the justice and truth of these claims."

Dr. F. E. Daniel and Mr. A. H. Graham welcomed the members of the Association on behalf of the physicians and citizens of Austin. Graham waxed sentimental as he paid tribute to the family physician as he liked to remember him: "If it were given me to select the brow upon which to place the richest crown in heaven's coffers, I could not imagine one more worthy to wear it than that of the gray-haired physician, who, bent with the weight of years, and spent with the toil of arduous duties, well performed, turns with weary steps to lay himself upon his last couch to rest."

On roll call by the secretary, ninety-three members responded. The acceptance of fifty-two new members would suggest an attendance a good deal higher than was recorded. President Nott made several recommendations in his opening remarks: the practice of economy in the financial affairs of the Association; the creation of a Board of Censors to compromise the "personal differences and minor grievances which must necessarily arise among members in a body so large as ours"; discontinuance of advertisements in the *Transactions;* and condemnation of physicians' use of proprietary medicines. All these recommendations were approved by a committee appointed to study the suggestions.

The Judicial Council reported the presence of fifteen lesser affiliated organizations. The following were included in the list and had not been acknowledged in two previous reports: Bosque County Medical Association, Brownsville and Matamoros Medical Association, Central Texas Medical Association, Galveston Medical Club, and Rockwall and East Collin County Medical Association. The presence of the word Matamoros in the second organization is interesting.

Despite the versified appeal for divine guidance at the outset of this Austin session, it must be recorded as one characterized by contention and discord, by charge and countercharge, unapproached in other years. The Judicial Council initiated the disagreeable business by recommending the expulsion of Dr. W. G. Hardin, of Terrell, and Dr. F. W. Kaiser, of Flatonia. Violations of the code of ethics were mentioned in the accusations but were not specified. Dr. J. D. Osborn and Dr. A. M. Douglass objected to voting on "the expulsion of a member without knowing of what he stood accused." Then the specific charges were read: that both men had consorted with quacks and had otherwise comported themselves unprofessionally. Their expulsion followed.

Dr. M. K. Lott, of Belton, had printed a pamphlet entitled "A Chapter on Medical Ethics as Practiced by Dr. H. C. Ghent." Dr. J. J. Dial brought charges against Lott for distributing the pamphlet to doctors and laymen alike, with "malicious intent of damaging the reputation of said H. C. Ghent, as a gentleman and physician." Long discussion terminated in the suspension of Dr. Lott for one year.

By way of retaliation, Dr. R. P. Talley, of Belton, preferred charges against his fellow-townsman Dr. Ghent, accusing him of conduct unbecoming a gentleman, in that "during the year 1884, he did, in order to get to be President of this Association, write several infamous and libelous letters in regard to members of this Association." For this and other conduct, Talley called Ghent "unworthy of the honor and benefits of membership in this or any other well organized Medical Association," and asked that he "be at once expelled." Dr. Ghent demanded immediate action on the charges.

134

The Judicial Council quickly found them "flimsy, puerile and entirely unsustained by the evidence produced, and absolutely unworthy of consideration. We exonerate Dr. Ghent of even a suspicion of guilt." Less fortunate was Dr. D. B. McMillan, of Johnson County, who was accused by Dr. J. D. Osborn, of Cleburne, of gaining admission to the Association by falsely representing himself as a graduate in medicine. The Judicial Council recommended his expulsion.

But the most distressing of these disagreeable experiences revolved about the personages of Dr. F. E. Daniel, of Austin, and Dr. J. R. Briggs, of Dallas. Dr. Briggs had received the prize-essay award in 1885. Dr. Daniel was functioning in the dual role of secretary of the Association and editor of *Daniel's Texas Medical Journal*. An article had appeared in this journal accusing the Committee on Prize Essay of partiality in its award to Briggs. The committee was exonerated of the charge. The next day Dr. Briggs, in a three-page presentation, asked Daniel's expulsion on the ground that he had falsely claimed his journal to be "the official Organ of the Texas State Medical Association"; that he had appropriated to his own use $175 from the funds of the Association; that he was a "firebrand, a stirrer up of strife and a fomenter of discord"; that he was vindictive and embittered because he had not been elected president of the Association; and that he was critical of two distinguished former presidents of the Association. Dr. Daniel, in a brief statement, branded "the entire allegations in every particular, as false as hell." He was cleared of all charges by the Judicial Council. Hardly had Daniel finished thanking the Association for "this act of simple justice" before a motion was made that Briggs be expelled. The motion was ruled out of order.

The next day, Dr. J. J. Dial brought charges "against Dr. J. R. Briggs for his action in preferring charges against Dr. F. E. Daniel," asking that Briggs "be either expelled or exonerated from your body at once." "I do this," said Dial, "both in justice to the Association, and Dr. Briggs and his friends." Daniel declined to appear or to give evidence. The result was that the Judicial Council vindicated Dr. Briggs: "We do not deem it a crime for one member to prefer charges against another in this Association." This controversy was altogether unfortunate. As a result of it, the Association was to reap a harvest of bitterness which would project itself far into the future. There seemed to be more criticism of Daniel as an editor than as secretary of the Association and chairman of the Committee on Publishing, for he continued in the two latter capacities for three years.

Austin was most generous in the way of entertainment. Governor and Mrs. Sul Ross honored the Association with a reception at the Executive Mansion. By way of reciprocation, the Governor and his staff received and accepted an invitation to sit on the platform at one of the Association meetings. The fact that the Section on Obstetrics was in session was not significant. On the night of the Governor's reception, Dr. and Mrs. J. W. McLaughlin entertained members at their residence. On Tuesday evening, "the grand opera of Belshazzar was given at the Opera House by the Austin Musical Union, under contract with the Committee of Arrangements, for the entertainment of the delegates." This performance "far surpassed our most sanguine expectations, and would have been creditable to any of the metropolitan cities, and we tender our sincere thanks to the members of the Musical Union, the hospitable citizens of Austin, and especially to the Committee of Arrangements, for providing us with such a magnificent entertainment." Visits were made to the "magnificent new Capitol," of native granite, then in process of construction, the new University of Texas, the Lunatic Asylum, the Institute for the Blind, the Asylum for Deaf Mutes, and the Confederate Camp and Soldiers' Home. The invitation to visit the university came from Leslie Waggener, its first president; that from the Confederate home, from General R. Lindsey Walker. The recorder was careful to explain that General Walker was the "late General R. E. Lee's corps commander of artillery in Virginia, and now commander of John B. Hood Camp Confederate Veterans."

The treasurer, despite good collections, showed a precarious balance of $20.07. But this did not include a note for $255.00 executed by the Committee on Publishing to defray the extra expense of printing the 1886 *Transactions*. Thus deficit spending came to the Association. The secretary reported the membership about stationary, with fifty-two new members and fifty dropped for nonpayment of dues for three years or longer. The secretary referred to 537 books in his possession which "can be made by proper care and attention —a *library*." These were mostly *Transactions* of the Association, but Daniel thought they were "worth the cost of a book-case, or other means for their proper care."

136

Dr. R. P. Talley, chairman of the Committee on Constitution and Bylaws, recommended several changes, but these were not considered until 1889. As an appendix to the constitution and bylaws, the committee offered the following:

Seven things any Chairman should remember

(1) Take the chair promptly at the time for the meeting to open.

(2) Always rise to your feet when putting a question. All your remarks to the House should be made standing.

(3) Order is best maintained by a rigid enforcement of Parliamentary Laws.

(4) Except in vote by ballot, the Chairman can only vote when the meeting is equally divided, or when his vote given to the minority would make the division equal.

(5) The Chairman should familiarize himself thoroughly with the purpose of the meeting.

(6) Common sense, decision and firmness are absolutely necessary to a successful Chairman.

(7) The Chairman's three duties are: to preserve order, to put questions and to keep the body strictly to the business on hand.

Six things any Secretary should remember

(1) Provide the necessary stationery for the performance of the duties of the Secretary.

(2) In reading minutes and papers, pitch the voice to the furthest person in the room.

(3) Do not attempt to write up the minutes during the meeting,—take full note of everything that happens.

(4) Preserve all papers carefully. Do not allow members to remove them after they are read.

(5) See to it that all Committees are properly warned of their appointment and the business they are to do.

(6) In writing minutes, make them as short as possible but include every important matter.

A timely address was made at the 1887 session by Dr. Thomas D. Wooten, chairman of the Board of Regents of the University of Texas. Dr. Wooten had succeeded Ashbel Smith, who had died on January 21, 1886. He spoke on the progress and prospects of the four-year-old university, a mile to the north. He deplored the action of the Legislature of 1883 in disposing of the two million acres of fertile land and granting to the university a large area in West Texas "vastly inferior in quality to the lands previously taken away." He attributed this result to "the fraudulent maneuvers of those who have from time to time exercised the functions of legislators." He could not have been expected to foresee that beneath that arid area was a pool of oil which would pour upwards of $165,577,000 into the coffers of the university by 1953. In 1887, income was only $47,000. The prospects for a medical department were unpromising. But the need was urgent. "We need a medical school," said Wooten, "to educate the hundreds of young men who yearly go elsewhere for their professional education; we need it as a nucleus for scientific enterprise and research in our chosen calling; we need it as a measure of professional culture, and a standard of professional attainment, we are entitled to it under the beneficent endowment of those who conceived the establishment of a State University, and we would have it today should the designs of those early patriots be fulfilled, and the honest claims of the institution be recognized by those who now exercise the prerogatives of government."

Several of the papers presented at the Austin session displayed a pioneering spirit in medicine. "Laparotomy for Intestinal Obstruction" was the title of a paper by Dr. John C. Jones, of Gonzales. A seventy-year-old man had had an obstruction for eleven days. Among other measures, "the patient was inverted and held by the heels, and large quantities of warm water were pumped into the bowels," without avail. On exploration, a constricting band was found and divided. The patient recovered. "Typhlitis" and "perityphlitis" were names given to inflammatory processes in the right lower abdomen. Drs. P. J. Bowers, W. H. Lancaster, and C. M. Alexander, of Coleman, reported such a condition in a little girl. After six weeks the child had died, and at autopsy the appendix "was lost in and completely obstructed by the inflammatory mass in the caecum." "Was there a time," they asked, "had the family been better advised, and sought advice earlier, that this could all have been successfully treated?" Had they followed the appendix more closely, they might have shared an important discovery with Reginald Heber Fitz, who had described the pathology of appendicitis a few months earlier. These Coleman doctors, in their final paragraph, were somewhat apologetic about the absence of the autopsy specimen. "We very much regret," they said, "that the condition of the parts involved in this pathological structure, together

138

with a very strict vigilance maintained over us during the autopsy, prevents the exhibition of the dried mass on this occasion."

Dr. C. F. Paine discussed "A Case of Haematemesis of Obscure Pathology." A large man of sixty, who "had been a free drinker for a number of years, and usually took his liquor straight," had two hemorrhages prior to the one which caused his death. One of these was, wrongly of course, "estimated at from 3 to 5 gallons." At autopsy, the gastric mucosa was found to be normal. "No erosions were to be found. . . . Duodenum presented nothing abnormal." Dr. Paine had the inquiring mind of an investigator, but he could not have known of the possibility of esophageal varices as the source of the bleeding.

In talking on "Scrofulous Glands in the Neck—Their Removal," Dr. Luther B. Creath, of Kinneyville, leaned to the view that scrofula was glandular tuberculosis, despite the opposing view of Rudolph Virchow, and cited inoculation experiments in animals, with reproduction of the lesions, as proof of his belief. He had dissected out two enlarged glands of the neck, one of which had formed a sinus, and three weeks later was able to report a well-healed wound in a much improved patient. He advocated early removal so that "we can dissect out the capsule entire, remove all the affected parts by a clean incision through healthy skin, and with antiseptic precautions secure first intention, leaving, in lieu of a disfiguring scar, a simple line or cicatrix, and thus remove the poison before it infects other tissue."

The title of a paper by Dr. E. J. Ward, of Waxahachie, "Ligation of the Popliteal Artery or Elephantiasis Arabum," may be misleading. A woman of thirty-five had had a swollen leg since childhood. At the time of the operation, the lower leg was greatly swollen, and there was an ulcer four inches in diameter on the posterior surface. Dr. Ward records that he ligated and severed the popliteal artery; one can but wonder, however, whether it was not the vein. At any rate, the previously severe pain disappeared, the ulcer healed, and the swelling greatly lessened. Improvement was hastened by use of a rubber bandage.

The presidential address of Dr. T. H. Nott took up some of the near-at-hand problems that faced the doctors of Texas. He lived in Goliad, "a village of 800 souls, thirty miles from the nearest railroad station or telegraph office. There is not a foot of railroad, nor telegraph wire nor a telephone in my county." He reproved the Legislature for its indifference in matters of health. "Our law-makers give the sheep owner abundant legislation to protect his flocks from disease," he argued, and yet they ignore the physical welfare of the people. Another of his concerns was purity of drugs and honesty in dispensing them. He called attention to the difference between an average druggist and a scientific pharmacist, and then pointed to the fraudulent claims in patent medicine advertisements. The average druggist, he charged,

always recommends that doctor who sends in the greatest number of prescriptions. He will furnish us with prescription blanks—no, not entirely blank—advertising his business. He fills our saddlebags when we go into the country, and to save our patrons from the consequences of our want of medical research, wraps the packages in printed advertisements, claiming curative properties for his patent nostrums, which you know are denied to the whole materia medica. . . . Patent and proprietary medicines, like quacks and charlatans, are boosted into notice by printers' ink and preachers' certificates, either bogus or from sources and authorities worse than bogus. Go to the religious press and you will find it teeming with advertisements and certificates of cancer specifics and infallible consumption cures, and the like. Competent judges indeed they must be of medicine and its virtues!

For the first time, more than one town asked for the next meeting. Invitations came from Galveston, Waco, Corpus Christi, and Cleburne. Galveston was chosen. The new officers were Sam R. Burroughs, Buffalo, president; R. T. Knox, Gonzales, first vice-president; A. M. Douglass, Osceola, second vice-president; and A. A. Terhune, Jefferson, third vice-president. Daniel and Larendon were again re-elected. For the first time, also, the president's picture was used as a frontispiece to the *Transactions*. This custom, with very few exceptions, was followed until the *Transactions* were discontinued in 1905.

The local newspapers were taking more and more interest in the affairs of the Association. Previously, they had printed items concerning the officers or some prominent member, such as a former Confederate surgeon. But at the Austin session, one paper published in twelve full columns the entire proceedings, along with sidelights and comments. It is rather obvious that the material was furnished by Secretary Daniel, since the wording is similar to his. There was a list of the 163 members in attendance; the *Transac-*

PAST PRESIDENTS

Taylor Hudson, 1901   S. C. Red, 1902

Frank Paschal, 1903   F. E. Daniel, 1904

PAST PRESIDENTS

J. E. GILCREEST, 1905   G. B. FOSCUE, 1906

C. E. CANTRELL, 1907   H. W. CUMMINGS, 1908

tions do not furnish this information. After listening to the multiple controversies of this session, the reporter concluded that "doctors know how to wrangle as well as lawyers." The Association was "composed of men who can estimate mankind as they really are, and among whom crankism is scarcely known." The reporter observed that "some of the doctors can talk well as well as prescribe accurately." [4]

Back in Galveston after an interval of eleven years, the twenty-second session of the Texas State Medical Association convened in Harmony Hall on April 24, 1888. Chairman H. A. West of the Reception Committee made the main welcoming speech. He wanted the doctors of Texas to know that Galveston was not "a dead town." He assured them that she would continue to rise phoenix-like from the effects of storm and tempest and fire. Recalling the Daniel-Briggs squabble, Dr. West expressed the sincere hope that the Association would "put into execution some plan whereby the time of the Association should not be consumed in the useless discussion of personal grievances. Life is too short and time too fleeting for us to spend it in this way. Rather let us, in a spirit of concord and brotherly kindness, examine these problems of life and death we are daily called upon to meet."

President Sam R. Burroughs responded in high-flown language typical of the times: "Eleven years have been unfolded from the womb of time and have been gathered into eternity by the inexorable cycles of measured nature, since last we enjoyed the pleasure of holding counsel in your midst, but decades, nor scores can ever deface from memory's records the grand, brilliant and charming reception with which the Texas State Medical Association was received on that memorable occasion." And then he proceeded to do some geographic and historical juggling. "From the foot-prints of a Pineda, a De Soto, a La Salle, to the anchorage of the buccaneer in your waters; and from the little village of Campeche to the populous, wealthy and magnificent city into which you have grown, Galveston and its Island have woven an eventful history."

President Burroughs recommended some changes in the bylaws and suggested plans for obtaining desired medical legislation. He called attention to the progress that was being made in completing the new state capitol and expressed the opinion that steps should

[4] *Austin Weekly Statesman*, April 28, May 2, May 5, 1887.

be taken to obtain a room in this "magnificent and spacious building for the purpose of collection, storage and preservation of all pathological specimens, books, essays, etc., etc., that may from time to time be presented to the faculty of the State, or spring from any other source."

Dr. J. F. Y. Paine, chairman of the Committee on Arrangements, announced receipt of a message from the Mayor inviting the Association "to visit the Artesian wells at their convenience, and stating that an excursion by rail to the Jetties in the bay, had been arranged for that afternoon." About 150 members and "many ladies of delegates' families" inspected the jetties. Further entertainment features were a reception, a ball, and a "grand banquet" at the Tremont Hotel, which should be described. "Exotic flowers and evergreens arranged here and there around the spacious room gave a touch of sylvan beauty to the surroundings, and the profuse display and artistic arrangement of bouquets of rare and beautiful cut flowers made the air redolent with the fragrance of sweet roses. The long tables fairly groaned under the weight of the numerous relishes incident to a well appointed banquet, with here and there a towering pinnacle of pyramid cake iced and decorated in such beautiful style that it seemed a pity to destroy such beauty simply in satiation of an appetite." Food at that time was plentiful and appetites voracious, and there was plenty of time. Here is the menu:

Berwicks on Half Shell, Celery

Green Turtle,   Consomme Colbert

Broiled Redsnapper, Lemon and Butter Sauce

Parisian Potatoes

Soft Shell Crabs a la Tartar. Calf's Brains

Sauté aux Fine Herbs

Turkey, Stuffed with Oysters, Cranberry Jelly

Tenderloin of Beef a la Neapolitan

New Potatoes, Cauliflower

Spring Chicken with Truffles,   Sweetbreads

French Peas, Asparagus

Punch a la Cardinal

Diamond Back Terrapin, Madeira Sauce

Lettuce, Tomatoes, Mayonnaise

Chicken Salad,   Olives,   Chow-chow

Horseradish,   Cucumbers,   White Onions

Strawberries with Cream,   Fresh Pineapple with Champagne

Imperial Jelly,   Vanilla Ice Cream

              Bisque Glace,   Assorted Confectionery
                          Bon Bons,
          Fruits,   Nuts,   Raisins,   Crackers
          Cheese—Edam, Roquefort and American,
                          Coffee [5]

Votaries of Susan B. Anthony were doubtless thoroughly displeased by this report: "In the general dining room, the lady visitors and lady guests of the hotel were having a banquet of their own in the ordinary." This was done "according to conventional custom." [6] The women's "ordinary," or *table d'hôte,* was in sharp contrast to the elaborate feast which the men were enjoying. "When the sparkling wine began to flow," the doctors drank toasts to the Association, the invited guests, the veterans in the ranks, the ladies (*in absentia*), the University of Texas, and the medical press of Texas.

The secretary and treasurer had nothing unusual to report. Dr. Larendon showed the Association to be solvent, but only by the sum of $28.97. Dr. Daniel's roster contained 416 names, one less than the previous year. He reported 22 "societies in affiliation," but he did not list their names.

From the beginning of organized medicine in Texas, the leaders of the Association had been urging the passage of laws for the protection of the people against medical charlatans. Dr. George Cupples, in 1853, had spoken out against the blatant effrontery of the charlatans and deplored the absence of legal restrictions, and every succeeding president had taken up the theme. But frank words, courageously spoken, had accomplished very little. So in 1887 a different mode of attack had been undertaken: a committee was appointed to take the matter directly to the people. The labor of this committee resulted in a letter of four pages addressed to the people of the state of Texas. Presented at the 1888 session, the letter deplored the growth of medical quackery: "The country began to be overrun by ignorant, immoral and dangerous swindlers, self-styled doctors, who preyed upon the unfortunate and ignorant, promising everything and accomplishing nothing for their amelioration or recovery from their ills." It pointed out that thirty-three

[5] Mrs. Sally Frampton, genial manager of the Menger Hotel, made this comment on this menu: "Should by a miracle anyone serve this type of dinner, it would probably cost them around twenty-five dollars per person, and I doubt if all the items would be available even at that price."

[6] *Galveston Daily News,* April 27, 1888.

states had passed laws calculated to curb charlatanry. "The best interest of the people's welfare," it declared, "demands a higher attainable standard of medical education and qualification, skill, and ability, as well as professional honor, integrity and morality, in order to secure the right to practice medicine within the limits of our State." The letter was ordered published in the *Galveston News*.

At this meeting, Dr. Daniel Parker, of Calvert, made some very sensible remarks in his "Plea for Early Surgical Interference in Epithelioma of the Skin": "In many cases," he said, "I believe we can effect an absolute cure, and thus save our patients from horrible disfigurement and untimely death. . . . At least so far as practical treatment is concerned, cancer is at first a local disease, and consequently . . . a recurrence after operation proves that extirpation was not thoroughly performed, or that the attack is a new one; . . . the earlier extirpation is attempted the better the prospect of success; . . . recurring attacks, after complete extirpation, are successively less active, and at greater intervals; . . . surgical interference has no unfavorable influences on the course of the disease, even if unsuccessful in the way of cure."

Less direct and less tangible was the report of Dr. H. A. West, of Galveston, on "Responsibility of Criminals." It was, in fact, a paper on insanity. The discussion became involved in such factors as heredity, criminality, alcoholism, total depravity, moral insanity, and irresistible impulse. He aptly criticized court procedures of the times with criticisms which could in some degree be leveled against the courts of today. What confusion, he asked, must the judge and jury alike experience when "there is the unseemly conflict in expert testimony, men possibly of learning, ability and experience, laboring upon one side to prove the sanity, and upon the other the insanity of the prisoner"? "In my humble opinion," West concluded, "there will be no remedy until an enlightened public judgment, in view of the acknowledged evils of the present system, forces the State to make some radical change, consisting in the adoption of some method whereby the State may employ and properly remunerate experts, who are such not in name only, but who possess the scientific knowledge, who by special training and years of experience are competent to aid the courts in arriving at correct conclusions in dealing with the many obscure cases they are called upon to decide."

144

There was full discussion of Dr. West's paper. Dr. E. J. Ward said that "if he had not known Dr. West, he would have taken him for a preacher, when he began his paper; a little later he thought he was a poet; and as he got well into the intricacies of the vexed question and made all so clear, he was convinced that West was a lawyer." Dr. J. H. Sears had a solution more direct and more permanent than that of Dr. West: he "never could see why a crazy criminal should not be hung, if adjudged guilty by the jury. He should submit to it the more cheerfully."

Mention has been made in an earlier chapter of the custom of inviting distinguished guests from outside Texas. Most of these invitations were graciously declined. Occasionally, some medical contribution accompanied the declination. This year, Dr. Thomas More Madden, of Dublin, Ireland, sent in a paper on "Displacements of the Ovaries," a very good presentation on herniation of the ovaries through the femoral and inguinal canals. The subject was discussed under the headings of symptoms, differential diagnosis, and treatment. In cases with acute symptoms, removal of the ovary was advised, although nothing was said about repairing the hernia.

President Burroughs followed rather closely the pattern of address set by his recent predecessors, speaking on the relation of medicine to science, hygiene, medical legislation, medical education, and quarantine. In closing, he referred to those medical martyrs who had fallen "in defense of life, health and happiness." And then he recalled, with deep emotion, the martyrdom of Dr. George W. Peete, health officer of Galveston:

Just here, memory bears upon her wings a worthy and chivalrous representative of this immortal throng. The eastern extremity of this beautiful island marks a spot where, in that memorable year 1875, when the lamented Dr. Geo. W. Peete was on duty, and the winds blew, the waters gathered and the elements were marshalled for a furious onslaught by land and sea—Medicine and Government sat in counsel. A place forever hallowed and made sacred by the holiest ties of friendship, affection and heavenborn love, an altar, whose fires unceasingly glow responsive to the heart throbs of loved ones, and whose erection crowned the union of Medicine and Government with an incandescent halo of glory as a last and best offering; and so long as mind governs matter, and the Levant sends the liquid wave to kiss the eternal shores of this continent, the memory of this martyr to professional and governmental duty, will live engraven in golden letters in the hearts of this people.

This is a good time to take stock of the Texas doctor of the 1880's. What manner of man was he? Where did he come from? What was his preparation for practice? For several years, it had been customary to print in the *Transactions* in tabular form the names of members along with post office, county, age, nativity, time and place of graduation, and year of election to membership. The list for 1888 comprised 451 names, although the secretary reported only 416 members in good standing. Opposite 133 of these names, no place of graduation is set down; this is in part due to lack of data. In other words, nearly three-fourths were reported as graduates of a medical school. This does not mean that all these were graduates of a good medical school, for 58 schools were represented. A large majority of members were born in the South and came from medical schools in the South. The University of Louisiana led the list with 55 names, and the University of Louisville came second with 26. Two each were graduated in Scotland and Germany, and 1 each in England and Denmark. Eleven were born in Europe; England, Scotland, Ireland, Germany, France, Sweden, Austria, and Denmark were represented. Fifteen states were carried as places of birth. It is interesting that 7 members gave their place of birth as "America." It might be recalled that that was the day when it was not healthy to ask a man why he came to Texas and what his name was before he came.

Another valuable feature of the *Transactions,* instituted several years prior to 1888, was a tabulation of the officers of the Association. Without exception, these tables began with the Houston meeting of 1869 under the presidency of Dr. T. J. Heard. Thus the two meetings in 1853, under the direction of Drs. Joseph Taylor and George Cupples, were regularly overlooked. These tables list the number of the session, date and place of meeting, president, first vice-president, second vice-president, third vice-president, secretary, and treasurer.

The mayors and councils of Waco, Paris, and San Antonio requested the next meeting of the Association. The last-named city was chosen. New officers for 1889 were J. F. Y. Paine, Galveston, president; H. K. Leake, Dallas, first vice-president; A. V. Doak, Taylor, second vice-president; and O. Eastland, Wichita Falls, third vice-president. No change was made in the offices of secretary and treasurer.

The second meeting of the Association to be held in San Antonio convened in Casino Hall on April 23, 1889. As before, Dr. Ferdinand Herff welcomed the assembled members. He called attention to the growth of San Antonio and the progress of medicine in the intervening years. With clear prescience he forecast the prevention of infectious diseases by use of vaccines:

Ten years ago San Antonio was an overgrown frontier village, easygoing, lazy, cut off from the world and without any of the improvements which the present generation count almost among the necessaries of life. All that was wanted then has been supplied within the last years. Three railroads, waterworks, parks, club and opera house, monumental business buildings, large hotels, ornamental private residences, electric lights and two large public buildings bear testimony to the change in the number and public spirit of the population and place our city in that rank to which she is entitled by her age and history. Great, however, as these changes are, they cannot be compared with the giant strides which the medical sciences have made on the road of progress during the last decade. . . . From bacteriology we have obtained the key to the riddle that has baffled the skill of sages and philosophers for over a thousand years. The large gap which had existed between pathology and therapeutics ever since the time of Hippocrates has been gradually filled up, and the physician who formerly groped his way in the dark, begins to see the aurora of a promising future. . . . We know further, that by cultures in proper medicines infectious microbes can be mitigated, so that their inoculation in the healthy system will protect the subject against the disease from which they have originated; in short, by using bacteria against bacteria and mitigated virus against dangerous infection, we will be able to stamp out cholera, yellow fever and typhus with the same success with which small-pox has been conquered by vaccination and hydrophobia by Pasteur's method. . . . I may state with satisfaction and pride that our Association has not lagged behind neither in writings nor deeds. The number of our working members has increased; we have more than a dozen affiliated societies; we can boast of several medical papers; our delegates to the National and International Medical Congress meetings have been conspicuous by their able essays and active participations in the discussions. This is the more creditable since we have neither large hospitals, universities nor pathological or microscopical laboratories.

President Paine, referring to the contemplated changes in the bylaws, urged caution. "Whatever may be done in the way of remodeling the Constitution and By-Laws," he said, should "conform to, and preserve the national code of ethics as the palladium of your honor." He brought up the rebellion of the New York State Medical Society when he questioned the "motives which actuated certain prominent doctors in some of the Northern States of this country a few years ago, in trampling upon the national code, and openly declaring their contempt for it." Damage suits against doctors received this notice from the president:

The increasing number of suits for malpractice furnishes a subject worthy of serious thought. Incompetence does not afford a solution of all the cases, because in some instances the defendants have been among the most prominent members of the medical profession. Physicians have always been held responsible for the unfavorable termination of cases, both medical and surgical, and are frequently the victims of calumny, but their arraignment before the courts has ever been a most exceptional occurrence. The reports of trials that have come under my notice bore the appearance of having been prompted by either malice or avarice on the one hand, or having been instigated by a doctor who had accused his associate of improperly treating a case, on the other. In each case honorable acquittal was the result, but still the accused were not uninjured, for they were not only subjected to the expense of lawyers' fees and loss from neglect of business, but professional standing was not unsoiled. It should always be borne in mind that a physician's reputation, like the character of a woman is a sacred thing, that may be irreparably damaged by a shadow of suspicion, and physicians should exercise unvarying courtesy and mutual protection in all the vicissitudes of professional life. They would not, of course, lend their influence unworthily, to shield a practitioner who, by ignorance or imposition, had gotten into trouble. There should be some local protection to society against the malevolence and rapacity of irresponsible harpies.

In closing his recommendations, Dr. Paine anticipated University of Texas President William L. Prather and John Lang Sinclair by fourteen years when he reminded his hearers that "the eyes of two millions and a half of people are upon you."

The secretary reported that the Association had failed to obtain rooms in the new capitol to be used as a library. "Quite a library of transactions and reports" had accumulated and were stored in the hall of the Travis County Medical Society. These quarters were now inadequate, he stated, and other space must be obtained. Twenty-four auxiliary societies were carried on the secretary's roll, and for the first time the complete list appeared in the *Transactions:* Austin District Medical Society, Bell County Medical Society,

148

Bosque County Medical Association, Brownsville and Matamoros Medical Association, Central Texas Medical Association (Waco), Dallas County Medical Association, Ellis County Medical Association, East Line Medical Association, Fayette County Medical Association, Fort Worth and Tarrant County Medical Association, Galveston County Medical Association, Grayson County Medical Association, Hill County Medical Association, Johnson County Medical Association, Leon County Medical Association, Long Medical Association (Bastrop County), North Texas Medical Association, Rockwall and S. E. Collin County Medical Association, Travis County Medical Association, Terrell Medical Association, Val Verde Medical Society, Washington County Medical Association, Waco Medical Association, and Western Texas Medical Association (San Antonio).

For several years Dr. George Cupples had acted as chairman of the Committee on Medical Legislation. Reports had been made from time to time, but this year (1889) the whole subject was reviewed, and sensible, practical recommendations were made. He established the need for medical legislation by quoting from his presidential address of 1853: "Charlatanism and imposture, the offspring of ignorance reign rampant in the land; no legislative check restrains the indiscriminate and unregulated practice of physic by unqualified persons, the incredible and destructive abuse of nostrums and secret remedies; humbug is the order of the day." Dr. Cupples reviewed the efforts to obtain a medical-practice act and recorded the results. A bill was passed in 1873 requiring the registration of medical diplomas. Three years later, boards of medical examiners were created, their duty being to examine all applicants for license. But soon this law was emasculated and the sole requirement was that county clerks record all diplomas from recognized medical colleges. What county clerk, he asked, is competent to say what medical colleges are recognized? And what county clerk could even read the diplomas? As a starting point Dr. Cupples made three suggestions:

First: A comprehensive and incontrovertible definition of what shall constitute the offense of practicing medicine or surgery without proper authorization.

Second: The appointment by the Governor of the members of the Board of Medical Examiners for the State of Texas, who shall devise an equitable mode for examination, which will insure, as nearly as possible, a uniform standard of qualification on the part of the applicants for license.

Third: An official register of all the qualified practitioners of medicine of the State under all the laws regulating the subject matter, which register shall be an official record, and prima facie evidence of what it contains.

Dr. Cupples then described a bill which he and his committee proposed:

1. It violates no constitutional provision. The State Constitution contains a clause to the effect that no discrimination shall ever be made in favor of any one school or system of medicine. It is true that this bill was drafted under instructions from the State Medical Association, representing the regular or Hippocratic school of medicine, of which there are over 4,000 representatives in Texas, while those of the Homoeopathic and Eclectic schools number less than fifty, yet we defy the most astute, the most acute lawyer to detect in this bill any evidence of its origin. There is no allusion to any difference of schools, any diversity of opinion.

It provides that a fair and impartial examination shall be made of all candidates for license, in anatomy, physiology, pathology, hygiene, surgery, chemistry and obstetrics, all which departments of science are recognized by all schools of medicine, and knowledge of them required by such, as the basis of all medical knowledge. Practice of medicine, on which alone the schools differ, is not included, nor is materia medica or therapeutics.

2. It has no retro-active effect; all legally qualified practitioners who have become such by prescription through length of practice, or by compliance with any law now or heretofore in force, retaining their status.

3. A single board of examiners appointed by the Governor.

4. An official register, which will be an authentic record and official proof of the professional status of those whose names shall be borne upon it. An objection may arise to the creation of a single board of examiners for so vast a territory. It is a self-evident truth that when responsibility and authority are exercised through many different agencies, it becomes inefficient.

The medical profession itself cannot be absolved from responsibility, the report continues. The root of the trouble—the *fons et origo mali,* as Dr. Cupples puts it—is found in

the multiplication of schools of medicine in the different States through the blamable facility with which charters are granted for that purpose.

... The natural and inevitable result is, that crowds of graduates have been let loose on the people, possessing a mere smattering of medical knowledge, acquired in some of these institutions in fifteen months; while in the great schools of the old world, from four to seven years are thought to be none too much for the purely medical education of well-trained and well prepared students. . . . [Restrictions in other states have] driven hordes of quacks of all known and unknown varieties from their accustomed haunts to seek more genial climes, and our fair land of Texas has been an asylum and a refuge, and they have come in swarms to prey upon our people.

A ray of hope was visible on the horizon: a bill had been passed by the Legislature regulating the practice of dentistry and pharmacy. So the medical profession must persevere. After all, "we are called on to prepare legislation for Texas, not as she is today, but for the time when she shall be in population as in grandeur and extent, in power as in resources, the peerless State of the Union." Every doctor in Texas, said Cupples, had a contribution to make in three different directions: "education of public opinion by the medical profession throughout the state by constant discussion in season and out of season; making the practice of medicine bill and board of health enactment an issue in the next election of state senators and representatives; a monster petition from the people throughout the state, urging these measures."

This report was "received with much applause" and widely discussed. The first thought was to distribute 5,000 copies to the people of the state. When it was called to the Association's attention that its "bank had run rather low," no action was taken. The reference to the condition of the treasury was an understatement. As a matter of fact, a cash balance of $44.91 was more than cancelled by $65.00 due to President Paine for funds he had advanced. But the question of publishing the report arose again the next day because Dr. Cupples felt that his conscientious effort was in vain and unappreciated. After full explanation had been made and deep appreciation expressed, several motions and amendments relating to the number of copies were made, all resulting in a decision to instruct the Committee on Publishing to publish in pamphlet form as many copies as the finances of the Association would warrant.

The subject of the prize-essay award came up again, and again it was the source of discord. The award was made to an essay on the "Ophthalmoscope in General Practice," written by Dr. J. R. Briggs, who had won the last award. Dr. F. E. Daniel voted in vain to disallow awarding the one-hundred-dollar prize again to Dr. Briggs. Then it was voted to discontinue the award, which had proved to be a source of unwholesome agitation and useless dissension.

The Committee on Constitution and Bylaws, appointed two years earlier, made its report. After a good deal of work and discussion, it proposed but few changes. The objects of the Association, set down in Article II of the constitution, were enlarged to include "advancement of State Medicine, i.e., of public hygiene; of medical education; of medical jurisprudence and public institutions for the sick and the infirm." Article III was amended so as to require all applicants for membership in the state association to be members of their respective county or district societies. One other change clarified and expanded the duties of the Judicial Council.

Since the reorganization in 1869, no special effort had been made to have the Association incorporated. The general assumption being that nothing was to be gained by incorporation, no charter had been issued since 1853. At this 1889 meeting, however, the president and secretary were instructed to apply for a charter without delay. Two months later the following charter was issued:

Know all men by these presents, That we, R. M. Swearingen, F. E. Daniel and T. J. Bennett, all citizens, of Travis county, Texas, and J. Larendon, a citizen of Harris county, Texas, and our associates, desiring to form ourselves into a body corporate and politic under the general laws of the State of Texas governing the creation of private corporations, hereby adopt and subscribe the following

CHARTER:
I. Name.—The name of this corporation shall be, The Texas State Medical Association.

II. Purposes.—The purposes for which this corporation is created are:

1. To organize the regular medical profession of the State in the most efficient manner possible.

2. To encourage a high standard of professional qualification and ethics.

3. To promote professional brotherhood.

4. To labor for the advancement of State Medicine, i.e., of public hygiene; of medical education; of medical jurisprudence, and public institutions for the sick and infirm.

III. Term of Existence.—This corporation shall exist for the full period of fifty years.

IV. Domicile.—The principal office of this Association shall be at Austin, Travis county, Texas, or wherever the Secretary of said Association may reside.

V. Trustees.—The business of the Association shall be managed by a board of nine trustees, and

J. F. Y. Paine, M.D., Galveston, Texas;
Sam. R. Burroughs, M.D., Raymond, Texas;
O. Eastland, M.D., Wichita Falls, Texas;
W. L. York, M.D., Decatur, Texas;
E. L. Thompson, M.D., Dallas, Texas;
A. G. Clopton, M.D., Jefferson, Texas;
G. W. Kerr, M.D., Waelder, Texas;
J. H. Sears, M.D., Waco, Texas;
A. N. Perkins, M.D., Sabine Pass, Texas,

are hereby declared to be the trustees for the first year.

VI. Capital Stock.—This Association has no capital stock; the estimated value of its assets is fifty dollars.

Witness our hand this the 20th day of July, A.D. 1889.

(Signed)   R. M. Swearingen, M.D.
       F. E. Daniel, M.D.
       T. J. Bennett, M.D.
       J. Larendon, M.D.

It is of passing interest to note that the 1853 charter had permitted the Association to possess property "not to exceed in value the sum of One Hundred Thousand Dollars." In 1889 "the estimated value of its assets is fifty dollars."

In another chapter, it was remarked that the strides of surgery were probably more rapid and more secure than those of medicine; this trend was accelerated by the work of Pasteur and Lister. The *Transactions* of 1889 devoted eighty pages to papers on surgery and only thirty pages to the section on medicine. At one point in the 1889 proceedings, in fact, an attempt was made to terminate the surgical section so that another section could resume. The motion was lost: there were too many surgeons present. The content of some of this surgical material, however, was open to serious question. For instance, there was discussion of abscess formation from perityphlitis, when Fitz, three years before, had shown the origin of such abscesses to be the appendix. Less forgivable was the continued advocacy of Battey's operation.[7] This operation meant removal of both ovaries in women who had "perverted ovarian func-

[7] Robert Battey (1828–95), of Augusta, Georgia.

tion," and it was performed with reckless and frequent abandon. As Dr. J. F. Y. Paine had said, "every aspirant for gynaecological distinction has a strong desire to hang to his belt of fame the ovaries of a woman, as has the Indian of the West to display the scalp of his white-faced victim."

Again, it could not have been expected that a doctor from Georgetown could throw a great deal of light in his paper on "The Functions of the Spleen." But his additional report of an abscess of the spleen leans heavily on his imagination. The abscess first ruptured into the pleural cavity and lung. Next, it found its way into the stomach, "which was followed by great discharge of pus and blood by the bowels, and with it a piece of the fractured rib, about one and a half inches long and half the thickness of the rib." The third rupture of the abscess was even more dramatic: "About six weeks after the second abscess, another formed in the lower part of the spleen, and broke into the peritoneal cavity. I was sitting by her bed at the time, trying to induce her to allow me to aspirate, when a severe paroxysm of pain came on, and the abscess broke. I could hear the pus and blood pouring into the peritoneal cavity."

This great upsurge of surgery did not go unchallenged. Dr. B. E. Hadra, of Galveston, had something to say about the occasional surgeon and the general specialist. Laparotomies, he said, can be performed "away in the bushes," but he doubted the wisdom of the practice except in emergencies.

I am sure that the very same practitioner who claims to know everything, and who represented a kind of a general specialist, if he should require grave surgical treatment himself, or if his wife or daughter should have to submit to a laparotomy, that he will not call in his next best colleague, but that he will travel, like a wise man to a surgeon in or without the State who has acquired an acknowledged reputation in the concerned branch. Now, let our clients have the same consideration you claim for yourself and family. Is it not strange, that the same man who would not dare to touch an eye for cataract, will readily jump at a laparotomy, which to him may be an equally unfamiliar operation? But in the first instance he dreads a failure as a perpetual monument of his inability, perhaps even as a drain on his purse; whilst in an abdominal operation he knows that the victim will be covered with God's pitiful earth, and that the previously warned relatives will be easily convinced that such a termination was unavoidable, considering the large incision and the great array of preparation and instruments!

154

As a contrast, there was a high point in the medical section when a modest but serious young man walked down the aisle with a microscope in his hand. His name was George Dock, professor of pathology and bacteriology in the Texas Medical School and Hospital. He was twenty-nine years old and only five years out of the University of Pennsylvania. The record states simply that "Dr. Dock gave an interesting demonstration of malarial parasites and was listened to with great attention." Dr. Dock summarized the facts about the parasite, beginning with the work of Laveran in 1881. He then proceeded to demonstrate the making of blood films and the examination of fresh and stained specimens. He described the parasite in its several forms and expressed himself as being convinced that it definitely was the cause of malaria. Despite the fact that not all of Koch's postulates had been established, "when a certain organism is uniformly associated with a particular disease, and found in no other morbid state, and when, in addition, it is so evidently affected by the drug which is a specific cure for the disease in question, it seems to us that no more is needed to establish its position as a causative agent."

Dr. Paine delivered his presidential address in a fast-moving world which, as one of his fellow-members had said, was menaced by "the multiplication of accidents, which inevitably attend the growing facilities for rapid locomotion, the sacrifice of human life by the improved engines of war, and the lengthening of the death-roll by the compounding of inherited disease." All this added up to a short life expectancy. Dr. Paine turned to statistics and mathematics to point out the need for improved public health under a capable health department: "Basing a calculation upon the population of Texas in 1880, the diminution of the death rate three per thousand would be equal to the saving of 4,775 lives annually; and it is estimated that for every death two people are sick the year round, which equals 730 days of labor lost for each death; now, if the total deaths (4,775) be multiplied by the days of labor lost for each death (730), the product will be 3,485,750 days of labor lost, which, valued at the low rate of 33⅓ cents per day, shows a clear loss to the State of $1,161,916 annually." He enumerated the principal causes of disease as "heredity, impure air, impure water, climate and soil, habitations, occupation, food, intemperance of various kinds, clothing, sexual errors, parasites, mental causes, including worry, errors in exercise, contagion, etc." Personally and practically, he felt that "good conduct, personal cleanliness and the avoidance of all excesses, are the first principles of health preservation; if to these be added, 'love the Lord and fear the devil,' there could scarcely be a more practical religious and moral code." With a record of 531 deaths from smallpox in Texas in 1880, he had a powerful argument in favor of compulsory vaccination of all citizens.

After the final session on Thursday, it was announced that the members would take a ride around the city and that hacks were waiting at the Menger Hotel. They returned in time for the "grand banquet" at the Menger that night. And then the next day, it was voted to suggest to future committees on arrangements that the banquet be discontinued. An excursion to Corpus Christi on Friday completed the entertainment.

Fort Worth was the place selected for the 1890 meeting. R. M. Swearingen, Austin, became the new president; A. Sims, McKinney, first vice-president; B. F. Kingsley, San Antonio, second vice-president; and I. E. Clark, Schulenburg, third vice-president. Daniel and Larendon were re-elected. In accepting, Dr. Swearingen had this to say: "We are all gatherers of knowledge; we are all workers in the field of science; the man from the country, from the town, the hamlet, the city; and we can all gather up our little facts and bring them together."

Before final adjournment, Dr. H. C. Ghent delivered a well-received address on the prospective Alamo monument. The following resolution, introduced by General J. B. Robertson, of Goliad, was passed: "*Resolved,* That the effort to erect a monument to the heroes of the Alamo meets our hearty approval, and we pledge ourselves to do all in our power to promote the laudable undertaking." [8]

[8] The monument was built by the state of Texas in 1891 and stands on the Capitol grounds in Austin.

XI

The Gay Nineties, 1890–94

THE LAST DECADE of the nineteenth century was a period of comparatively hard times in Texas. This period was punctuated by the national panics of 1890 and 1893. In the nation, the situation resulted from unsound railroad finances, agricultural depression, and bank failures. In the state, all these factors were operative, but emphasis rested on the farm situation; cotton declined to less than five cents a pound. This led to the formation of the Farmers' Alliance and the Populist party. The already unsteady railroads and insurance companies came in for more and more regulation, especially at the hands of Governor James S. Hogg, the great commoner of Texas. These general economic conditions were reflected in the medical profession of Texas, influencing its membership, its finances, and even its temper.

As chairman of the Committee of Arrangements, Dr. W. P. Burts opened the twenty-fourth annual convention of the Association at the Fort Worth Opera House, April 22, 1890. He welcomed the members "to our growing city; to its health-giving air; to its well paved streets; to its electric street cars; to its beautiful churches; to its magnificent libraries, and—to the best article of artesian water in the world." He remarked on the changes in the Association as it had developed from infancy, through boyhood, to mature manhood. Graciously, he noted the presence of a few of the learned men who had undergirded the Association in its formative years, men whose "heads show the whitening effects of many winters, and their faces exhibit the furrows dug by remorseless time." In his reply, President Swearingen pointed to the harmonious sessions of 1888

157

and 1889 as evidence that the period of stormy youth had been forgotten in the higher life of serene and matured manhood. He deplored the fact that "for nearly forty years we have knocked in vain at the door of legislative halls." No protection was afforded the people; with equally disastrous results, a young mother and her baby could fall into the hands of a kind-hearted simpleton or a bold and reckless impostor.

The secretary reported a membership of 506, this being the first year in which the membership had reached 500. This figure, however, was not maintained. The new members from year to year hardly equaled the deceased and delinquent members; the membership in this period stabilized itself at about 425.

The treasurer collected dues in the amount of $1404.50, of which all was expended except $78.00. The principal items of expense were: E. Von Boeckmann for publishing 650 copies of the *Transactions*, $567.00; salary of the Committee on Publishing, $300.00; secretary's salary, $200.00; treasurer's salary, $100.00; and prize essay, $100.00. The committee appointed to examine the secretary's report was satisfied with everything except that they wanted an explanation concerning "voucher No. 7, where he paid $7.50 for clerical work." Illness of the secretary, which necessitated the employment of assistance in mailing 3,000 copies of the report of the Committee on Medical Legislation, was accepted by the committee as a satisfactory explanation. The necessity of employing secretarial help was recognized in a resolution by Dr. H. A. West, of Galveston: "*Resolved,* That the general Secretary be authorized and empowered to select a competent stenographer and typewriter to assist in reporting discussions and proceedings of the Association at each meeting." [1]

Two other resolutions of importance were adopted. One had to do with the length of papers to be read. For some years twenty minutes had been the limit. In this fast-moving era, impatience was asserting itself. This time a committee was created to regulate the length of papers, and those requiring more than twenty minutes were to be presented in abstract. The second resolution gave full recognition to the microscope and the part it had come to play in Texas medicine: "*Resolved,* That a Committee on Microscopy and

---

[1] The first practical typewriter was put on the market by E. Remington in 1874. It had an inked ribbon and had only capital letters. Visible writing was not perfected until 1893.

Pathology be added to the standing committees of this Association, to the end that these branches of study be thereby fostered and the wants of the profession in these directions met by competent investigators." It was altogether proper that Dr. George Dock was made chairman of this committee. The other members were Drs. J. W. McLaughlin, of Austin, and E. J. Ward, of Waxahachie. After Dr. Dock left Texas, another eminent man of medicine, Dr. Allen J. Smith, replaced him as chairman.

Dr. Q. C. Smith, who had an inventive turn of mind, on several occasions had exhibited surgical instruments which he had devised. This year he showed some obstetrical and rectal instruments. Dr. H. A. West said Smith's ingenuity "reminded him of a man who had an improved speculum which could be used at will, either as a speculum or as a tongue-depressor."

In his annual address President Swearingen spoke on "Conservation of Forces." Since he spoke from notes, the address was not available for publication. The *Transactions* record that it was delivered "at the Opera House to a brilliant audience."

The first paper in the Section on General Medicine was by Dr. J. W. McLaughlin. The subject was "An Explanation of the Phenomena of Immunity and Contagion, Based upon the Action of Physical and Biological Laws." [2] Thirty-six pages on a subject rather unclear to both reader and hearer no doubt stimulated the aforementioned resolution dealing with the length of papers. The subject matter became rather involved as Dr. McLaughlin presented the various theories of infection and immunity as championed by Metchnikoff, Prudden, and others. The speaker's first premise was sound: "A person with an infectious fever may infect a hundred or more persons with the same disease." Infection as a cause of disease had not been embraced by all the older doctors. Dr. J. H. Sears, of Waco, a graduate of 1851, in discussing a paper on a similar subject, denied the influence ascribed to "so-called germs." Dr. H. A. West grew a little impatient with his elder colleague, retorting that he

[2] This paper was expanded and later published as a 240-page book: *Fermentation, Infection, and Immunity: A New Theory of These Processes, Which Unifies Their Primary Causation and Places the Explanation of Their Phenomena in Chemistry, Biology, and the Dynamics of Molecular Physics* (Austin, Texas, 1892). A noteworthy aftermath came sixty-two years later. A geologist son of Dr. McLaughlin died in California in 1952 and left most of his one-million-dollar estate to the Medical Branch of the University of Texas to be used in investigations in the field of infection and immunity.

"did not know that there was an educated physician in Texas who refused to accept the theory."

The papers presented at the 1890 section meetings were for the most part not noteworthy. One by Dr. J. D. Burch, of Aurora, on "Cerebro-Spinal Meningitis" reported sixteen cases with seven deaths. The detailed symptoms were rather typical except that the skin and joint manifestations were more extreme than they usually are today. Dr. H. L. Fountain, of Bryan, presented a "Report of Five Cases of Cranial Surgery." He said that in the past the human brain had been "a dark and unexplored region through which there was neither path nor guide to lead to any special area." Now, this was all changed by the advent of antisepsis and localization of brain function as worked out by Broca. The report included three fractured skulls and two brain abscesses. All recovered.

From time to time, attempts had been made to appraise the medical profession of Texas. These evaluations were not unduly critical or in poor taste; rather, they were honest efforts to point out the shortcomings of the Association and to indicate needed changes. Using the title "Our Troubles as a Profession—Their Cause and Cure," Dr. C. M. Ramsdell, of Lampasas, offered this diagnosis:

The profession of medicine in the United States is sick; it is very sick. For many years it has been ailing, and of late, its maladies have so increased in number and the symptoms have become so alarming as to cause great anxiety in the minds of its friends. It is infected by parasites, disfigured by ulcers and tumors, warts and excrescences. It has chills and fevers and night sweats. It shows symptoms of softening of the brain and locomotor ataxy, and has become so generally debilitated as to need crutches, braces, supporters, pads and plasters innumerable. Its crowning woe, the natural outcome of its miserable condition in other ways, is that it has lost the respect of mankind.

Among the deforming growths upon the fair body of medicine may be mentioned homeopathy, eclecticism, so-called, Baunscheidtism,[3] Christian science—in which is to be found neither science nor christianity—and that hemorrhoidal tumor of recent development and evanescent character, A. Wilford Hall's method of rectal irrigation.

The young man who left the plow or the yardstick and who did not know Greek from Choctaw when he saw them in print, Dr.

[3] Karl Baunscheidt, of Germany, who had died thirty years before, had advocated the treatment of chronic rheumatism and other diseases by acupuncture, using a multipointed instrument dipped in an irritant such as oil of mustard.

Ramsdell declared, could not be expected to make a good doctor. He might meet with some success, but a day of fearful reckoning could be expected. "Must he not at times think with horror of that day when he shall meet, in the shadowy world, the reproachful glances of those whose souls he sent, by his ignorance and incapacity, before their time, to the abode of spirits?" Education for the profession was paramount. "The physician should be, by long odds, the best educated man in the community in which he lives. When this becomes universally the case then the death-knell of quackery will have been rung. Knowledge is power, and men who really feel that their family physician is their superior in all other departments of knowledge and the superior of his neighbors as well, will be quite ready to listen to him on matters pertaining to that art for the practice of which he is known to have made special preparations." Education of the layman was likewise of great importance. "There will always be impostors," Ramsdell said, "and fools to believe in them; every good thing will have its counterfeit, but with increased intelligence and education among the masses, there will be a corresponding decrease in all kinds of humbugging, and while education will not prove a panacea for the ailments of medicine, it will heal many of her diseases and mitigate the suffering from others. At all events 'more light' is the first, great requisite."

The next meeting was awarded to Waco. The new officers were W. P. Burts, president; and J. C. J. King, Waco; M. D. Knox, Hillsboro; and W. W. Reeves, Wills Point, vice-presidents. Daniel and Larendon were continued as secretary and treasurer.

The twenty-fifth annual session of the Association convened at the City Hall in Waco, April 28, 1891. Mayor C. C. McCulloch in a gracious address welcomed the membership to the Queen City of the Brazos and the Athens of Texas, "the greatest artesian city in the world and the great cotton market of the state." He reminded his auditors that the people have come to look upon the physician "not alone as our medical attendant, because in most instances friendly ties spring up which create lifetime bonds of friendship, esteem and affection."

Dr. W. H. Wilkes, speaking for the medical profession of Waco, addressed the assemblage in a humorous vein; he dealt principally with the artesian wells of Waco and the cotton-picker factory. It is interesting to note the repeated emphasis that was placed on the existence of artesian wells, especially at Waco and Fort Worth. When a speaker at this meeting was asking, "How dare a man prescribe for a patient when his brain is filled with alcohol?" it may be that the desire was to call attention to the value of water. In reality, this emphasis on artesian water was evidence of civic pride. The wells at Waco were 1,800 feet deep, and the water was hot. "We only live nearer the great water heart of nature," Dr. Wilkes explained, "and therefore our welcome is all the warmer and more cordial— as deep as our vast geysers, and as warm as the limpid, fervid streams that gush from them, clear as crystal and healthful as the ambrosia of the gods."

It will be news to most of us that a mechanical cotton-picker was in prospect at that early period.[4] And yet a factory for its production did exist in Waco. The far-reaching social and economic implications of this invention were foreseen by Dr. Wilkes. He spoke of "the cotton picker, that wonderful invention which is destined to revolutionize the labor of the South. This discovery will largely release 'the poor downtrodden colored man' from the engrossing cares of the cotton field, and allow him more time for the study of political economy, and how to utilize the glorious right of suffrage guaranteed to him by an enforced amendment to the constitution, and raise the commercial value of his vote from fifty cents to a five dollar note!"

With these formalities over, President W. P. Burts took the gavel and opened the meeting for business. Instead of the usual recommendations for the good of the Association, he was content with making "a few appropriate remarks." He then asked for the secretary's report. This report pointed out that 128 members were delinquent. This situation, the secretary thought, had developed because of the decision to issue badges and send the *Transactions* only to those members who had paid their dues. This meant, he asserted, that less than half of the members had been carrying the financial load of the Association. This meant also that 311 copies of the *Transactions*, dating back to 1884, had accumulated. Despite this lost revenue, the treasury showed a balance of $448.04. This sum, however, was not to last very long. Frank C. Pierce, "a skilled stenographer and type-writer," was employed to take down the discus-

[4] The first patent on a cotton-picking machine was issued to Samuel S. Rembert and Jedediah Prescott on September 10, 1850.—*Farm and Ranch,* September, 1950, p. 28.

sion. The compensation agreed on was $15.00 per day, and twenty cents per hundred words copied, several copies to be furnished if desired. This entailed an expenditure of $175.00, an amount obviously above the financial ability of the Association to pay. In subsequent years, a flat sum of $50.00 was paid.

A wag, with some accuracy, could have dubbed the *Transactions* of the period the "Transgressions of the Texas State Medical Association." Controversy and discord continued to fill the pages. As in other years, these differences were not particularly serious but were personal and persistent. The Daniel-Briggs and Talley-Ghent controversies that had begun in 1887 came up again in 1891. The latter was speedily disposed of by the Judicial Council with the ruling that it had been closed by a previous decision. The former was not so easy. It will be recalled that both Dr. Daniel and Dr. Briggs were exonerated by the Judicial Council in 1887. Under the surface, during these several years, there must have been more to this matter than is now evident; certainly there was more than the well-paid stenographer was able to set down. In 1890, Dr. Daniel had resigned as secretary, for the sake of "harmony in the ranks and prosperity of the Association." His resignation was accepted, but he was reappointed to serve until his successor was elected. Dr. Briggs had been active and had continued to use his *Health Journal* [5] in accusing Dr. Daniel of "conduct unbecoming a physician and a gentleman." At the 1891 meeting, the Judicial Council went over all the evidence again and brought in a report absolving Dr. Daniel of all accusations and at the same time, by unanimous action, recommending the expulsion of Dr. Briggs from the Association. Dr. C. B. Raines, of Mineral Wells, moved that the report of the council be not received. At this point, Dr. Daniel played his trump card: he rose to his feet, reviewed his services to the Association, recalled his

[5] The *Texas Health Journal* was published from July, 1888, to June, 1889. The first issue contained a very captious editorial dealing with a paper which D. R. Wallace, one of the oldest members of the Association, had presented two years earlier. After quibbling over whether a Latin expression should be *de gustibus non est disputandum* rather than *de gustibus nil disputandum,* Dr. Briggs closed with this harsh suggestion: "Dr. Wallace, we suggest that you devote less attention to such long, windy and senseless literary fabrications and give your time to the care of the unfortunates over which you are alleged to preside." Such an unprovoked diatribe against a faithful member could not be calculated to benefit one already enmeshed in serious professional problems. In recording the 1889 meeting of the Association, however, the *Health Journal* commented on the "peace and good will to all" that prevailed.

desire to resign as secretary the previous year, and renewed his request that his resignation be accepted. He was actuated, he said, "by a sincere regard for the best interests of the Association, and solely with the desire to secure and preserve peace and harmony." "The Texas State Medical Association," he concluded, "is a grand body, and its destiny is to become one of the foremost in the ranks of science. This I have labored for, and its welfare is my dearest wish." His resignation was accepted, and the recommendation of the Judicial Council concerning the expulsion of Dr. Briggs was confirmed. Later in the meeting, Dr. M. S. Crow, of Stephenville, made an attempt to have the Association reconsider its decision, in the interest of fair play and the welfare of the Association, but to no avail. Briggs's name does not again appear on the roster of the Association. He appealed to the American Medical Association, and as late as 1893 the Judicial Council of the state association refused to alter its decision. As for Daniel, he became president in 1904. If any good came out of these contentious experiences, it is to be found in this resolution by the Judicial Council: *"Resolved, That members of the Texas State Medical Association be requested and urged to hereafter endeavor to keep out of the State Association or its judicial council all matters of a personal character, and that we all strive to cultivate and promote a spirit of unity in the bond of peace."*

The presence of three visitors at this Waco meeting should be noted. One was "Dr. J. M. Meyer, A.M., M.D., of Danville, Ky., member of Kentucky Medical Association, and graduate of the Transylvania University, who is now here with us and wishes to read a paper on Practice before the Association." The fact that Dr. Meyer read his paper may seem somewhat unusual to us, but we must admit that the Association was generous and courteous. A second visitor was President R. C. Burleson of Baylor University, who addressed the Association and invited the members to visit the university. The third visitor, Judge J. C. Walker, of Waco, undertook to address the Association on "Evolution of Life and Mind." The paper was described by the secretary as lengthy. Judge Walker set out "to account for life, including mind, upon natural causes in regular logical sequences, and it appears to me clear [that] the antecedents and sequences are equal. If this be true, then there is no necessity to resort to 'special creation' to account for life or mind, when natural causes are plain and sufficient to account for all the phenomena of life." He dealt with the researches of Huxley, the nebular theory of Laplace, elementary monads, the diversified forms of living matter, and the perturbations of the planet Jupiter. Darwin and Huxley, it will be recalled, were not too popular in those days, even among doctors. As the Judge developed his theme, it became necessary for the presiding officer to remind him that his time was running out. It is not recorded whether the time element alone dictated this action or whether the speaker's advocacy of the theory of evolution played a part. In either case, the next day the Association repented of its seeming discourtesy and adopted a resolution thanking the Judge and expressing regret that there was not sufficient time "to enable the learned judge to complete the reading of the paper."

For several years, a Committee on Necrology had been in existence. Dr. J. W. Carhart, of Lampasas, had served as chairman for three or four years. This year, eight members had died. An hour was set aside for memorial services, and Dr. Carhart made the address. While he did not know any of the deceased members, he thought it appropriate that the members should "pause a little in the rush of business, in the pursuit of knowledge, in pursuing our investigations, and that we should quietly and reverently look over the road we have come, and note the fall of those noble men who have stood by our side in the struggle in which man is engaged. It is proper for us to pause a moment here and speak words of sympathy for the bereaved; to pay at least some slight tribute of respect to the memory of those men who have been accustomed to be with us year after year, and who have assisted us so nobly in this grand work."

Several papers read at Waco are worthy of notice. Dr. W. A. Morris, of Austin, a man of about eighty years and the father of Dr. Seth M. Morris, of the University of Texas, provoked much discussion by his paper on "The Responsibility of the Medical Profession in the Use of Alcoholic Stimulants." He felt that at times, when properly used, alcohol is almost invaluable. But the doctor should never forget that it "is a good servant but a bad master . . . it takes away and gives nothing in return; it helps the present at the expense of the future. It visits upon the children the iniquities of the fathers." Some physicians, in certain ailments, were advocating the use of fifty-six ounces of brandy a day, "besides champagne freely administered." This was certain to court disaster. Dr.

Morris quoted a Washington bureau which estimated that there were 5,000,000 heavy drinkers in the United States. Figuring six months per man per year as a conservative estimate of time lost, then the nation was deprived of 2,500,000 years of time each year. And to this must be added "the insane, the homicides, the suicides, the epileptics, the imbeciles, the inherited tendency to vice and crime, and the poverty and moral depravity that inevitably follows in the train of alcoholic abuse." Not very accurately, Dr. Morris listed the physical ailments which Demon Rum inflicts: "diseases of the brain, spinal cord and nervous system, paralysis, locomotor ataxia, ulceration of the stomach and bowels, cirrhosis of the liver, fatty degeneration of the heart, valvular troubles, degeneration of the arteries, renal diseases and dropsies—the bloated face and tottering gait of the man that was made in the image of God—a wreck, morally, physically and intellectually." In substantiation, he brought in the case of Margaret Juke and the long train of crime, disease, and depravity that followed her through many generations.[6]

This serious sociological problem, Dr. Morris held, could be solved only by the combined effort of physician, statesman, and philanthropist. The physician should set the example. Never should he forget that the social cup is "as insidious as the sirens' song." Nor should he be caught up in the plaint of some human wreck: "The doctor prescribed it for me. I acquired the habit, and you see what I am. Not fit to live, and afraid to die." Of the seven who discussed Dr. Morris's paper, six were in thorough accord that the hazards of alcohol were as serious as the solution was difficult. Dr. H. W. Dudley, of Hillsboro, however, demurred. He was a man who had always done his own thinking. His personal plan was to begin taking alcohol in small amounts and gradually increase the dose day by day. Thus, he said, he "let nature and old Alcohol go it between themselves." The result was that alcohol got the upper hand, so that he drank awhile and quit awhile and then drank some more. Therefore, he said, "I must say I know something about the effects of alcohol on the human brain, and I move that the doctor's paper be accepted with the thanks of the Association, and with the assur-

[6] R. L. Dugdale, *The Jukes: A Study in Crime, Pauperism, Disease and Heredity* (New York, 1877). Dugdale says (p. 4): "I am informed that $28,000 was raised in two days to purchase a rare collection of antique jewelry and bronzes recently discovered in classic ground, forty feet below the *débris*. I do not hear of as many pence being offered to fathom the *débris* of our civilization, however rich the yield."

166

ance that it is one of the best papers we have ever had read before it." Reform and live longer, was the advice given Dr. Dudley by Dr. D. R. Wallace, of Waco.

One of the early papers on laboratory techniques, "Some Points of Interest in the Clinical Examination of the Urine," was offered by Dr. J. H. Wysong, of Galveston. He utilized observations in the naked-eye appearance of urine, described the Fehling test for sugar and the heat and nitric acid test for albumen, and demonstrated a very comprehensive chart showing many laboratory methods of urinalysis.

Dr. B. E. Hadra reported a case in which he wired fractured vertebrae so as to effect immobilization. A figure-of-eight suture of silver wire was carried around the spinous processes of the sixth and seventh cervical vertebrae and fastened tightly. The patient had had definite evidence of compression of the cord, which was relieved by the operation. Dr. Hadra should receive credit for priority for this procedure. He could find no case in the literature where wire fixation of fractured vertebrae had been used.

Dr. J. W. Carhart, in his paper on "Legal Control of Marriage," expressed some very sensible ideas, ideas which the state of Texas has only recently accepted. His presentation was in fact a strong plea for the practice of eugenics. His solution lay in the appointment of "competent medical men to examine all candidates for matrimony, as to all conditions, diseases and habits that would constitute a sufficient bar to marriage."

President Burts chose the all-inclusive title "Life" for his annual address. For a definition and origin of life, he enlisted the assistance of Plato, Socrates, Huxley, Humboldt, and others. He recognized the individual cell as the basis of all life. From this beginning, other and more complex forms appeared. And then came man, God's masterpiece. "Who," asked Burts, "but a divine architect could accomplish such a structure?" The Darwinian theory had some substance and fact behind it, Dr. Burts thought; but "whatever may be the outcome of scientific investigation on this subject, science can never controvert religion. Science is man's interpretation of God's laws, as far as understood by man. Religion is a revelation of those laws still less understood by man, and when both are better known they will, they must, harmonize; they can not clash. What man endowed with ordinary intellect, be he ever so skeptical, can study the development of the human infant from the embryo as we have just shown, and reflect that within that atom of matter, undistinguishable from the germ of an oyster, there dwells the possibility of a Newton, a Gladstone, a Napoleon or a Washington, and not acknowledge a supreme being, a creator, an all-wise and beneficent God?"

Before Tyler was decided on for the next meeting, the following officers were elected: W. H. Wilkes, Waco, president; P. C. Coleman, Colorado City, first vice-president; W. L. Rodgers, Temple, second vice-president; and B. H. Vaughan, of Vaughan, third vice-president. H. A. West, of Galveston, succeeded F. E. Daniel as secretary. In accepting, Dr. West said, not without some presumption, "It appears that for some reason I have been selected as the exponent of peace and progress; that I am the man upon whom you all look in the office of secretary to promote that welfare and good feeling in the Association."

In 1892 the Association came back to Tyler for the second time. The other occasion was in 1883. The chairman of the Committee on Arrangements called the meeting to order at the Opera House on April 26. Along with the mayor of the city, former Governor Hubbard was on hand again to welcome the visitors, despite his boasted 240 pounds. It was explained that one of the best hotels had been destroyed by fire, but four hundred private homes had been thrown open to meet the emergency. A round of lavish entertainment was announced:

Tuesday evening—Receptions by the Tenneha Club and Benevolent Patriotic Order of Elks, and their ladies, at their club rooms.

Wednesday—Receptions at the homes of our citizens. The Quid Nuncs will receive at the home of Hon. H. M. Whitaker; the Pathfinders will receive at the home of Hon. Horace Chilton; the Chautauquans will receive at the home of Mr. L. L. Jester; the Atheneans will receive at the home of Mr. Dick Reviere.

Thursday evening, after the address of our president, Dr. W. H. Wilkes, a banquet will be given to the visiting doctors by the medical profession and citizens of Tyler.

The freedom of the Tenneha Club, next door to the opera house, has been generously tendered the visiting doctors.

Dr. H. A. West, in his first report as secretary, called attention to a very obvious defect in the annual programs of the Association. Heretofore, chance and perhaps carelessness had been permitted to play too important a role. A member or visitor would often announce at the meeting that he desired to read a paper. Dr. West felt that the program should be arranged and published ahead of time. "The fault belongs largely to officers of sections. It appears to me that, with proper effort upon their part, the titles of papers could be secured in time for publication. Members can not prepare for intelligent discussion unless they know the subject of papers. I shall consider it to be my duty to inquire of each chairman and secretary of sections as to their intention of serving, and I would respectfully suggest to the nominating committee that no man's name is an ornament to the pages of the Transactions if he fails or is negligent in the performance of his work."

The program at this Tyler meeting came in for criticism from another source: "It was in point of scientific interest, nearly barren in results. Only two of the Section chairmen were present, and few of those absent sent reports, few secured any papers, and with one or two exceptions, the papers that were read were not up to the usual standard." [7] This same critic accounted for the small attendance (117) on the ground that Tyler was comparatively inaccessible. He thought that in future only the larger cities of the state should be called on to entertain the Association.[8]

These criticisms were not without justification. At this 1892 meeting, there was not much in the way of papers which requires comment. Dr. J. P. Tucker, of Overton, was still writing on "Perityphlitis," which gave Dr. James Kennedy, of San Antonio, a chance to say, "The moral to be deduced from these cases of ours, and similar cases in other hands with like results, is this: Operate early in case of appendicitis where the diagnosis is clear." No just criticism could be brought against the paper of Dr. C. H. Wilkinson, of Galveston: "The Status of Surgery Today." The author deplored the great and perhaps unjustified increase in abdominal surgery. "Following in the footprints of Sims, protected by the talisman of Lister and encouraged by the shouts of Tait, the whole world today seems moving down upon the abdomen; men skilled and unskilled in the use of the knife; the patriarch with trembling hand, as well as the tyro in his professional swaddling clothes, all alike are rushing on into this territory." Dr. Wilkinson stressed several of the newer surgical procedures: early operation in appendicitis; lateral anasto-

[7] *Texas Sanitarian,* I (1892), 393–94.
[8] *Ibid.,* 397.

mosis and the contribution of Nicholas Senn, closure of intestinal perforations, in typhoid fever; intravenous and intra-arterial injection of normal salt solution in severe hemorrhage; and early operation for intestinal obstruction. He called attention to the steady increase in the incidence of cancer and spoke wisely about the management of this serious disorder: "Remove early and thoroughly, is a maxim which applies to no other morbid process with more vehemence than to cancer."

Likewise in surgery Dr. Irvin Pope, of Tyler, reported successful removal of the median lobe for prostatic obstruction by the suprapubic route. A paper, published in the *Transactions* but probably not read, "The Radical Cure of Inguinal Hernia—Bassini's Method Illustrated, with Remarks on Recurrent and Ventral Hernia," by Dr. Samuel E. Milliken, of New York, described ligation of the sac, transplantation of the cord, and overlapping of the fascial layers in a way similar to that used today.

In the Section on General Medicine, Chairman T. J. Bell, of Tyler, gave a creditable summary of recent medical progress. He emphasized the increasing part which bacteriology, pathology, and physiology were to play in the future of medicine. The prevention and treatment of disease would go forward, he said, as the cause was discovered. He cited, as illustrations, the discovery of the typhoid bacillus by Edwin Klebs and the influenza bacillus by Richard Pfeiffer only a few months before.

So it can hardly be said that the Tyler meeting was a water haul, particularly when some other items on the program are considered. One of these was an address by Dean J. F. Y. Paine of the Medical Department of the University of Texas. This department had opened on October 1, 1891, with the state of Texas, the city of Galveston, and the John Sealy Hospital co-operating. Heads of departments were Drs. A. G. Clopton, William Keiller, James Kennedy, S. M. Morris, Edward Randall, Allen J. Smith, James E. Thompson, and H. A. West. Such a distinguished faculty assured this institution a top rank in the decades ahead. Dean Paine had come before the Association to make a report of the school's first year. In fact, he repeated the report which he had made to the Board of Regents at the school's first graduating exercises. He reported that only twenty-four students had attended during the first year; of these, Thomas Flavin, Houston T. Quinn, and Jessie Porter Hendrick were awarded diplomas. This small number was due partly to high requirements for admission. Graduates of recognized high schools and colleges were accepted without examinations. All others must write a short essay as a test of orthography and grammar and pass an examination in elementary physics. Graduates of regular medical schools in good standing were admitted to the third year without examination. Dr. Paine wanted his institution to be of assistance in discriminating "between true science and the assumption of ignorance and empiricism." Many of the five hundred or more Texans who were attending medical schools outside of Texas should utilize the facilities offered at Galveston. Proudly Dean Paine concluded: "The faculty stand committed to devote their time, energies, what of talent and ability they possess, to the advancement of medical education and to the making of this institution what its projectors intended it should be—a source of pride to the State, a credit to the profession of medicine, and a blessing to mankind." [9]

"Medical Progress" was the title of the address of President Wilkes. During his speech a heavy hailstorm came up; the noise on the roof was so great that he could not be heard. One elderly member cried out, "We can't hear you; sit down till the storm is over." One generation, he told his uneasy audience, had seen many changes in the practice of medicine: "The young physician of today stands on a higher plane, and his armament is vastly more elaborate and comprehensive. He must not only be able to examine the tongue, and feel the pulse, and distinguish normal and abnormal thoracic sounds by the ear, but he must skillfully handle the stethoscope, the otoscope, the laryngoscope, the ophthalmoscope and now the gastroscope." A physician who would "keep his head within breathing distance of the top waves of scientific medical progress" must work industriously and untiringly.

Dr. Wilkes proposed, and the Association passed, a resolution endorsing a memorial which the American Medical Association had sent to the authorities in Washington urging the creation of a bureau of public health with a physician of cabinet rank as its head. The American Medical Association had sought such a bureau since 1888 and has persistently worked for it these many years, but in vain. A hope was expressed by Dr. Wilkes that the bureau, if created, would be kept in the hands of competent physicians and sani-

[9] Dr. Paine's address appeared in the *Texas Sanitarian* (I [1892], 385–91), as well as in the *Transactions* of the Association.

tarians and "not be gobbled up by greedy politicians for their own selfish ends."

Great as medical progress had been, Dr. Wilkes continued, the profession could look to the future with hope and faith. "Deep and untiring experiment and research are boring down into the artesian depths of medical wisdom, and perennial streams of knowledge will gush forth to water and replenish the mind of every physician who remains a student, and give him a deeper insight into, and a keener appreciation of the mysteries which surround his noble profession."

During the year, four members of the Association had died. One of these was Dr. W. W. Reeves, superintendent of the State Lunatic Asylum, who was shot down by a recently discharged patient. In his memorial address, Dr. E. P. Becton, of Sulphur Springs, said:

One year ago four of our fellow members were with us in the enjoyment of health, of happiness and of the privileges and pleasures that we this day enjoy. Now, they sweetly sleep beneath the shade of the trees on the other side of the river. Life's duty done, they have no more to do with the things of earth; their lives, like ours, were hard, hard ones. Those who live in the cities, where everything is well regulated, have comparatively an easy time. Not so with the Texas country doctor. He goes at midnight hour, amid the raging storms, exposed to the dangers of the lightning's flash; goes at midsummer, exposed to the burning rays of the summer's sun; and even the surging waters deter him not from the discharge of his duty. How often these brethren had done this; how often were they saddened over the disappointments and vexations incident to human life; how seldom did they, and how seldom do we, receive the words of encouragement that we sometimes so long for. But when they do come, they come with a perennial freshness; they fall as gently as the dews of heaven upon the tender flower, and sink as softly into our hearts as the prophet's prayer for the redemption of his people. But the supreme moment came, and all that was left for them to do was to bid farewell to the wife and the little ones, sunder the ties that bound them to earth and cross over the river to the great beyond. Let us indulge the fond hope that they looked back on a life well spent in the faithful discharge of every duty. . . . Let us indulge the fond hope that these four brethren, dying with harness on, having faithfully discharged the duties of life, that their immortal spirits leaped from the cold waves of the Jordan of death, scaled the highest battlements of the celestial city, and this moment are a part of the brightest of the coruscating retinue that vie around the blazing throne of the eternal God.

As leaders for 1893, the Association chose J. D. Osborn, Cleburne,

172

PAST PRESIDENTS

W. B. Russ, 1909   John T. Moore, 1910
David R. Fly, 1911   J. H. McCracken, 1911

PAST PRESIDENTS

John S. Turner, 1912   Marvin L. Graves, 1913
F. D. Boyd, 1914   G. H. Moody, 1915

president; T. J. Bell, Tyler, first vice-president; F. M. Pitts, Jr., Hubbard City, second vice-president; and T. J. Bennett, Austin, third vice-president. West and Larendon were re-elected secretary and treasurer. Dr. Osborn was very sincere when he said, "Today you have honored me by placing upon me the highest position of trust in your power. I hope you will never have cause to regret the same, and that this arm of mine will wither and decay whenever I fail to do my duty for the high standard of medicine."

Late on the last day, the president announced that the members would meet that night to have a group picture made. If the picture was taken, it is not in the records. It would be a priceless possession for the Association today. Then, after selecting Galveston for the next meeting, the Association expressed its gratitude to the people of Tyler "with a lingering taste of ambrosial delicacies, a dream of sweet music and fair ladies from flower-decked bowers, and under the refining and ennobling influence of Tyler's social circles."

As it had done five years earlier, the Association convened in Harmony Hall in Galveston for its twenty-seventh annual session. The date was May 2, 1893.[10] After a few welcoming words from Mayor R. L. Fulton, Dr. George H. Lee of the Reception Committee spoke for the doctors of the Oleander City: "May the soft south breeze, fresh with the brine of the ocean, gently dispel all thought of care, past and future, and may your stay in Galveston leave an impression like the soothing refrain you catch from the distant murmur of the Mexico gulf." In response, President Osborn said: "The sound of the waves, the balmy gulf breezes, the odors of beautiful flowers, the songs of tropical birds and the other beauties and attractions of this charming city are one thing and the duty we have to perform is another. We are here not for pleasure, but for work, and the sooner we get at it the better."

Dr. Osborn then went on to lay stress on the necessity of higher standards for admission to medical schools. Requirements, he thought, should include proficiency in spelling, grammar, English literature, and the classics. After suggesting the creation of three scholarships at the Medical Department of the University of Texas and after referring to the inadequacy of the laws having to do with

[10] The *Galveston News* carried a full day-by-day account of the meeting. The names and addresses of 127 physicians in attendance were given.

public health and the practice of medicine, he expressed the hope that the session might be harmonious and "replete with good fellowship."

The secretary announced that a preliminary program had been sent out in advance of the meeting. This was the result of a recommendation he had made the year before. Now, he was suggesting that the several chairmen of the sections appoint certain members to discuss the papers. This way, he thought, the discussions would be more relevant and the work of the Association would be enriched.

A series of entertainments, comparable to that of Tyler but of an entirely different nature, was offered:

Tuesday afternoon at 5:30 o'clock—Visit to Medical college and Sealy hospital. 8 o'clock—Commencement exercises Medical Department State University at Harmony Hall.

Wednesday evening, 8 to 11 o'clock—Reception by Hon. and Mrs. Walter Gresham, Fourteenth and Broadway.

Thursday evening, 6 to 11 o'clock—Concert, buffet banquet and dance, given by the medical profession and citizens, at the Garten Verein. President Osborn's address at 8 p.m. at the Garten.

Friday afternoon at 4 o'clock—Sail on Galveston Bay.

Important business of this session included revision of the constitution and bylaws. Since the revising committee could not agree on the suggested changes, the matter was thrown into the lap of the Association, where long and heated debate took place. There were three major points of disagreement between what came to be known as the Waco group, led by Dr. J. H. Sears, and the Galveston group, led by Dr. H. A. West: qualifications for membership, prior membership in a county or district society, and trial of offending members. Article III of the constitution used the word *man* in setting out the requirements for admission. Dr. C. M. Rosser thought that this "would exclude ladies and admit colored people." Dr. William Keiller felt that "learning made all men akin and that color had nothing to do with it." Dr. A. G. Clopton reminded the gentleman that he "had not been long enough in the south to appreciate the prejudice which exists in the minds of the southern people against anything like social equality between the whites and negroes." Article III was amended, almost unanimously, to read: "Every regularly educated physician within the limits of this

174

state, who is a graduate of a regular medical college in good standing, and who adopts and conforms to the Code of Ethics of the American Medical Association, shall be eligible to membership in this body, except those of the negro race."

There was ample discussion of the relationship between the state and local organizations. The opinion presented by Dr. West prevailed, and the clause adopted four years before, "provided they are members in good standing of their respective county or district medical societies," was stricken out. This change was a distinct and obvious setback to the trend toward closer union between the state and local organizations.

In the problem of dealing with offenders against the code of ethics, the disagreement came over whether or not the state association should initiate proceedings. On the local level, personalities were more likely to enter in. As in the case of the mice in the fable, who, they asked, would bell the cat? The outcome was that the state association retained its authority, through the Judicial Council, to supervise the professional conduct of its members. Certain changes were made so that the accuser must submit his charges in writing beforehand and then be present at the hearing.

There was some discussion over abolishing the Nominating Committee and permitting nominations from the floor. The old plan of nomination, however, by a committee comprised of one member from each county, was continued. Dr. T. J. Heard spoke for the majority when he advised the Association to "remove not old landmarks." [11]

The *Transactions* continued to record frankly the uninhibited behavior of the members. Dr. David Cerna, of the Department of Physiology at Galveston, read a twenty-page paper on "The Action and Uses of Pental," a new anesthetic drug which had found favor in some quarters. Dr. Cerna asked permission to publish the paper in a journal other than the *Transactions*. Dr. J. Van Gasken, of Luling, could see no objection, since the drug was "no good" anyway. Indeed, after careful experiments in the laboratory, Dr. Cerna had concluded that pental was not a safe or efficient anesthetic agent and was definitely inferior to ether and chloroform. His purpose in desiring a wider medium of publication was to discourage the use of this dangerous drug.

The Judicial Council had two duties to perform at the 1893

[11] Good authority was being quoted here: Proverbs 23:10.

meeting, one unpleasant and one pleasant. The Western Texas Medical Association had become ensnarled in quarrels that touched the state association. Irregularities and insubordination, individual and organized, had been exposed. The Western Texas Medical Association was directed to purify itself by expelling all members who did not observe the code of ethics. The expulsion of Dr. James Kennedy was approved, but his reinstatement was advised after mutual apologies had been offered. The pleasant duty concerned Dr. John M. Litten, one of the group of ten Austin physicians who had initiated the organization of the state association forty years before. Because of infirmities of age which rendered him "unable to discharge the duties of an active member," the council recommended that he be made an honorary member. This was done.

The program was enriched by papers from several members of the faculty of the new Medical Department: J. E. Thompson, Allen J. Smith, William Keiller, H. A. West, J. F. Y. Paine, and David Cerna. Dr. Thompson, professor of surgery, presented two papers, "Whitehead Operation for Haemorrhoids" and "Operative Treatment for Perforation in Typhoid Fever." The anatomy of the lower rectum was thoroughly described. Then followed a clear description of the operation, in which the entire pile-bearing area was removed. Four illustrations, initialed "J. E. T.," accompanied the article. The other paper reported an operation in a case of typhoid fever which had perforated four days before. Death followed in twelve hours. He collected sixteen cases from the literature, of which only four had recovered.

Dr. Smith, professor of pathology, talked authoritatively on "Generalization of Cancer of the Stomach." He reviewed the literature on the known modes of metastasis: direct extension, transference by the blood, and transference by lymph vessels. To this he added his own wide knowledge of the subject—in a way, doubtless, which aided in effecting his own transference to the University of Pennsylvania a few years later. Dr. Keiller, professor of anatomy, spoke on "Pelvic Peritonitis and Cellulitis." Dr. Paine, professor of gynecology, reported a "Case of Splenectomy." Dr. West, professor of the theory and practice of medicine, spoke on "The Association of Diseases and Morbid Processes."

Dr. Q. C. Smith was on hand again with some new instruments. His title was "Placenta Praevia with New Instruments for Treating

176

Same." This paper was discussed at length by Drs. Paine and Keiller. It may be that Dr. Smith and others felt that these newcomers from the medical faculty were inclined to usurp the prerogatives of the Association, and that they seemed to speak ex cathedra. At any rate, it is recorded that "to both of these gentlemen Dr. Smith replied in a very energetic and slashing style." He may have been emphasizing the difference between scientific surgery and successful cutting.

The most important portion of the "Report on Surgery," by Dr. A. B. Gardner, of Bellville, had to do with appendicitis. Even yet there was no agreement as to the necessity or the time of the operation. Such men as "McBurney of New York and a host of others" were insisting that "all cases should be considered with a view of surgical interference." [12]

The presidential address of Dr. Osborn dealt with the code of ethics. To him, the code was sacred:

Our Code of Ethics is looked upon by the masses as a safeguard thrown around us by ourselves to protect us in our conspiracies. . . . This should not be so. We should endeavor to instill into their dull minds that our Code is our law next to the Bible, and that by it we govern our actions to our professional brothers, and by it our patients' interests are protected, and by it a protecting arm is thrown over the public; that in it lies their safety and protection as well as ours. . . . The true physician should have his mind imbued with the greatness and the sacredness of his mission. His conscience is the only tribunal by which his acts of carelessness, ignorance and neglect can be judged. . . . To share and have part in the sorrows of our friends broadens the vision, tempers the heart, and makes golden the light that falls upon the hearthstone where he with loved ones dwells.

A sidelight on the practice of medicine by members of the Texas State Medical Association is found in the charges made by the doctors of this period. A fee schedule used by the physicians of Austin in 1893 is available. If these charges are typical, the doctors did not fare so badly—provided they collected a good part of their bills. Here are a few selected charges by way of illustration:

[12] It was about this time that McBurney, sitting beside John D. Rockefeller at a banquet, facetiously suggested that every child should have the appendix removed before the age of five. Mr. Rockefeller replied, "McBurney, that would beat Standard Oil."

For day visits (old city limits)	$ 2.50
For night visits	double
For ordinary prescription or advice	1.00 to 2.00
For consultation with another physician, first visit	10.00
For visit to the country, per mile (city visit extra), one way	1.00
For consultation and written opinion	5.00 to 25.00
For visits to contagious diseases (small-pox, yellow fever, cholera, diphtheria), from	50% to 200% extra
For administering anesthetics	5.00 to 10.00
For examination of urine for albumen and sugar	2.50 to 5.00
For microscopic examination of urine	5.00 to 10.00
For microscopic examination of pathological specimens	10.00 to 25.00
For natural delivery (4 hours)	20.00 to 30.00
For twins	35.00 to 50.00
For cæsarian section	250.00 to 500.00
For laparotomy	200.00 to 500.00
For perineorrhaphy, old	50.00 to 100.00
For extirpation of uterus	250.00 to 1000.00
For ovariotomy	250.00 to 1000.00
For capital operations	100.00 to 1000.00
Fracture of femur	40.00 to 100.00
Fracture of leg, arm, or fore-arm	15.00 to 50.00
Venereal practice, in advance	5.00 to 50.00 [13]

Austin was selected as the site of the next meeting. J. H. Sears, Waco, became president; C. M. Rosser, Dallas, first vice-president; E. M. Rabb, Hallettsville, second vice-president; and W. A. Watkins, Kemp, third vice-president. No change was made in the offices of secretary and treasurer.

There was an amusing echo to this Galveston meeting. Dr. H. A. West, as chairman of the Committee on Arrangements, took it on himself to substitute "the buffet banquet and concert, where ladies could grace the occasion by their presence and smiles," for what he termed "the traditional drinking bout and maudlin speech making, ordinarily called a banquet, which has heretofore prevailed." He

[13] *Texas Sanitarian,* II (1893), 34–36.

used these injudicious words in a letter published in the June, 1893, issue of the *Texas Medical Journal* and hailed the experiment as a "charming success." Dr. D. R. Wallace castigated "the zealous doctor" who "pro bono publico, of course . . . descends into the arena as a reformer." Dr. Wallace continued: "I have known the Texas State Medical Association from its first meeting. I have never witnessed, never heard of any drinking bouts or maudlin speech-making, much less that they were traditional. *He* substituted—*he* tried the experiment. There were banquets with wine, and banquets without wine, long before this great reformer and experimenter became a member." Dr. West's letter, said one member, was an "unjust, uncalled for, gratuitous insult to gentlemen, his peers in every respect." [14] The editor of the *Texas Sanitarian* resorted to ridicule in answering Dr. West: "Some of the old members who have worked so long and hard to keep the Association alive and prosperous, who have trotted it upon their knees these score of years, and furnished it pap and chucked it under the chin, as a proud father does his young hopeful, will be made unhappy when they learn that all of their honest and faithful efforts at entertaining and being entertained, heretofore, were failures—only 'drinking bouts.' " [15]

A tentative program of the 1894 meeting appeared in the April issue of the *Texas Medical Journal*. The Committee on Hotels promised to care for their guests in "comfortable and elegant style," even though they "must lodge at least two in a room." Rates at the principal Austin hotels were listed as follows:

Driskill, board and lodging per diem	$2.50
Hotel Salge, board and lodging per diem	2.00
Avenue Hotel, board and lodging per diem	2.00
Hotel Orr, board and lodging per diem	1.50
Austin House, board and lodging per diem	1.25

"Come, brethren, and let us have a royal good time," the committee exhorted. And the editor of the *Journal* added: "Austin will have on her loveliest spring attire in April. Strawberries will be ripe, and roses in bloom. Our sweet south breezes will be laden with the breath of violets."

Forty-eight papers appeared on the preliminary program. Of

[14] *Texas Medical Journal,* IX (1893–94), 79.
[15] *Texas Sanitarian,* II (1893), 395.

these, thirty were read. Eleven papers were presented which were not on the preliminary list.

When the Association convened in the Senate Chamber on April 24, "the attendance was smaller than for years,—attributable to 'financial stringency,'—about one hundred members and delegates being present the first day; increased next day to perhaps one hundred and fifty. As usual, there were about fifty old stand-bys, who attend all meetings; but it was noticeable that there was a large attendance of doctors whose faces were not familiar—new doctors and young doctors." [16]

President Sears congratulated the Association on having "finished our boyish misunderstandings and 'scraps,' and arrived at years of full maturity to do the work of men in a most harmonious manner." He was apprehensive about the numerical stagnation of the Association: 431 members out of nearly 5,000 "regular medical men" in the state. He was concerned, too, about the finances: a balance of $34.30. It had cost $881.03 to publish the *Transactions*, this being $1.54 per volume and consuming more than half the income of the Association. He touched on the wisdom of establishing a state health department and of making certain desired changes in the law creating a State Board of Medical Examiners. He urged the passage of a law requiring that all patent medicines be plainly labeled as to chemical content "so that all can understand what they are swallowing."

Vice-President Rosser had been assigned by President Sears the task of inquiring into the status of the local and district medical organizations in the state: their number, their membership, and whether "they were prosperous and doing a good work." Dr. Rosser took his assignment seriously and brought in a good report. By this time, there were twenty-nine affiliated auxiliary associations. Only thirteen of these were found to be active and alert. Most of the remainder, including those at Dallas and Fort Worth, indicated "the mournful fact that these have lapsed into a state of inactivity." All of the inactive societies, he hoped, were looking forward "to an early resurrection day, when it shall be discovered that they were not dead, but sleeping." The Hill County Medical Society and the Waco Medical Society were commended for their high quality of work. The thirteen active organizations were listed in tabular form.

[16] *Texas Medical Journal*, IX (1893–94), 571–72.

PAST PRESIDENTS

J. M. INGE, 1916   E. H. CARY, 1917
S. P. RICE, 1918   R. W. KNOX, 1919

PAST PRESIDENTS

T. T. Jackson   I. C. Chase, 1920
President-Elect 1919   Joe Becton, 1922
T. J. Bennett, 1921

	Membership	Average attendance
North Texas Medical Association	300	120
Central Texas Medical Association	105	50
Austin District Medical Association	106	35
Lone Star Medical Club	35	25
Galveston Medical Club	24	12
Grayson County Medical Society	37	15
Houston District Medical Association	30	14
Johnson County Medical Society	27	14
Collin County Medical Society	40	15
Travis County Medical Society	25	10
Hill County Medical Society	25	10
Waco Medical Society	30	15
Western Texas Medical Society	35	20

The affairs of the American Medical Association came in for adverse criticism on two counts. The first took the form of a resolution opposing the majority report which advocated some rather radical changes in the code of ethics which had been in effect since 1848. This matter had been before the national association for two years and had been debated heatedly. The solution came at the 1894 session, when it was announced that no changes would be made, since twenty-one out of twenty-five state associations were in favor of retaining the code as originally promulgated by Thomas Percival in 1803.

A more barbed shaft was launched against the American Medical Association in a resolution by David Cerna, of Galveston: "*Resolved,* That this association likewise express its disapprobation of the practice of inserting advertisements of secret preparations in the columns of medical journals, such action being an insult to the intelligence of the profession, and a degradation of journals indulging therein to the level of the patent medicine almanac. Especially to be condemned is the action of the *Journal of the American Medical Association* in admitting such advertisements."

This matter of accepting the blatant advertisements of patent and proprietary medicines in medical journals had occupied the minds and consciences of doctors for a long time. It was brought to a head in 1892, when the medical society at Philadelphia, under the leadership of Dr. Solomon Solis-Cohen, urged the *Journal of the American Medical Association* to set the example. The editor of the

Journal defended the practice and suggested that these advertisements would be discontinued if the Philadelphia doctors would
repay the association for the lost income, which ran from six to eight
thousand dollars annually. The problem was faced slowly. Progress
was registered in 1895, when the Board of Trustees instructed the
editor to accept no advertisements "which do not give a formula
containing the official or chemical name and quantity of each composing ingredient to be inserted as a part of the advertisement." [17]
But it was not until 1904 that all such advertisements were refused.
Although the American Medical Association permitted monetary
considerations to influence its sluggish decision, the Texas State
Medical Association had accepted no advertisements in its *Transactions* for a number of years.

This subject of proprietary preparations came in for further castigation in a paper on "Embarrassments of Medicine," by James H.
Bell, of Philadelphia.[18] After commenting on the purposes and
accomplishments of legitimate medical journals, Dr. Bell said that
the doctors as a group should refuse to countenance or support
those periodicals "which, under the establishment and control of
proprietary medicine, are engaged in advertising, through a thinly
disguised and utterly worthless rehash of scientific matter, the secret
preparations of selfish enterprise."

One week after the meeting, the *Austin Daily Statesman* published a vitriolic article entitled "The Reason Why Doctors Object
to Patent Medicines, as Explained by One of Them." This article
purported to set down what the reporter had heard in the discussion
on patent medicines: "No doctor who has any consideration for
his calling will prescribe a patent medicine compound for a patient.
If he is a doctor at all he will write a prescription containing the
same ingredients. By this means the druggist is enabled to make his
percentage on the prescription and the doctor gets a rebate. Now,
if the doctor prescribes a patent medicine, the druggist only gets
a small margin of profit and the doctor gets nothing at all. So in
consideration of this fact, if for no other, a doctor should never
prescribe a patent medicine." Dr. J. W. McLaughlin, newly elected
president, and a group of Austin physicians inserted in the *Austin
Daily Statesman* a resolution which branded the article as "false

[17] Fishbein, *History of the A.M.A.*, 169.
[18] This is probably the James Hall Bell who moved to San Antonio and
became a member of the Association in 1899.

182

and libelous," "a misrepresentation of facts, and an unmerited insult to the entire medical fraternity of this city and State." [19]

Dr. Allen J. Smith, in his notable address on "The Relative Importance of Pathology in the Medical Curriculum," proceeded to place pathology in its proper position and to convince his auditors that "pathology deals with living, moving questions, as well as with the dead and offal of disease." He saw this subject as an introduction to the study of diseases which every doctor would meet in his everyday practice. Pathology, as he saw it, was more than the study of abnormal tissues; it was more than the study of bacteria and effects on tissues; it comprised also the field of pathological physiology, which concerned itself with altered function of organs as well as the reasons for symptoms of disease. Knowledge of true pathology "makes of a man an intelligent practitioner of medicine," and ignorance of it "makes of him the routine follower of other men's methods." Dr. Smith's many students at the University of Texas and the University of Pennsylvania will recall his deep sincerity as they read his words: "The failure to thus acquire the habits of pathological reasoning, of comparing the diseased with the normal structure, the diseased function with the normal function, of seeking for the influences such changes may have upon the rest of the body, and their probable sequences; the failure to thus acquire the habits of study of the natural history of disease, leaves a man hampered in his medical life to a degree that years of study, even a lifetime may never overcome."

Another piece of good research work, on anesthesia, came out of the three-year-old Medical Department of the University of Texas. Drs. Edward Randall and David Cerna presented the results of their investigations in a paper entitled "A Contribution to the Study of the Action of Chloroform." Tables and tracings helped to confirm their conclusion that the danger from chloroform lies in respiratory failure rather than cardiac paralysis. They felt that both possibilities, however, should be constantly in the mind of the anesthetist: "Both the circulation and the respiration should be watched at the same time, and not one function alone."

President J. H. Sears was a medical pioneer. He was sixty-eight years old and had been a member of the Association since 1869. Logically and with a tinge of nostalgia, he spoke in his presidential address of things as they were. Despite the efforts of the regular

[19] *Texas Medical Journal*, IX (1893–94), 596–99.

profession, Texas was "cursed with a larger and more energetic horde of quacks, charlatans and frauds than are to be found in any other state of the union." And an apathetic Legislature showed no concern: "Dear liberty accords to every man the right to have himself and family maltreated, robbed and cheated as much and as often as he may choose, without let or hindrance." Time and conditions had changed, and the people had changed. Too many foreigners were drifting in. "Why not retain this territory for our children and their descendants?" These interlopers would corrupt the character of our people and undermine the very foundations of government. "How do you think these tramps would vote? Would they not vote for free lunch; for distribution of funds by the public for their support?" The hope of Texas lay in the "conservative, native, inborn influence" of "a class that upholds the majesty of the law, believes in God and honors woman." [20]

A note of interest is found in the graduating exercises of the Medical Department of the University of Texas a few days after the Association adjourned. Dr. Allen J. Smith spoke on the influence of medical studies upon religious thought. The degree of Doctor of Medicine was conferred on Malone Duggan, Walter N. John, George Sparks, Jacob H. Sampson, and Ernest A. Thompson. It was announced that Mr. John Moore "of the first year class, was awarded the prize in histology offered annually by the professor of pathology, the prize this year being a copy of the last edition of Carpenter on the Microscope and its Revelations."

An Austin physician, J. W. McLaughlin, was elected president; W. L. York, Decatur, first vice-president; W. R. Blailock, McGregor, second vice-president; and W. H. Lancaster, Moulton, third vice-president. Dallas was to be the meeting place for 1895.

[20] This address in its entirety, along with the *Proceedings* of the Association, appeared in the *Austin Daily Statesman,* April 26–28.

XII

The Old Century Ends, 1895–99

THROUGH THE YEARS it became increasingly obvious that the Texas State Medical Association was making little or no progress in the direction of membership or finances. Each succeeding president expressed anxiety about the situation. Various remedies were offered: better programs, shorter papers, reduction in annual dues, abolition of entertainment, and acceptance of individual responsibility, especially on the part of those whose names appeared on the program. All this might have been interpreted as natural in a new and ambitious organization. However, it was more than this. It was at least partial recognition of the fact that organized medicine in Texas lacked some greatly desired, but still unknown, ingredient. In reality, it was the reaction of a young organization in ferment, going through the stages of growth and development, meeting with successes here, only to encounter disappointments yonder. It was, in fact, a constant reaching-out toward a long-sought goal, which was not to be attained until 1903. In that year, organized medicine in the United States underwent a thorough reorganization, in which the county society became the unit of organization in each state and the combination of all state associations comprised the American Medical Association.

The organizational problems received a thorough airing in letters to, and through editorials in, the *Texas Medical Journal*. The editor, Dr. F. E. Daniel, about whose head many a storm had broken, led off with an editorial, "Shall We Abolish the State Medical Association?" He recalled that the membership in 1882 had been 280. In twelve years, well over 800 had been admitted to membership, and yet the net increase was only 74. A membership of 354 was a poor showing for the 5,000 doctors in Texas. Dr. Daniel recognized the difficulty: "We are working upon a wrong plan, and our efforts are as futile as pouring water in a sieve." But his solution was not simple or easy; he advised that an effort be made to enroll every physician in some local society and that each society should send delegates to the state association, which would meet in Austin.[1] The several correspondents felt the need of some radical change, and each had some remedial plan to suggest. Dr. P. C. Coleman, of Colorado City, to be elected president at the next meeting, went to much trouble in collecting data to prove that Texas, by comparison, was faring less badly than at first appeared: in Alabama, 61 per cent of the physicians of the state belonged to the state medical association; in Nebraska, 32 per cent; in Mississippi, 23 per cent; and in Georgia, 15 per cent. So the figure of 9 or 10 per cent in Texas was not to be severely criticized when the size of the state and distances involved were considered. And, besides, Texas should be proud of her 71 members in the American Medical Association.[2]

This discussion was wholesome but not fruitful. In the meantime, the affairs of the state association continued about as usual. The *Texas Medical Journal,* in its April issue, carried a preliminary program of the twenty-ninth annual session, to be held in Dallas, April 23–26. President McLaughlin urged a good attendance. The local medical societies, he said, should not be regarded as rivals of the state association. Rather, it was his ambition to "unite the separate medical organizations of Texas as members of a grand State Medical Association."[3]

The 1895 meeting was held in the auditorium of the City Hall, up four flights of steps. According to the *Texas Medical Journal,* the registration was about 150, this number tapering down to about 30 at the end. For the first time, badges were issued to the members. Dr. John O. McReynolds, chairman of the Committee on Arrangements, was one of the orators and thinkers of the Association. His words of welcome deserve more space than can be allotted to them:

I come before you today as an unworthy representative of the most glorious brotherhood of the greatest city of the greatest state of the grandest government on earth. . . . In medicine more than in any other

[1] *Texas Medical Journal,* X (1894–95), 133, 177.
[2] *Ibid.,* 221–23.
[3] *Ibid.,* 526.

department of scientific research do we find an imperative demand for organization; not for the purpose of protection against powerful combinations of wealth and influence; not for the purpose of securing individual emolument or honor, but that we may receive the richest fruits of our combined experience and study, to the end that we may become more efficient and faithful servants in the vineyard of mankind. The span of human life is so short, individual experience and observation so restricted, the influence of climate and environment so varied, habits of thought and methods of investigation so widely different, and our field of labor so important and so sacred that no one can with justice to himself and those committed to his care follow alone the feeble rays of his own dimly burning lamp. . . . He that would build best a monument to his memory in the hearts of his fellowmen must come to the sweet and sacred shrine of truth, around which alone do lasting laurels grow. . . . Your influence touches not only that heart which beats and bleeds and must pass away, but it penetrates into the inmost recesses of that heart which is to live forever. Your duty calls you to administer with impartial hand to suffering humanity wherever found, in the splendid palaces of the rich or the humble cottage of the poor.

Introduced as guests of the Association were Professor Richard Douglas, of Vanderbilt Medical College; Professor Landon Carter Gray, of New York; Dr. J. M. Kellar, of Hot Springs, Arkansas; and Dr. G. W. Wells, medical director of the Manhattan Life Insurance Company.

After the secretary had reported that it had cost $1.72 per volume to publish the last *Transactions* and that there was a resulting deficit of $179.27, there came a report from a committee appointed "to consider the best means of increasing membership and advancing the interests of the association." This committee, composed of Drs. J. T. Wilson, D. R. Wallace, and T. D. Wooten, chairman, made a careful and perhaps constructive report; and yet, between the lines, it is not too difficult to detect the note of futility: the same ground had been covered many times before, the same suggestions had been made, the same negative results had followed. The committee was certain that the welfare of the Association would be furthered if its meetings were devoted "to a terse, pertinent and vigorous discussion of recent discoveries, approved experience and well-attested facts in the domain of medicine and its allied branches" instead of "idle speculations, imaginary exploits or vapid generalizations." A further thought, somewhat different from that of former committees, concerned the election of officers. To offset the plans of those who would seek office, it was proposed that no man could be named for any office by the Nominating Committee "who has directly or indirectly solicited the same at the hands of the committee or any member of it."

One goal of the Association, touched on in this report, was the ingathering of all eligible doctors in Texas. From time to time, various methods had been offered for accomplishing this much desired purpose. So far nothing had been said or done which would make membership in the Association necessary, attractive, or even very desirable. These several efforts led to the ultimate realization of the goal nine years later. In discussing the report, Secretary H. A. West read a circular sent out by the secretary of the American Medical Association. This showed that the national organization was thinking along the same lines and that the plan of reorganization adopted in 1903 was being formulated this early. The circular read, in part:

WHEREAS, This association has long recognized the advantages to be derived from the more intimate relation between the state medical societies and the American Medical Association; it is hereby

Resolved, That we request the various state medical societies to perfect their local organizations, so as to include as far as possible, in the membership of their district societies every regular practitioner within the state;

That these local societies shall actively co-operate in urging a general attendance upon the annual meetings of the state societies. . . . We further direct that the permanent secretary of the American Medical Association enter into correspondence with the secretaries of the several state medical societies, and furnish annually a written report of the membership of the state societies and the working effectiveness of their organizations.

Up to this time, specific remedies in disease were nonexistent. They had been much sought and long awaited. Claims of specificity were always received with skepticism; disappointment after disappointment could breed only skepticism. The subject of diphtheria antitoxin well illustrates this feeling of mistrust so well expressed by Alexander Pope:

> Be not the first by whom the new are tried,
> Nor yet the last to lay the old aside.

Emil von Behring made his claim for specificity of diphtheria antitoxin in 1894. The next year two papers on the program of the
Texas association dealt with the subject: one by Dr. A. H. Schenk,
of Kenney, and one by Dr. William Gammon, of Galveston. Dr.
Schenk wrote as one who was almost persuaded. He had had no
personal experience. He spoke of the unwisdom of "enthusiastic
haste" and urged utmost caution in the interpretation of results.
In the meantime, he would not cast the old aside: he would still pin
his faith on calomel, tincture of iron, and strychnia. Calomel by
inhalation was used for its local effect. Dr. Gammon, close to the
clinical laboratory of the University of Texas, accepted diphtheria
antitoxin at its full value. He described with clarity and conviction
the theory on which the preparation was made, the laboratory technique of manufacture, and the practical application of the product.
Two cases were reported, both of which cleared up rapidly. The first
case developed paralysis of the soft palate. The second, a medical
student with initials "O. S. H.," [4] reacted with urticaria on the
seventh day. This reaction was correctly explained as being "due
to a difference between the serum of the animal from which the
antitoxin was obtained and the blood serum of man."

The paper by Dr. J. T. Wilson, of Sherman, on "Menstrual Disorders in School Girls" invaded a field which must have been considered as the terra incognita of medicine. Dr. Landon Carter Gray
praised the author for his courage in making public things which
every medical man had known to exist. After touching on the pet-
ting, pampering, and spoiling of the American girl of that day, Dr.
Wilson continued: "She must be confined indoors and her complexion bleached; then her figure must be changed, and she is
moulded out of shape with a tight corset, diminishing her size to
one-fifth or one-third. Around this are tightly tied and hung several
heavy skirts, compressing the heart and pushing it up out of place,
squeezing the liver, interfering with the portal circulation, displac-
ing the stomach, disturbing the digestion, dragging and pushing
down the abdominal and pelvic organs, producing congestion and
displacement, interfering with their functions, arresting the development of the body, embarrassing respiration and productive of

[4] Ollie Spence Hodges, of Beaumont. W. J. Maxwell, *General Register of
the Students and Former Students of the University of Texas* (Austin, 1917),
361.

hysteria." All this could only result in weak backs, morbid appetites, poor nutrition, habitual constipation, cold feet, and serious menstrual disorders. Under proper care, however, he thought these ailments could be corrected. "There would then be less use for the gynecologist with his 500 or 1000 laparotomies with the uteri or appendages on exhibition in his museum; there would be fewer weakly, neurotic children with their hereditary predisposition to countless troubles peculiar to their sex, and menstruation might be what it was intended to be, a physiological process and not a pathological condition."

Less kind was the reception accorded the paper of Dr. J. W. Hunter, of Waco, on "Asthma in Its Causation and Treatment, with Report of Cases." Hardly had he closed when he was accused of advertising a proprietary medicine. It developed that Dr. Hunter was the agent for a preparation claimed to be "good for asthma." His paper was refused publication in the *Transactions*.

There was nothing significant about the "Report of a Case of Haematocele," by Dr. S. B. Kirkpatrick, of Commerce. The condition was not recognized as a ruptured ectopic pregnancy. But it did give young Bacon Saunders, of Fort Worth, a chance to make this apt observation: "The average man who has not had large experience in abdominal surgery had better puncture the vagina and trust to drainage, cleanliness and the Lord." Two up-and-coming ophthalmologists, Dr. John O. McReynolds, of Dallas, and Dr. H. L. Hilgartner, of Austin, read papers which did justice to their specialty.

President McLaughlin titled his address "Theoretical Reflections upon the Manifestations and Modus Operandi of Drug Action upon the Living Organism." It was "an elucidation of a theory of the dynamic and therapeutic energy of drugs." The address might have been more acceptable to a group of physicists and, in reading it today, a physicist is needed to determine whether it is bulging with scientific profundities or illusory theorizing. For twenty-five pages, Dr. McLaughlin dealt with atoms and molecules, atomic and molecular collisions, the indestructibility of matter, the properties of ponderable and imponderable matter, and the kinetic and therapeutic energy of drugs. Therapeutic energy of a drug, Dr. McLaughlin theorized, is determined by its molecular waves: "The effect produced in the organism may result from the molecules of the drug coming within the range of the activities of certain free or loosely combined molecules of the body, such as the albuminoid molecules of blood and lymph, or the drug may affect more remote tissues by means of the nervous system." The address was well written and well thought out; but the close attention which he enjoined several times during its delivery was really needed by his auditors.

Dr. George Cupples had died on April 19, 1895, four days before the meeting had opened. Resolutions of respect were prepared by Drs. T. D. Wooten, Ferdinand Herff, and Frank Paschal. Of Dr. Cupples it was said: "His life was surely one to be praised, and the world is always poorer when such men as Dr. Cupples die; for history furnishes few examples of devotion so sincere, duty so faithfully discharged, and humanity more dearly loved." This was merited praise for this great man who looms large in the story of medicine in Texas. In the May issue of the *Texas Medical Journal,* Dr. F. E. Daniel published a panegyric on Dr. Cupples, closing thus: "In the bright Empyrean realms, far beyond the skies,—the abode of noble souls,—illumined and made glorious by the presence of Eternal God, may his gentle spirit find its guerdon of rest; and when the arch-angel shall recount his many benefactions to suffering man, may a crown of glory, too, be his. Amen." At San Antonio, memorial services were held, at which prominent physicians and laymen spoke. Thus, in those days, the great of the earth were properly appraised and worthily honored.

The meeting of 1896 was assigned to Fort Worth. P. C. Coleman, Cleburne, became the new president; J. T. Wagley, Cleburne, first vice-president; N. B. Kennedy, Hillsboro, second vice-president; and T. B. Bass, Terrell, third vice-president. In his speech of acceptance, Dr. Coleman referred to a new stability of the Association: "There was a time when it seemed that the old ship would be engulfed in the billows of dissension, but not so now. Far beyond the breakers in her majestic grandeur she is sailing on the mighty ocean of scientific truth without one ripple to disturb her motion."

The stability to which Dr. Coleman referred was evident mostly in his optimism and the optimism of other stalwarts like him who believed with unshakable faith in the ultimate dominance of the Texas State Medical Association as the voice of all the doctors of Texas. When the Association convened in the Tarrant County Courtroom, Fort Worth, on April 28, 1896, it was clear that there would be much ado about the welfare of the Association. Words of welcome from Mayor B. B. Paddock included a reference to the newly established medical school in Fort Worth. Dr. Bacon Saunders was all-inclusive in his greeting: "I shall not ask whether you are from hamlet, village, town, or city; whether from the boundless, treeless plains of the northwest; or whether from the east, where the air is musical with the murmur of the pines and redolent with the perfume of the peach and apricot; or whether from the center of the State, where the land is waxy, where the corn grows tall and cotton is king; or from the south, where the live-oak grows and the magnolia and oleander bloom, and where the mosquito sings his 'cute' song all the night long; if you are but Texans, or friends of Texans, you are the salt of the earth, and our hearts and our doors are open to you."

Secretary West reported that 1,000 eight-page programs had been mailed out at an expense of $34.55. Yet fewer than 100 members were present, and later in the meeting only 27 voted on an important question. There was growing realization that the Association was gradually stagnating and that none of the many suggested solutions had aided. Of the sincerity, the foresight, and the industry of those who would advance the interests of the Association, we today can have no doubt. And yet all efforts toward progress had proved ineffectual. At the 1895 meeting the president had appointed a committee to study the situation and to report on "the best means of increasing the membership and thereby the usefulness" of the Association. This was a strong committee, composed of T. D. Wooten, of Austin; J. F. Y. Paine, of Galveston; M. D. Knox, of Hillsboro; Bacon Saunders, of Fort Worth; and J. T. Wilson, of Sherman. Previous to the meeting, they had inserted a long letter in the April issue of the *Texas Medical Journal,* urging a large attendance at the Fort Worth meeting. They appealed for the support of "every medical man in the State, who honors his profession, who loves his people, who has a conscientious regard for their welfare, who desires the promotion and progress of science, who feels the great necessity for improved State medicine and sanitary laws, and who desires his own advancement and firmer professional standing, with a just pride for a higher condition of medical matters in his State."

The report of this committee was the result of much time and thought, most of which was supplied by Chairman Wilson. A long evening session and most of the next morning were devoted to the

192

discussion. First of all, the committee recommended certain changes in the constitution and bylaws; these were adopted. Chief among them were the abolition of the initiation fee of five dollars and the reduction of the Nominating Committee from its former unwieldy size to thirteen members, one from each congressional district.

A large part of the report was vague and repetitious. It referred to unity, harmony, industry, elimination of politics, reduction of dues, good section work, and pleasant meetings. However, all vagueness and all repetition came to an abrupt end when the committee got around to recommending a bill creating a board of medical examiners composed of "six physicians, *four homeopaths* and *two* eclectics" (the italics belong to the *Texas Medical Journal*). A contemporary editor thus described the resulting turmoil and the unexpected reaction: "There was firing all along the line, heaviest in the center, where the homeopaths and eclectics were entrenched, as it was claimed, behind the State constitution—that 'no preference shall be given any school of medicine'—a heresy, a bugaboo—that served to whip into line even some of the vaunted 'old guard.' The old guard surrendered—but under protest—and one sole survivor still kicked,—the editor of the Red Back. The gentlemen 'took their medicine' with the meekness of the proverbial lamb." [5]

Later, when a feeling of repentance set in, it was resolved that the Association recognize homeopaths and eclectics only so far as the statutes and constitution of the state specified, and that any member of the Association who so lowered the "dignity of regular medicine as to meet them in consultation" should be expelled. Still later, when penitence became full grown, the "offensive clause" was stricken out. "These men on the outside," President Coleman insisted, "just wouldn't do."

This heresy of the homeopaths was little more than a diverting interlude, a digression which held the attention of the Association for the moment. The main purpose of the committee—that of increasing the membership and usefulness of the Association—could not be long forgotten. The question of "journalizing the transactions" came up and was rejected. A Committee on County Societies was created to foster the organization of local societies and to stimulate interest in the state association. With the initiation fee abol-

[5] *Texas Medical Journal,* XI (1895–96), 635.

ished, it became possible for a member of a county or district society to join the state association by presenting a certificate signed by his local president. But all these suggestions did little or nothing to avoid the era of decadence which was being predicted for the Association in certain quarters. Hard pressed financially, the Association retrenched by cutting the salary of faithful Treasurer Larendon in half in his twenty-fourth year of service. The doctors of Texas could not be attracted into the Association. In 1896 the membership had fallen to 379, and the next year it had dropped to 270, the lowest for many years. Indeed, it was difficult to stay above 300 until 1903, when the Association underwent the stimulating experience of reorganization. Then in 1904, there was a phenomenal increase to 2,415.

Several resolutions with a decidedly modern ring were passed at this Fort Worth meeting. One had to do with maintaining all life insurance examinations at five dollars, a figure that was not to be increased for more than fifty years and then by only a few companies. The secretary was instructed to communicate with Texas senators and representatives in Washington, "urging them to oppose the enactment of the pending bill for prohibition of vivisection by every means in their power." The claim was advanced by Dr. J. O. Williams, of William Penn, Texas, that he had performed the first three symphysiotomies in the United States. This claim had gotten into print, and a controversy had arisen. A committee was appointed to establish the facts and to report on whether "Texas deserves the honor of this priority." If the committee made a report, it does not appear in the records.[6]

President Coleman injected a note of sentiment when he presented a gavel to the Association. Previously a black stone had been used. Dr. Coleman had asked the secretary of the Kentucky State Medical Association to send him a block of wood taken from near the grave of Ephraim McDowell. From this he had a gavel made, and on it were engraved the names of Rush, McDowell, Gross, and Sims.

Nervous and mental diseases were well represented on the pro-

[6] Williams was no doubt sincere in his claim, but his date of publication does not support it. His article appeared in the *Southwestern Medical Record*, I (1896), 193–203. Dr. C. Jewett had preceded him with a paper in the *Brooklyn Medical Journal*, VI (1892), 790–92.

gram. Dr. Frederick Peterson, of the College of Physicians of New York, began with a good paper setting forth what was then known on the subject. Rest, diet, massage, hydrotherapy, and electricity were the sheet anchors of treatment. Dr. F. S. White, of Terrell, presented a strong plea for a state-supported institution for the care of epileptics and those suffering kindred ailments. In "A Plea for Reform in Criminal Jurisprudence," Dr. F. E. Daniel, of Austin, talked on methods of curbing the increasingly large number of mental diseases. He urged legal restrictions on the marriage of the mentally unfit. He was very emphatic in his belief that castration was indicated in dealing with all "natural criminals" and the criminally insane, thus closing the "flood gates of evil" and denying the unfit the chance to inflict their progeny on the next generation.[7]

If the papers read at this meeting are any criteria, surgery was making slow progress. Dr. A. H. Schenk brought up the subject of appendicitis and concluded that the "disease is not purely surgical, but it can be treated scientifically by an intelligent general practitioner"; that conservatism should be practiced "unless general symptoms indicate danger"; that "morphia, if intelligently used, relieves the patient, and does not obscure the symptoms unless given in poisonous doses"; and that "saline laxatives or castor oil, combined with minute doses of tincture of opium, deodorized, and aconite, are indicated, and can be used with safety." Dr. A. W. Fly, of Galveston, made a rather awkward report on "Three Cases of Cholecystotomy." His arithmetic was obviously bad. The third case did not come to operation because the patient was moribund when first seen. "For that reason," Dr. Fly recorded that he "did not use the knife, being as much opposed to the free and unlimited cutting of human flesh in such conditions of affairs as I am 16 to 1 financially."

President Coleman spoke on the subject "Of Medicine and of Doctors." He reviewed the history of medicine and referred to the fact that in other days physician and priest were one, this relationship being illustrated by an old advertisement which he had found: "Wanted for a family who have had bad health, a sober, steady person in the capacity of doctor, surgeon, apothecary and man mid-

[7] Texas had a much earlier and more radical advocate of this doctrine, Dr. Gideon Lincecum.—Nixon, "A Pioneer Texas Emasculator," *Texas State Journal of Medicine*, XXXVI (1940), 34–38.

wife. He must occasionally act as butler, and dress hair and wigs. He will be required sometimes to read prayers, and to preach a sermon every Sunday. A good salary will be given."

Two years after it was published, Dr. Coleman was quoting from Ian Maclaren's *A Doctor of the Old School* and was reminding his auditors that all over this land of ours counterparts of Dr. William MacLure lived and labored. He lauded the work of the pathfinders of medicine and accorded to them a place high in the world's history. "To my vision the hand of God is as manifest in the life work of Thomas Sydenham, John Hunter and Edward Jenner, as it is in the life work of Martin Luther, John Calvin and John Wesley."

Beyond the confines of the Association, medical affairs went on as usual. Even then, the doctors were drifting toward the cities, as we know from such notices as this in the *Texas Medical Journal:* "A doctor is needed at Lititia, a small station on the M., K. & T. R. R., twenty-five miles west of Houston; nearest doctor nine miles. Mr. F. V. Daniel, at Addicks P. O., Harris county, will give particulars if asked. A sober doctor wanted." [8] One reply to this notice was as follows: "Dear sir I notic in Danels Tex Medical Journal that a physician is wanted at ———, hence I rite the ask in regard to the location and what the population of the place and surrounding country has, and do you think the it will support a Dr, and give me any othe information you have." [9]

And down at Galveston at the fifth commencement, forty-two graduates were presented with diplomas. Caps and gowns were worn—mortarboards and expansive gowns with balloon sleeves. Two students rebelled at such clowning, and their names were not read at the exercises. Rumor has it that their diplomas were awarded in private.[10] The Nominating Committee at the 1896 meeting made an innovation by bringing in two names to be voted on for president: Bacon Saunders, Fort Worth; and J. C. Loggins, Ennis. The first received 10 votes and the second 16. A. N. Denton, Austin, was elected first vice-president; J. S. Letcher, Dallas, second vice-president; and David Cerna, Galveston, third vice-president.

[8] XI (1895–96), 648.
[9] *Ibid.,* XII (1896–97), 48.
[10] Dr. John T. Moore, of Houston, who was present, states in a personal communication, that these two men were E. B. Osborn, of Cleburne, and A. F. Lumpkin, of Amarillo. They were not permitted to sit on the rostrum but were given their diplomas at the end of the exercises, "amid applause." See also *Texas Medical Journal,* XI (1895–96), 706.

PAST PRESIDENTS

A. C. Scott, 1923   M. F. Bledsoe, 1924
C. M. Rosser, 1925   William Keiller, 1926

PAST PRESIDENTS

Joe Gilbert, 1927   Felix P. Miller, 1928
Joe Dildy, 1929   D. J. Jenkins, 1929

Paris was chosen as site of the next meeting. "A woeful mistake," commented the editor of the *Texas Medical Journal*. "Too far from Center and South and East and West; not sufficient hotels, and members don't like to be quartered on the town." [11]

Paris is located far up in northeastern Texas, very close to the Red River. As predicted, the attendance was unusually slim. No quorum was present at the first meeting of the 1897 session, so that it became necessary to await the arrival of the noon train, which brought several delegates. Those areas which normally sent sizable delegations fell far short this time: one came from Fort Worth, six from Dallas, three from Galveston, two from Austin, and none from San Antonio. This disappointing attendance came in spite of the publicity given to the meeting in the March and April issues of the *Texas Medical Journal* and the publication of an attractive program of forty-nine papers. Hotel accommodations had been advertised at from one to two dollars per day. Dr. F. E. Daniel paid the higher figure and recorded that his stay at the Lamar House was a nightmare. The food and accommodations, he said, were "generally pronounced 'rocky.' " [12]

The usual opening formalities were observed at the afternoon session at the City Hall. The prayer of the Rev. G. A. Farris was not recorded, but it could well have been a prayer for the Association's survival. The meeting had made little progress before reports of financial deficiencies were offered. Assessments and sight drafts were discussed as methods for meeting the situation, but the practical expedient of passing the hat was followed. It produced $145.

The only business of importance to come up in 1897 was the report of the previously appointed Committee on County Societies, to which had been assigned the difficult task of organizing local societies over the state and then bringing them into the fold of the state association. Chairman W. R. Blailock, of McGregor; E. A. Woldert, of Tyler; L. L. Shropshire, of San Antonio; J. D. Becton, of McKinney, and S. E. Hudson, of Austin, comprised this committee. Sometime prior to the meeting, letters had been sent to all doctors of the state, appealing to their pride and conscience, but replies were few. The size of this undertaking was emphasized by the fact that only 91 out of 246 counties were represented in the

[11] XI (1895–96), 642–43.
[12] *Ibid.*, XII (1896–97), 630.

Association; in other words, members of the Association resided in only 37 per cent of the counties. After setting forth the problems involved and expressing the belief that some progress had been made, the committee recommended that the secretaries of all local societies be joined together as a committee on medical societies and that a sincere effort be made on the local level to enlist memberships in the state association. The recommendations were accepted, and the presidents of the local organizations were added to the committee. This was a rather unusual procedure in that there was no organic relation, so far as the membership was concerned, between the state association and the lesser societies. The composition of the committee proved immaterial, for a year later the president reported that the committee had not "met with any marked degree of success." An opinion expressed by Dr. H. A. West, however, anticipated events: "The time is coming, and I believe is near at hand in the interest of a more perfect organization of the medical profession of this country, when a man cannot acquire membership in the American Medical Association except through his State society. When that period is reached he ought not to be able to enter the State body except through his local society."

The disappointments of the Paris meeting elicited from one editor this wise observation: "It is remarkable how a man loses interest in the Association after he has been president." [13] Even today it is still likely to be true that election to high office in many organizations terminates the usefulness of many worthy men. At Paris, former Presidents J. H. Sears and J. F. Y. Paine were present.

As visitors, "nearly the entire Faculty of the Gross Medical College," of Denver, seven in number, were present. Three visitors came from St. Louis, including Professor Emory Lanphear, who presented a paper with the title "Remarks upon Cancer of the Uterus Based upon a Personal Experience of Ninety-Seven Hysterectomies with Only Four Known and Eight Suspected Recurrences." This title was grossly misleading in that only twenty-two cases had been done for as long as three years and only eight cases as long as five years. These results, coupled with an operative mortality of 13 per cent, must have been a source of discouragement to his auditors.

Dr. J. H. Sears, of Waco, chose the title "Hotchpotch" for a paper dealing principally with malaria. He quoted Sir William Osler,

[13] *Ibid.*, 632.

198

whose famous textbook had come out five years earlier: "It is worthy of comment that three of the greatest benefits conferred on mankind, beside which it would be hard to find three of equal importance, have been in connection with fevers: The introduction of cinchona, the discovery of vaccination, and the announcement of the principles of asepsis. . . . I have spoken of the discovery of cinchona as one of the three greatest benefits conferred upon mankind in relation to the fevers, an event fraught with more memorable consequences than any, perhaps, in the history of medicine. It has made waste places habitable, the wilderness to blossom like the rose, and has been one of the greatest factors in the expansion of European civilization." The fact that this man of many years quoted from the young man whose writings were to bring modern medicine to the average doctor did not deter him from speaking out in defense of those things he had come to have faith in and those medical precepts he had come to live by. One of these was quinine, a drug "capable of snatching precious life from the icy arms of our greatest enemy, *death*." This paper was, in substance, his valedictory. In medical harness for forty-six years, he was bound, in good conscience, to interpret things as he found them. Seven years before, he had found the germ theory unacceptable; and even now he felt that "the whole microbe and antitoxin theory will have to be reconstructed or in a few years abandoned." [14]

The case report on "Entero-Lithiasis" by Dr. B. J. Neathery, of Van Alstyne, is interesting as an illustration of how much abuse the gastro-intestinal tract will tolerate. As demonstrated by late operation, the patient had a large enterolith high up in the jejunum. Three days before operation, the following list of purgatives was administered: six compound cathartic pills, five ounces of saturated solution of magnesium sulphate, and one pint of castor oil. After this, it was noted that the patient was "gradually becoming weaker." The next day, a consultant advised repetition of this medi-

[14] Sears was not the last of the unbelievers. Two years later, Dr. Thomas J. Pugh, of Hearne, reported that a local druggist decided to castrate himself. "He proceeded to do the operation on a quick and non-expensive, non-aseptic plan. He applied cocaine solution to his scrotum till all sensibility of the parts was destroyed, and with a common tobacco pocket-knife opened the scrotal sack and took out his testicles, severed the cord, and put the organs away in a pickle bottle, and has them preserved in alcohol." There was much bleeding but no infection. "The success of this operation, without any regard to the 'aseptic regime,' certainly knocks out that fad."—*Texas Medical Journal*, XV (1899–1900), 13–14.

cation plus an unspecified amount of calomel. The third day, two consultants agreed on calomel and only a half-pint of castor oil. No one took issue with the author's conclusion: "It is, gentlemen, in this class of cases where waiting too long brings the surgeon into disrepute and fills his mind with regret, and by all such cases dying, causes our patients to view an operation as an ante-mortem procedure, and consented to for the gratification of the surgeon."

When Dr. J. T. Benbrook, of Rockwall, got up to speak at this Paris meeting, he suggested that because of the small number present his and subsequent papers be dispensed with. Had his suggestion prevailed, we would have been deprived of two rare case reports. A woman had been wounded by a .44-caliber pistol. The bullet had passed between the eighth and ninth ribs on the right side and ranged downward toward the crest of the ilium. Three days later, uterine cramps developed and the bullet was passed *per vaginam.* The second patient was a man. A bullet from a .32-caliber rifle had penetrated the skin near the right anterior superior spine of the ilium and ranged toward the midline. A few days later, it *almost* passed by the penile urethra. At operation it was found directly against the urethra.

On this program was a young surgeon, A. C. Scott, of Temple, who was to become a part of the era uniting the old surgery with the new. He reported two cases of osteomyelitis of the lower jaw, which he had treated by resection. The operations were done intra-buccally, and both patients got a good result. Dr. H. L. Hilgartner, of Austin, reported on "Hypertrophy of the Pharyngeal Tonsil." In the way of treatment, if general treatment and cod liver oil failed, he advised "complete extirpation." "For this purpose three means are available—the unarmed finger, the forceps or the curette. Of these methods, either the use of the long-handled curette or the index finger will commend itself to the unpracticed operator."

President Loggins devoted his entire address to legislation relating to the practice of medicine in Texas. He showed how adequate legal restrictions had been established in such places as England and New York. And then, by contrast, he pointed out how wholly insufficient was the Texas law, passed in 1873 and modified in 1879. He found the local boards of medical examiners blameworthy, and especially did he single out the Galveston board for castigation. What can we expect, he asked, when in the very shadow of our great medical school at Galveston, "we have a District Medical Examining Board, composed of seven members, eminent in the profession in this State, and one of whom fills a professorship in the medical department of the University, who have so little regard for proficiency on the part of those whom they license to practice medicine as to grant license to first and second year men from our State school[?] . . . so eager are they to thus accommodate the applicant for a license, that they have reduced the fee from fifteen to five dollars, and have a board meeting every Saturday evening."

Hardly had Dr. Loggins ceased speaking when Dr. A. W. Fly was on his feet, eager to correct "an erroneous impression upon the mind of our honored ex-president." [15] The applicants referred to by Dr. Loggins were poor medical students to whom "a $10 bill is as big as chicken to the missionary in foreign lands." The "unblushing infidelity" which Dr. Loggins attributed to this board was in reality nothing less than undefiled pity for a group of struggling medical students. And besides, these second-year men were better doctors than many of those practitioners who had been turned loose on the unsuspecting people of Texas.

The mayor of Temple asked for the 1898 meeting, but it was awarded to Houston. As candidates for president, the Nominating Committee brought in two names, Bacon Saunders, of Fort Worth, and J. T. Wilson, of Sherman. When the votes were cast, Saunders received 20 to Wilson's 12. S. C. Red, Houston, was elected first vice-president; A. C. Scott, Temple, second vice-president; and C. M. Alexander, Coleman, third vice-president. No change was made in the offices of secretary and treasurer.

The Houston meeting served as a much needed stimulant to the Association. When it was called to order at Turner Hall on April 26, the attendance was the largest in several years. Because of accessions at this meeting, the secretary's report showed an increase in memberships from 270 to 355. Among the recruits were Dr. M. L. Graves, of McLennan County, and Dr. Joe Gilbert, of Travis County. And the treasurer added a note of hope by announcing a cash balance of $249.33. Entertainment planned for the session included an excursion down the bayou to San Jacinto on Wednesday, a streetcar ride over the city on Thursday, and a reception at Turner Hall Thursday night.

President Bacon Saunders included in his annual message two

[15] "Ex" by only a few seconds.

references to the national medical scene. One concerned the anti-vivisection bill then before Congress. Saunders had informed the senators and representatives from Texas of "the iniquities of the proposed law," and all had agreed to oppose the legislation. In fact, the situation was not so serious as it sounded, since the bill applied only to the doctors of the District of Columbia, and was easily defeated. The other reference was an appeal to the pride and patriotism of the membership in contributing to a fund to erect in Washington a monument to the memory of Dr. Benjamin Rush. This project had been begun in 1885 by the American Medical Association and was not completed until 1905. Texas doctors had given $37.50 in 1888, but those of other states were equally slow.

The Committee on Legislation reported another failure in its dealings with the Legislature. A bill endorsed by the Association had managed to get by the Senate, but the House of Representatives had taken no action on it. Despite this rebuff by the Legislature, the committee urged that the Association persevere. Thirty-one states already had satisfactory medical-practice acts. And "Texas with its splendid domain, the fascinating romance of stirring history, the grandeur of its achievements, the glorious possibilities of its rapidly developing future, the ability and scientific attainments of its golden-hearted medical men and the jealousy with which it guards its peerless honor, should not be the last in the union to protect its citizens from the inroads of the quacks and charlatans and ignorant pretenders, the head of whose column is turned in this direction and marching rapidly in, unchallenged and unmolested."

The Judicial Council recalled that of those members who had participated in the reorganization of the Association at Houston in 1869, six survived: D. R. Wallace, D. F. Stuart, J. H. Sears, T. J. Heard, R. T. Flewellen, and R. H. Jones. On the recommendation of the council, these were elected honorary members.

Tuberculosis, responsible for about 10 per cent of the deaths in the state, was the subject of two papers: "What Shall We Do with Our Consumptives?" by Dr. A. B. Gardner, of Bellville, and "The Prevention of Tuberculosis," by Dr. M. M. Smith, of Austin. Sixteen years after Robert Koch had proved the contagiousness of the disease, there was still an alarming ignorance and carelessness as to its hazards. The old dogma of heredity was still abroad in the land. Both authors realized that prevention rather than cure was paramount. Both advocated education of the public and construction of state sanatoriums.

Several new surgical procedures were described. Dr. A. C. Scott reported a case of gunshot wound in which fourteen inches of intestine were removed, and anastomosis was effected by use of a Murphy button. Dr. Joseph A. Mullen, of Houston, who signed himself a fellow of the American Laryngological, Rhinological and Otological Society, explained the use of adrenal extract in eye surgery, following the experimental work of Dr. J. J. Abel, of Baltimore. Dr. Robert F. LeMond, professor of diseases of the eye and ear, Gross Medical College, Denver, Colorado, presented a case in which the cornea of a rabbit was transplanted to the eye of a man. The result was indifferent. However, the paper which provoked the most interest at the Houston meeting and which reflected the thinking of physicians over the state was Dr. H. A. West's "The Differential Diagnosis Between Dengue and Yellow Fever, with Some Account of the Epidemic of 1897 in Texas." Epidemics of yellow fever had occurred in Texas throughout the nineteenth century, notably the latter half. As early as 1840, Dr. Ashbel Smith had published a book on the subject. In 1853 and 1867, Texas was hard hit by the disease, particularly in the coastal region. The question which concerned the physicians of Texas was the diagnosis between yellow fever and dengue, because the prognosis was entirely different in the two diseases. As will be seen, there was wide divergence of opinion. The subject was of sufficient importance to enlist the interest of Sir William Osler, who remarked, "The difficulty in the differential diagnosis of these two diseases lies in their frequent coexistence, as during the epidemic of 1897 in parts of the Southern States. During the autumn in 1897 the profession of Texas was divided on the question of the existence of yellow fever in the State, some claiming that the disease was dengue, others, including Guitéras and West, that yellow fever also existed." [16]

Dr. West made a thoroughgoing survey of the entire subject. The epidemic began late in July in Galveston, Houston, and San Antonio, and then spread out rapidly for about a hundred miles in every direction. Sixty to 90 per cent of the population was affected. Dr. John Guitéras, professor of pathology at the University of Pennsylvania, was sent to Texas by the Marine Hospital Service.

[16] *The Principles and Practice of Medicine* (6th ed., New York, 1906), 237–38.

Dr. West recognized in the epidemic a source of widespread potentialities: "A complete paralysis of commerce, the wheels of industry arrested, enforced idleness with consequent poverty and suffering of thousands, enormous depreciation in property values of every kind, universal fear and panic, and the possibility of widespread death and desolation." He traced the history and progress of the epidemic, set down the symptoms in great detail, contrasted the symptoms of yellow fever and dengue, and quoted all available authorities. He noted that the epidemic subsided with the advent of cold weather and theorized that the disease was "transmitted by persons and things to other persons." [17] His conclusion was that both yellow fever and dengue were present in Texas. This conclusion was shared by Professor Guitéras and confirmed by at least one autopsy report from Professor Allen J. Smith. But West's views were vigorously opposed for eight pages of the *Transactions* and, indeed, over the state generally. The controversy reminded an editor of "the old preacher who begged to differ with Brother Paul about something Paul had said in his epistles to the—Marines—no, the Corinthians or the Ephesians." [18]

In his presidential address, Dr. Bacon Saunders touched on medicine as it was practiced in his day and sounded a warning: "Beware of the doctor that could have saved the patient if he had been there fifteen minutes earlier." Then he took a look into the future:

More people, perhaps, than most of you are aware of are tainted with the idea—as the story goes—that if the son of a family is too mean to be a preacher, not smart enough for a lawyer and too lazy to follow a business life, he is therefore good material out of which to manufacture a doctor. It is probable if those who enter the study of medicine now, at the close of the century, are prepared to take up the investigation of subjects now being carried on by hosts of capable workers all over the world, the first decade of the coming century will see more brilliant achievements in medical knowledge than the world has seen from the beginning of the science up to this time. What we have accomplished hitherto will seem as the first streaks of dawn that are the heralds of the coming of day in all his noontide glory. Can a brighter hope or nobler object stimulate the zeal and fire the ambition of man than this?

[17] In 1881, Dr. Carlos J. Finlay advanced the theory that yellow fever is transmitted by the mosquito. In 1900, Dr. Walter Reed and his co-workers carried out their epoch-making research which proved the correctness of this theory.

[18] *Texas Medical Journal,* XIII (1897–98), 242.

PAST PRESIDENTS

John W. Burns, 1930   J. O. McReynolds, 1931
J. H. Foster, 1932   A. A. Ross, 1933

PAST PRESIDENTS

S. E. THOMPSON, 1934   J. H. BURLESON, 1935
H. R. DUDGEON, 1936 CALVIN R. HANNAH, 1937

For some years an orator had been elected by the Association, but for the most part no oration was delivered. This year at Houston, Dr. I. N. Suttle, of Corsicana, made such an address. He spoke in praise of the doctor, what he had accomplished, and what he stood for. "To the cultivation of true science," he concluded, "to the alleviation of human suffering, to the divine business of going about doing good, and to the leaving to our beloved profession something better and richer than we found is the goal toward which we should set our steadfast feet. The accomplishment of these aims implies on our part a lifetime of laborious days, and nights devoid of ease, of unwearied patience, of constant mental and physical exertion; of utter self-abnegation. The way is rugged but the reward sublime."

The *Transactions* record that Dr. Charles L. Gwyn, of Galveston, had been appointed chairman of the Section on Obstetrics and Diseases of Children. Since Gwyn failed to pay his dues before the Houston meeting, his name was automatically dropped from the roll. This seemed natural enough, but it resulted in a fist fight on the rostrum. "A big burly fellow from Galveston sought to whip the secretary . . . for calling him a liar out loud in meeting, when he had 'risen to a point of personal privilege' and complained, as we learn, of having been dropped from the roll of membership for non-payment of dues." To an onlooker, it was a scandalous scene: "These gentlemen passed the lie to each other; there was a collision, and the first phase of a prize fight ensued on the floor of the convention." [19]

Nominated for president were J. T. Wilson, of Sherman, and A. B. Gardner, of Bellville. When Gardner withdrew his name, Wilson was elected by acclamation. Chosen to serve with him were J. M. Fort, Paris, first vice-president; Taylor Hudson, Belton, second vice-president; and R. W. Knox, Houston, third vice-president. San Antonio was decided on as the place of meeting in 1899. Then, after thanking everyone, including "the queenly matrons and maids of Houston," the members returned to their homes, carrying with them "sweet memories of their experiences at this meeting—tender memories walking to and fro, weaving garlands of immortelles and causing us in after times to turn with grateful hearts to the sunny days of April, 1898, passed by all of us in the enterprising city of Houston."

[19] *Ibid.*, 632–33.

Outside Association circles, medical affairs in Texas were active. New medical schools were springing up. The Fort Worth Medical School was in operation with 150 matriculants. Dallas had a school in prospect. The College of Physicians and Surgeons, of Weatherford, offered unusual conditions for admission: "To enable poor young men to secure medical education, the faculty, not being pressed financially, will accept in lieu of cash, cord word, Johnson grass, chickens, eggs, or any other commodity the faculty can consume." This institution insisted, however, that "the candidate must be advanced as far as 'Baker' in the old blue-backed speller and know the multiplication table thoroughly. The candidate must be of good moral character, and at least have no present indictment pending, and in event of having served a term in the penitentiary, he must have had his citizenship restored by the governor." [20]

When Drs. H. A. West, A. G. Clopton, and David Cerna resigned, apparently under pressure, from the faculty of the Medical Department of the University of Texas, at Galveston, there was a demand that these positions be filled by members of the profession in Texas. This demand was partially satisfied by the appointment of Dr. J. W. McLaughlin, of Austin, to succeed Dr. West.

Other doctors, too, were on the move, as indicated in this notice: "*A Good Practice* in six miles of one of the best middle-sized cities in Texas can be secured, on favorable terms, by applying to the *Journal.* Country practice in a thickly settled German settlement,— most of them speak English, and have the cash on hand to pay the doctor. Nets $1800 to $2400. This practice can be had by buying the incumbent's property; it consists of three acres of land, a five-room cottage and office, a good barn and other outbuildings. $2000, half cash; the incumbent will induct purchaser into practice, and retire at any time. Address, enclosing 2-cent stamp for reply, *The Texas Medical Journal,* Austin, Texas." [21]

In welcoming members of the Association to the 1899 session, at Turner Hall in San Antonio, now a city of sixty-five thousand people, Mayor Marshall Hicks paid eloquent respects to the medical profession, of which his brother, Dr. F. M. Hicks, was a prominent member: "All that a man hath will he give for his life and yet that life he implicitly places in the hands of his family physician.

[20] *Ibid.,* 86.
[21] *Ibid.,* 371.

The profession of law guards and protects property, but the client with all the goods and chattels of the world, if he hath not health is not a happy man. The theme of the ministry, and the future state of man, and his relation to his fellow man, and his family, are noble themes, but a man with an acute attack of indigestion is a most miserable man."

This session was to produce severe denunciations of the Legislature for its continuing failure to enact adequate medical practice and public health measures. Early in his address of welcome on behalf of the Western Texas Medical Association, Dr. James Hall Bell declared: "The most consummate fools, the most brazen and unmitigated scamps, are permitted by the absurd and amazing enactments of legislation, and the complacency of a civilization too careless of its own welfare to think, to exaggerate its inherent weaknesses, asperse its character, and to exercise its intricate and delicate functions on terms of equality with the most profound and disciplined minds."

About 250 doctors were said to have been in attendance, probably a high estimate.[22] The membership of the previous year (355) had been reduced to 297, mainly because 93 names were dropped for nonpayment of dues. For this meeting, Dr. Frank Paschal designed a badge which was worn by the members—"a button on white satin ribbon, and on the button is enameled a Texas star in white on a blue ground, encircled by a laurel wreath."[23]

Dr. Larendon made his last report as treasurer. It must have gladdened his apprehensive heart to report a positive balance of $414.56. After twenty-eight years of loyal service, he asked permission to retire. Very humbly he said, "It remains for me to again thank the Association for its long continued confidence, and regret that in leaving the treasury solvent I can not leave a more abundant surplus." His resignation was accepted in a most casual manner. But two days later Dr. W. R. Blailock, of McGregor, introduced this resolution, which was promptly passed: *"Resolved,* That this body manifest by a rising vote its appreciation of the honest, efficient and faithful performance of duty of its worthy Treasurer, Dr. J. Larendon, who is retiring from his official duties by resignation." Dr. Larendon was made an honorary member of the Associa-

[22] One of the local papers gave the number of members in attendance as 158, with 26 visitors.—*San Antonio Daily Light,* April 26, 1899.
[23] *Ibid.,* April 25, 1899.

tion. Here he was in good company with such men as Dr. Hunter McGuire, of Richmond; Dr. Louis S. McMurtry, of Louisville; Dr. Thomas More Madden, of Dublin; Dr. Edmond Souchon, of New Orleans; and Dr. John A. Wyeth, of New York.

President Wilson's annual message dealt with the two problems which had regularly plagued his predecessors: apathy of the Legislature in dealing with measures sponsored by the Association, and some method of increasing the scope and influence of organized medicine by multiplying local societies. In addition, he recommended that some action be taken on a resolution passed by the American Medical Association the previous year at Denver. This resolution denied membership to all teachers and graduates of medical schools the standards of which did not conform to the minimum standards of the Association of American Medical Colleges. Later the committee appointed to study Wilson's message advised delay and caution on this resolution. Indeed, the American Medical Association itself did not enforce it. This and other suggestions were forerunners of the Council on Medical Education of the American Medical Association, which was created in 1904 under the able chairmanship of Dr. Arthur Dean Bevan, of Chicago.

It is a source of real surprise that neither Dr. Wilson nor his predecessor referred to the Spanish-American War, which had been fought and won the preceding year and in which bacilli were said to have killed more men than bullets did. In fact, no reference to the war can be found in the *Proceedings*. Texas took a vital part in the war: the Rough Riders were organized and trained at San Antonio by Dr. Leonard Wood and Colonel Theodore Roosevelt. Texas supplied ten thousand soldiers, more than double her quota, and the doctors of Texas, as always, offered their services. It was all done without fanfare.

The memorial services this year were not impressive. No previous preparation had been made, and the result was hardly worthy of the three former presidents who had died since the last meeting: Drs. T. J. Heard, R. T. Flewellen, and R. M. Swearingen.

At this 1899 meeting in San Antonio, reports were made on the lack of progress in dealing with the Legislature. About all the Committee on Legislation was able to report were "assurances of a political kind," which the committee did not consider worth recording. The Committee on State Board of Health made a comprehensive report. It had succeeded in getting a bill to the Legislature, only to have the bill waylaid in the legislative hopper. The committee brought in a long memorial to Governor Joseph D. Sayers, deploring sanitary conditions in Texas and imploring his help in this unequal struggle. All this was accepted by the membership in subdued silence.

Then Dr. W. W. McGregor introduced a resolution calling the attention of the Legislature to "the vicious and self-destroying habit of using morphine" and other narcotics, and asking legislative relief. Silence was no longer subdued. Dr. A. B. Gardner offered this frank appraisal:

I am opposed to any resolutions or memorials or lobbying in any way with the legislature of the State of Texas for any bill regulating the practicing of medicine, or for anything that emanates from this body, not that I do not think and feel that this would be a good bill and that we need legislation, but it is on account of my respect for this Association, that I object to its trying to secure legislation in this State. I have been a member of the Association twenty years, and in that time there has hardly been a meeting that we have not adopted some resolution favoring legislation for the good of the people, not for the benefit of this body, which has been refused. We have sent committee after committee, and in all that time we have never accomplished anything, and have hardly been accorded a respectful hearing. We have been spurned with contempt, our requests have fallen upon a stone, a deaf ear has been turned to us. I think it is time for us to stop and let them run it to suit themselves. We are not lawyers, politicians or shop keepers, and have no influence with the voters, Governor or the legislators. Our self-respect dictates that we stop trying.[24]

This sentiment was vigorously endorsed by several other speakers. Dr. R. R. Walker, of Schulenburg, was bluntly frank: "I do not wish to reflect upon Governor Sayers, but if you want to buy the other crowd, take a ten dollar bill down to a certain saloon and deposit it there and you can get anything you want."

But calmer opinions prevailed. Drs. S. C. Red, H. C. Ghent, H. A. West, and others believed that the efforts of the Association should not be relaxed. Dr. J. H. Sears resorted to an apt Biblical analogy in supporting the latter view. "There is an account in the scrip-

[24] Had Gardner been able to look ahead fifty-three years, he would have been glad that his advice was not taken too literally. The influence of the medical profession has increased until in 1952 President Harry Truman complained that "a lot of lawmakers jump when the American Medical Association cracks the whip."

tures," he said, "of a woman brought before an unjust judge, who had no respect for God or man. That judge is just like our legislature, but he was importuned until he heard her cause, and I think we ought to ding dong the legislature one hundred years if necessary in order to accomplish the desired end."

President Wilson delivered his annual address at the Grand Opera House. His theme was "The Mission of Medicine." He referred to the heroic struggle which had occurred at the Alamo, just across the plaza. He acclaimed the dauntless courage of Travis, Bowie, and their followers: "The lone star banner waved undaunted and defiantly above them, and was hauled down only when every gallant defender lay cold in death." [25] Then he gave a learned summary of the history of medicine. The medical profession of Texas had proved itself worthy of its heritage. In the future, "the profession at large must be better organized, must evince a greater interest in medical legislation, give more attention to the urgent requirements of the day, spend a little more time for the public good and work in harmony together," remembering "how divine a thing it is to labor and to wait." He closed in a flight of oratory, submerging for the moment the sturdy individualism which characterized his generation:

The future is heavily laden with grand possibilities. The veil of mystery will be lifted and clearness of vision will bring many things to light that now seem impenetrable. The clouds will pass away and the bright rays of a luminous sun will reflect in beatific splendor a glory that was never dreamed of.... The time may be far distant, but it will come when accident and old age will be put down as the chief causes of death. Life will be more satisfactory, more enjoyable, the rosy tints of its morning resplendent with that freshness which unfolds the petals into full blossom, the noontide rich with the vigor of a perfect day. The evening calm and gentle in its sweet repose, whose lingering twilight passes like the slowly ebbing tide, will enable him

> By an unfaltering trust approach thy grave
> Like one that wraps the drapery of his couch
> About him and lies down to pleasant dreams.

The Section on Medicine was given over principally to discussion of infectious diseases: smallpox, diphtheria, meningitis, la grippe,

[25] Wilson was in error. The flag which the Texans unfurled at the Alamo was the Mexican flag with "1824" on it, indicating loyalty to the Mexican constitution adopted in 1824.

and pneumonia. Dr. T. W. Shearer, of Wallisville, presented a case of actinomycosis, confirmed by the microscope. Dr. S. C. Red, in step with progress, advocated "free purgation with the mild chloride of mercury" in place of "the old-time bleeding" in the treatment of pneumonia. "Whiskey, the gentleman's drink" would be found useful up to a pint and a half a day. Convalescent serum had its advocates, but he had had no experience with it.

The program of the Section on Surgery was highlighted by two papers on surgery of the liver: "The Surgical Treatment of Hepatic Neoplasms," by James E. Thompson, of Galveston, and "Some Points in Operating for Abscess of the Liver," by B. E. Hadra, of San Antonio. Dr. Thompson successfully removed a tumor from the liver, which Dr. William Keiller reported to be a gumma. The syphilitic history had been "carefully concealed by the patient," he explained. However, this case afforded Dr. Thompson an opportunity to review the literature of the subject and to record some experimental work he had done. Dr. Hadra's paper dealt with two large liver abscesses which he had attacked by resecting a piece of rib. Both cases succumbed. A contribution to the result was made by the "nurse, who, with a furious activity, combined the utmost contempt of Listerian theories."

Two papers read at this meeting were the vanguard of the violent assault on misplaced uteri and floating kidneys in Texas: "Cervical Flexions—Their Importance and Means of Curing Them," by T. J. Bell, of Tyler, and "Nephroptosis—Report of Case—With the Operation of Bi-Lateral Nephropexy," by G. W. Allen and W. H. Lancaster, of Flatonia. Dr. Bell was content to deal with his cases by means of dilatation, curettage, and packing the cervix. Drs. Allen and Lancaster classified floating kidneys in three forms: painful, dyspeptic, and neurasthenic. If gain in weight and a properly fitted belt did not correct the trouble, then the kidney should be stitched up.

Dr. Hugh H. Young, of Baltimore, read a paper on "Operative Treatment of Hypertrophied Prostate, with Report of Four Cases of Total Excision." A short time before, Dr. Young had given up his practice in San Antonio to become a member of the surgical staff at Johns Hopkins. This was one of the earliest reports on prostatectomy made by Dr. Young. His first published article appeared three years later. Unfortunately, his paper was not printed in the *Transactions*.

Waco was to be the place of the next meeting. A. B. Gardner, Bellville, was elected president; B. E. Hadra, San Antonio, first vice-president; George H. Lee, Galveston, second vice-president; and F. D. Thompson, Fort Worth, third vice-president. R. F. Miller, Sherman, became the new treasurer.

Despite repeated legislative rebuffs, two encouraging developments took place in 1899, which were in part referable to the efforts of the state association. One was the passage by the Legislature of a bill creating an asylum for epileptics at Abilene. This project had been strongly advocated by Dr. F. S. White in 1896. Another legislative success was getting the "occupation tax" law repealed. And in the experimental field the medical profession was not idle. Dr. Rudolph Menger, of San Antonio, had done some very creditable work, which he published under the title "Photo-Micrography as Related to Medical and Scientific Research." [26] In the political field also, some physicians were active. "Dr. A. W. Fly, the plucky mayor of Galveston, on August 29th, placed himself at the head of the police force, and, pistol in hand, quelled a serious labor riot." [27]

[26] *Texas Medical Journal,* XIV (1898–99), 671–81.
[27] *Ibid.,* 153.

XIII

A New Century and a New Association, 1900–1904

The new century brought to Texas an era of calm and unruffled confidence. Joseph D. Sayers and S. W. T. Lanham, the last former Confederate soldiers to serve as governor, projected their high idealism and mature judgment into the affairs of the state. This was in pleasing contrast to the contentions and controversies which erupted about the head of Jim Hogg. Farmers and ranchmen were in good financial condition. The cotton crop of 1900 was valued at $139,000,000. Industrial development, while still backward, was making headway. In 1901, the great oil field at Spindletop was brought in. In 1900, the population of Texas was 3,048,710, double what it was in 1880. Texas thus rose in population from eleventh to sixth among the states. The distribution of physicians was definitely involved in the fact that 85 per cent of the people lived in the country in 1900; in 1950 that figure had been reduced to about 50 per cent.

Dr. Jarrette D. Law, of Belton, before the 1901 session, gave expression to the impelling buoyancy of the new era in these words: "The old century is dead; we stand on the threshold of the new where honor is to him who will win it; there is scope for the broadest culture, for the highest ambition and grandest attainments. A mighty thrilling force permeates land and people, the counting house, the mill, the machine shop, the laboratory, the forge, the furnace. . . . The medical profession has taken position in the front surge of the battle as humanity struggles on to perfection." Proof

213

that big things medically were developing in Texas at that time is found in a case report by Dr. Arthur E. Spohn, of Corpus Christi: "Multicystic Ovarian Tumor Weighing 328 Pounds." [1]

From the depressing situation of 1899, the affairs of the Texas State Medical Association and the medical profession in general made steady and, at times, almost spectacular progress. The membership of 297 grew to 384 in 1902 and swelled to 2,415 by the time of the 1904 meeting. The cash balance of $414.56, which Dr. Larendon had proudly reported in 1899, became $1,628.35 in 1902 and two years later was $4,795.57. Another measure of the expansive mood of the Association was found in the marked increase in the size of the *Transactions*. The 1897 publication had been spoken of as "a very cheap affair, (not 'worth looking at')." [2] And the same was to some extent true of the 1898 and 1899 issues. The last was a volume of 351 pages. By 1902 it had grown to 587 pages, and by 1904 to 648 pages, published at a cost of $1,809.50.

When the 1900 meeting of the Association convened in the Waco auditorium, there was an air of confidence and assurance. Never had there been a meeting under more favorable circumstances than this thirty-fourth, President Gardner asserted. No noteworthy increase in membership had taken place, but Secretary West was able to report that only twenty-four had failed to pay dues. And a balance of more than $1,000.00 in the treasury gave the Association a comfortable feeling. There was a pervading impression that the Association was finally on its way.

A prominent citizen of Waco, Dr. W. L. Prather, who had just been elected president of the University of Texas, was asked to address the Association. He spoke of the "noble character" of the doctors of Texas and mentioned the state university as an associating bond between the medical profession and himself: "The medical college at Galveston, and the general interests of the University of Texas, desire to join hands with you in an earnest effort to uplift and establish upon a permanent basis the profession of medicine, a basis where the people can trust it, where the citizenship of Texas can firmly rely upon the man who carries his degree as a doctor of medicine that he is in truth and in fact prepared for his vocation." At this session, President Prather was made an honorary member of the Association.

[1] *Texas State Journal of Medicine*, I (1905–1906), 273–74.
[2] *Texas Medical Journal*, XIII (1897–98), 630.

The Committee on County Societies made a full report on its activities for the year. Data on forty-six local societies had been assembled. Location, date of organization, date and cause of demise if inactive, number of members, and names of officers were recorded. Twenty-four organizations were active, and of these, fourteen were affiliated with the state association: Austin Academy of Medicine, Austin District Medical Society, Bell County Physicians' and Surgeons' Association, Brazos Valley Medical Society, Brenham Medical Society, Central Texas Medical Association, Corsicana District Medical Association, El Paso County Medical Society, Hill County Medical and Surgical Association, Houston District Medical Association, Johnson County Medical Society, South Texas Medical Association, Waco Medical Association, and Western Texas Medical Association. There were ten unaffiliated societies: Briggs Medical Society, Cook County Medical Association, Dallas Clinical Association, Dallas Medical and Surgical Society, Delta County Medical Association, Grayson County Medical Association, Kaufman County Medical Society, Lamar County Medical Association, Panhandle Medical Association, and Practitioners' Society of Dallas. Assigned causes of failure were indifference, professional jealousy, and local prejudice. This report did not include the North Texas Medical Association with its 350 members, which had come to be a near rival of the state association.

At the previous meeting, it had been agreed to assess each affiliated society five dollars for each twenty members or fraction thereof. At the Waco session only one society paid this assessment, the South Texas Medical Association, which paid twenty-five dollars for its more than eighty members. Realizing that this levy had been a mistake, the state association returned this money and abolished the assessment.

The Committee on Legislation brought in its usual report, enlivened by some engaging words: "Your Committee . . . has come with its third biennial report, and lament the fact that after a valiant fight we are here, but come in no triumphal procession with flying banners and martial music amid loud cries of victory; we can lay no trophies at your feet, but have dropped in one by one to report that after a gallant attack in front and flank and rear we were repulsed, and come as vanquished knights to acclaim a dismal failure." It was altogether disheartening to this committee to have its legislative efforts referred to "the usual committee, and there lost in the dust and cobwebs and debris of ancient pigeon holes," especially when the strongest antagonists of desirable medical legislation were legislators who were also doctors. And yet this committee had ready a workable medical-practice bill, when and if the Legislature should show any inclination to accept it.

In line with this report were two papers read before the Section on State Medicine and Public Hygiene: "Maladministration of Public Medical Affairs in the State of Texas," by H. A. West, and "The Public Health and the State's Duty to Protect It," by M. M. Smith. Dr. West dealt with conditions in the hospitals for the insane, conditions that were "abhorrent in the extreme"; the inadequacy of the State Health Department, which consisted of a state health officer and a few quarantine officers at the principal ports and along the Mexican border; and the medical-practice act then in force, which he considered worse than useless.

Dr. Smith discussed, among other things, medical education and criminal abortions. He commented critically on inequality in the former: "We have upon the one hand the Medical Department of the University of Texas, which requires an entrance examination before young men can go there and take up the study of medicine, and requires a four years' rigid course, with every facility for teaching medicine in all of its branches. Upon the other hand we have the same State issuing a charter to an institution like the one in San Antonio." He was referring to the New York Medical College of San Antonio, which had been chartered the year before. The faculty consisted of one physician, his wife, and his brother, a layman. The matter was brought to the attention of the attorney-general of the state, who brought suit which later resulted in revocation of the charter. To obtain evidence, the West Texas Medical Association took up a collection of fifty dollars, the amount charged for a diploma, and enrolled a colored porter from the Hicks Building as a student in the college. After seventeen days in attendance, he received his diploma, signed and properly documented. As for criminal abortions, Dr. Smith deplored the presence in Texas of doctors who "follow such work as a business" and produce abortions for as little as fifteen dollars, doctors "who will murder an innocent infant in its mother's womb, placed there for its protection and life, for money." His closing sentence brought applause from his hearers: "If I were an artist and could paint a picture I would select as my subject the horrible face of the criminal abortionist; I would make

216

him the central figure of an immense picture, and all around him I would have the beautiful innocent faces of little children pointing at him and condemning him for his horrible deeds."

The discussion which followed these two papers covers fourteen pages of fine print in the *Transactions* and was participated in by fourteen men. All were in complete agreement. In the past, discussion had often meant disagreement; and in the future, further disagreements would come. But here was full accord, and it may well be that this unanimity as to medical practice, medical education, public health, quackery, and malpractice was a factor of importance in welding the medical profession of Texas into a solid state medical association three years later. This unified attitude prompted the Association to appropriate two hundred dollars to be used in organizational work. In its fight to prevent the indiscriminate practice of medicine, the Association received support from an unexpected source in the form of a resolution from the medical school at Galveston, offering united assistance, and signed by W. D. Jones and 121 other students.

The Association can be accorded the full credit for one important milestone in public health in Texas, the foundation of which was laid at this Waco meeting. Dr. Frank Paschal introduced a resolution creating a committee to influence the passage of legislation looking toward construction of institutions for the care of consumptives. As chairman of this committee, Dr. Paschal worked without ceasing for eleven years, and in 1912 the Carlsbad Sanatorium was opened to patients.

When the name of Dr. J. M. Litten was read at the memorial service, a thread of recollection traveled back through the years to a day in December, 1852, when a call had been issued for the purpose of organizing the Texas Medical Association. Dr. Litten was one of the ten men who signed this call. He was described as a pioneer doctor, a man of strong convictions, who "moved among his fellowmen without any outward display." He was the last but two of these signers to pass on, the remaining two being Drs. R. N. Lane and W. A. Morris. From the time when Dr. Lane was the first secretary of the Association, in 1853, to the time when he became the first president of the Maverick County Medical Society, in 1905, was a period of fifty-two years, more than half the lifetime of the Association. Dr. Morris died in 1902 at the age of ninety, having practiced medicine for more than sixty years. Also at this memorial service, Dr. F. E. Daniel eulogized the late R. M. Swearingen, an assignment given to him the year before. He had prepared a six-page memorial, well organized and beautifully written. This memorial in its entirety can be read today with profit to both heart and mind. Even now a feeling of pride wells up as we read:

Like the white plumes of Navarre, always riding above the storm of battle where the strife was deadliest, the crest of this modern knight could be seen as he battled with the hosts of darkness and death. When his native State, Mississippi, was in the throes of the great yellow fever epidemic of 1878, and the peaceful and happy little town of Holly Springs, under the impulse of generous sympathy and that hospitality ever characteristic of the South, threw open her doors to the terror-stricken refugees from the beleaguered towns, and became, herself, the storm-center of the pestilence, Swearingen and Manning,—the brave, the gallant, the lovable Manning,—were prompt to go to her relief. Manning fell. Many noble volunteer physicians and nurses fell, laying down their lives cheerfully in the cause of humanity,—in obedience to that power that impels a heroic soul to self-immolation in the discharge of duty. Swearingen held the hand of the dying Manning, and later, before this Association, paid a tribute to his memory in an oration of love-inspired eloquence which today illumines the pages of the Association's archives, and lives in the memory of those present.

President A. B. Gardner addressed this thirty-fourth session of the Association, at Waco, on medical conditions in Texas as he saw them and on the prospects for their improvement. Before getting very far, he sideswiped the politician: "There are in Texas thousands of politicians of every party, who can solve the problem of governing Cuba and Porto Rico, can tell just how to control Hawaii, and know just what course the president should pursue with the Philippine Islands, and what effect expansion would have on our economic conditions, and bring about, in a word, the millennium, yet they have never taken time to think of the problem how to lower the rate of mortality in the State, and improve the physique of the rising generation and make our State more healthful than it is." His main theme was tuberculosis, which was taking an annual toll of 100,000 lives in the United States. Rest and isolation in sanatoriums offered the best solution. Other countries such as England, France, and Germany and other states such as New York, Pennsylvania, and Illinois had taken the lead in this matter. Texas should not lag behind. "The medical profession everywhere is agreed that

218

this course is the solution of this problem; what will you do? Will you sit calmly by and see the rising generation of our glorious State deteriorate, or will you lend your aid to stay the progress of this dread monster, which threatens to undermine the vitality of our manhood? Why expend millions annually on the education of our youth and allow them physically to grow weak? What can we hope for from an over-trained mind and an enfeebled body? They will show forth brilliantly for a short time, but like a meteor on an autumn evening, soon fade away to be seen no more."

Dr. Joe Becton, of Greenville, was one of the last of the orators of the Association in the days when oratory was still in flower. His oration centered about the loyalty and dignity of the doctor. From Hippocrates to Sims, he spoke of those who had walked across the medical stage, made their contribution, and then passed on. Always, the medical profession had struggled upward, so that today "there is no higher calling; there is no life so self-sacrificing; there is none who gives his all to his fellowman as does the doctor. He is the same yesterday, today, and will be forever. In the even tenor of his way he goes from the squalid hovel, where poverty nurses as a child and misery lends a helping hand, to the splendid palace, where opulence is a burden and lucre is a plaything. The same gentle demeanor characterizes him at all times, and none but his co-laborer, the minister, knows how the world lives from the cradle to the grave. The one fact of which I am the most proud of all is that God never made a coward and a true doctor in the same man."

Two masterly papers, typical of the scientific progress that was being made by the Association, were presented at this 1900 session: "On the Anatomy of the Renal Vessels and Pelvis of the Kidney in Relation to Digital Exploration of That Organ in the Operation of Nephrotomy," by William Keiller, and "Stone in the Bladder and Lithotomy," by Frank Paschal. Dr. Keiller set out to explain anatomically the long-known fact that at the operating table an incision can be made into the kidney along the convex border, with little resulting hemorrhage. By a method of arterial injection and parenchymal maceration, he proved that from an arterial standpoint the kidney is divided into three parts: dorsal and ventral areas, where the blood supply is very free, and a central area that is comparatively avascular.

While practicing in Mexico, Dr. Paschal had had an unusual experience with vesical calculi. He reported on forty-three cases, the largest stone weighing 450 grains. His report gave the history of cutting for stone which dates back to antiquity, the causes for the formation, classification into age groups, the methods of diagnosis, the choice of operative routes, and the results to be expected. Two deaths occurred in the forty-three operations, excellent results under the worst surroundings imaginable, where "nothing but an undressed sheep skin served as a bed." Dr. Paschal used the perineal operation. His most famous case was "the celebrated thief known as the Peacock." This man ran afoul of Mexican law and received a .44-caliber bullet just above the pubis. Temporary hematuria without leakage of urine into the tissues did not detain him very long. Five years later, he returned with a stone in his bladder. Surgery was advised, but he chose to return to robbing and stealing. Two years passed before this Robin Hood was seen again, with aggravation of symptoms. Before he could accept the proffered operation, he was arrested, put in the *calabozo,* and then inducted into the army. Army life in the era of Porfirio Díaz was not attractive. After six months, "he sent me word that if I would get him out of the army he would let me cut him." One day in the hospital, and he was gone again. After a lapse of six years—thirteen years from the time he was wounded—he returned and submitted to operation. A large stone was removed. At its center was found the .44-caliber bullet. With a twinkle in his eye, well remembered by his friends, Dr. Paschal concluded: "He made an uninterrupted recovery, but the knife that I cut him with was stolen from amongst my instruments that I left at his house to be cleaned."

The first session of the Texas State Medical Association in the twentieth century adjourned after selecting Galveston for the next meeting and electing B. E. Hadra, then of Waco, president; Taylor Hudson, of Belton, first vice-president; L. Ashton, of Dallas, second vice-president; S. T. Turner, of El Paso, third vice-president; R. F. Miller, of Sherman, treasurer; and H. A. West, of Galveston, secretary.

On September 8, 1900, however, a most devastating storm struck the Texas coast, venting its greatest fury on Galveston Island. "Friday we see a city of forty thousand inhabitants, prosperous and beautiful and happy; Saturday we see it submerged, storm beaten and in darkness; and Sunday we see over six thousand dead, thousands of houses wrecked, and millions of dollars worth of property destroyed." [3] Doctors and nurses from all over the United States moved in with trainloads of supplies. The American Red Cross, under the personal leadership of Clara Barton, brought relief to the stricken city. Destruction, death, and disease were evident on all sides. The dead were buried in trenches and at sea. Many were cremated.

In the face of such a disaster, it would have seemed logical for Galveston to ask to be relieved of the responsibility of the 1901 meeting of the Association. But it did no such thing. At the opening session at the Harmony Club, Dr. George H. Lee announced that such a possibility had been firmly declined by the people of Galveston: "They said without hesitation the State Medical Association has honored us by the acceptance of our invitation, and crippled though we are, we will exert ourselves that much more to entertain them as they deserve, and to make their stay pleasant." A representative of the mayor, in welcoming the Association, was grateful to the doctors: "In the hour of our direst misfortune none stretched forth more promptly the hand of help and spoke the word of encouragement and ministered to the wants of the needy and suffering than did your honored profession." President Hadra expressed the Association's admiration of the courage, endurance, and self-reliance of the people of Galveston. And later in the session, he was able to announce "the largest attendance, the largest list of new members, the largest receipts by the Treasurer, that had been had for many years."

Secretary West's report brought up two subjects of importance. The first concerned the charter of the Association. At the 1900 meeting Dr. West had announced, with a little chagrin, that the charter had been forfeited by action of the secretary of state the previous May. It seems that failure to pay the franchise tax of ten dollars had resulted in the forfeiture. There was disagreement as to the wisdom or necessity of renewal. Dr. M. M. Smith offered an argument which influenced the Association to authorize its secretary to renew the charter: "We have a very treacherous libel law in the State of Texas. As we stand today, any action of the Association might make the membership individually responsible under the libel law. . . . [Without the charter,] as individuals of the Association we are liable under the libel laws of this State for the acts of the Association." Under date of May 25, 1901, the new charter was

[3] *Texas Medical News*, IX (1900), 700–701.

issued. With two exceptions, it is similar to the charter of 1889. One difference was change of name: the Texas State Medical Association became the State Medical Association of Texas.[4] The secretary stated that to get the new charter "it was necessary to make a slight change in title." The other important difference was in the location of the headquarters of the Association. The 1889 charter had stated that "the principal office of this Association shall be in Austin, Travis County, Texas, or wherever the Secretary of the said Association may reside." The new charter omitted the qualifying clause. This omission assumed tremendous importance in 1948, when the Association had under discussion the question of moving its offices from Fort Worth to Austin.

In addition to the new charter, the secretary reported on a communication from the American Medical Association. This proved to be the earliest effort at reorganization of the national association, an effort which was soon to succeed in making the county society the basic unit of the state associations, and the several state groups the component parts of the national organization. It was predicted at the American Medical Association meeting in 1900 that "the profession throughout the country in five years would be welded into a compact organization whose power to influence medicine would be almost unlimited and whose requests for desirable legislation would everywhere be met with that respect which the politician has for organized votes." [5] The plan which was submitted, after a year of most intensive study and work by the committee assigned to the project, was readily accepted. Aside from the relationship of the national association to the state and county organizations, the most salient change was the creation of the House of Delegates, which was composed of delegates from the state associations on a proportionate population basis, and which was to transact all the business of the national association.

The following excerpt from a communication received by Secretary West from Secretary George H. Simmons epitomizes the confusion in which the medical profession was floundering and emphasizes the urgent need for relief: "At the last meeting of the American Medical Association a committee was appointed, as follows: Drs. J. N. McCormack, Bowling Green, Ky.; P. Maxwell Foshay, Cleveland, Ohio; George H. Simmons, Chicago, to consider and recom-

[4] See above, Chapter 3, n. 1.
[5] Fishbein, *History of the A.M.A.*, 202.

mend a plan for a thorough organization of the medical profession of this country. At the present time there are about 1,300 regular medical societies, most of which were organized, and are acting, independently of each other. This independency of organization and of action applies to State as well as other societies, each being based on a plan of its own, scarcely any two being organized alike. The result is a lack of uniformity or concert of action among these bodies." It was clear that changes would have to be made in the constitution and bylaws of the Texas association to make them conform to the plan of the American Medical Association, and the following committee on revision was appointed: J. T. Wilson, J. E. Gilcreest, R. F. Miller, S. C. Red, and H. A. West.

The Committee on Legislation, whose efforts through the years had proved to be fruitless and disappointing, at last succeeded in getting an amended medical-practice act on the statute books. Strangely, the bill was passed by the Legislature with very little difficulty, the vote in the house being 98 to 2. The plan of having a joint board of medical examiners—composed of allopaths, homeopaths, and eclectics—which had been advocated in 1896, had been abandoned. Instead, the act called for three boards: the Board of Medical Examiners, the Board of Homeopathic Medical Examiners, and the Board of Eclectic Medical Examiners. Christian Scientists and kindred practitioners were exempt from the provisions of the act. Exempt also were all those who were practicing medicine in Texas prior to 1885, those who had recorded their diplomas since 1891 and could produce evidence that they had been issued by "medical colleges of respectable standing," and those who came from other states whose requirements for the practice of medicine were equal to those of Texas.

The act defined the practice of medicine or surgery and fixed the penalty for violating the law at fines from fifty to five hundred dollars and imprisonment not to exceed six months. Applicants were to be examined in the following subjects: anatomy, physiology, chemistry, materia medica, therapeutics, histology, pathology, practice of medicine, surgery (including diseases of the eye, ear, nose and throat), obstetrics, gynecology, hygiene, and medical jurisprudence. Meetings of the three boards were to be held at least twice a year. Each applicant was charged fifteen dollars. All funds were to be divided among the members of each board "as compensation for loss of time." An applicant who failed to pass the examination given by one board could not be examined by either of the other two boards.

The organization of each school of medicine was required to submit to the governor a list of eighteen names, from which a board of nine would be appointed. The first board chosen from the list suggested by the state association consisted of J. T. Wilson, of Sherman; S. R. Burroughs, of Buffalo; J. C. Jones, of Gonzales; Frank Paschal, of San Antonio; J. M. Reuss, of Cuero; J. W. Scott, of Houston; J. H. Evans, of Palestine; D. J. Jenkins, of Daingerfield; and M. M. Smith, of Austin. Wilson, Burroughs, and Smith were elected president, vice-president, and secretary of the board, respectively.

This bill was not all that was desired by the Association, but it was a tremendous improvement over the old district-board plan, which lent itself readily to abuses. In the words of the editor of the *Texas Medical Journal*, it was grounds for great rejoicing: "Texas is now redeemed from the odium so long attached to her as the dumping-ground of the refuse of other states." [6]

President Hadra addressed the Association on the social standing of the physician as compared with that of members of "other so-called learned professions." He had no intention, he said, of being put in the position of "that ugly bird that soils its own nest." He merely wanted to present the facts as he saw them. He noted basic differences in the professions: history would not assign to all "seats in the same row." However much the medical profession had accomplished through the centuries, "no one doctor has become a historical figure." Out of 859 names of Englishmen of "high degree of excellence" collected by the *Popular Science Monthly*, the names of only 7 doctors appeared on the list. Similarly, no physician was represented in the Hall of Fame for Great Americans erected the year before by New York University. [7] Such events served to prove that "it makes a great difference whether a man invents a cotton picking machine or whether he detects a new law in the conduction of the nerve power." Why, he asked, should not a man who has saved thousands of lives be as worthy of recognition as one who has killed thousands in battle? America may not boast a Jenner,

[6] XVI (1900–1901), 360.

[7] At that time, only 29 names had been selected. By 1935, the list had grown to 69, and the name of Dentist W. T. G. Morton was included. The first physician, Dr. Walter Reed, was selected in 1945. In 1950, the number of names was 83, and General William C. Gorgas, M.D., had been honored.

a Lister, a Pasteur, a Virchow, or a Koch, but who will gainsay the claim of McDowell, Sims, or Long? If the medical profession in the United States had failed to raise up any mental giants, the explanation lay in the preoccupation of the people of a new country with "food and shelter, life and freedom." Logical thinking and trained minds must be based in the fundamentals of learning. A thorough training in the classics had convinced Dr. Hadra of "the value of that heavenly perfume emanating from the work of the old founders of our civilization." By the very nature of his work, the doctor in his search for truth must submerge his own interests in the welfare of his people: "He may be better loved by the community, loved by more people than the lawyer, thought more of as a man and a citizen; still he will have to stand back when it comes to the loud public honors of the street and the political arena."

The papers presented at the Galveston session require no extended comment. Two names appeared which were to mean much to medicine in Texas, those of M. L. Graves, of San Antonio, and I. C. Chase, of Fort Worth. They spoke on "Jury Trials of the Insane" and "The Value of Calcium Carbide in the Treatment of Inoperable Carcinoma of the Uterus." Dr. H. A. West read a paper on "Medical and Sociological Aspects of the Galveston Storm," emphasizing the prevalence of typhoid fever, malaria, and dysentery during the several months after. Dr. James E. Thompson, with his usual thoroughness and with the aid of diagrams, demonstrated the technic of the "Treatment of Harelip." Dr. A. C. Scott talked on "Normal Salt Solution," which he considered "a great and neglected weapon for good." He thought that every doctor should carry a fountain syringe with suitable needle. Ninety grains of salt and a quart of boiled water were available in every household. Six methods of administration were mentioned: intravenous, intra-arterial, subcutaneous, rectal, abdominal, and pleural. The subcutaneous route was the most generally useful, but in an emergency Dr. Scott advocated direct injection into the common femoral artery.

Two other papers read in Galveston deserve notice: "Preliminary Communication on the Relation of the Parathyroids to the Thyroid Gland," by Dr. William S. Carter, professor of physiology, and "Anchylostoma Duodenale in Texas," by Dr. Charlotte M. Schaefer, the first woman mentioned as appearing on an annual program. In a large series of experiments, Dr. Carter had excised the thyroids of dogs, in part or *in toto,* removed one or more parathyroids, and transplanted the two glands in varying combinations. To him, there was much that was obscure and mystifying; to us, his work was trailblazing. "The conclusion that the parathyroids can assume the functions of the thyroids or are more important to the animal economy than the thyroids," he said emphatically, "is entirely unwarranted. Each gland is separate and distinct in structure and probably in function. What the function of the parathyroids is, remains for the future to determine."

Dr. Schaefer, working as an interne in the laboratory of Dr. Allen J. Smith, was interested in intestinal parasites. The subject of hookworm infestation in Texas and in the South was new. In 1893, Dr. Smith had demonstrated the ova of the parasite in a specimen of stool taken from "the general closet of the Medical School," but had been unable to find the person who was host to the parasite. One year later, Dr. Ferdinand Herff had found the parasites at autopsy.[8] The patient reported by Dr. Schaefer was a sailor who had been in the Orient and had lived in Mexico. The ova were found in the stools, and after the administration of thymol, more than one hundred parasites were expelled. Following this experience, Dr. Smith again found hookworm ova in a mixed specimen of stool which he was using for the purpose of class demonstration. He examined the blood of all the students and found marked eosinophilia in two individuals. With this as a clue, he examined the stools of these two students and was able to demonstrate ova of *Anchylostoma duodenale.*

Officers elected for the coming year were Taylor Hudson, Belton, president; S. C. Red, Houston, first vice-president; J. W. Nixon, Gonzales, second vice-president; W. A. Watkins, Kemp, third vice-president; H. A. West, Galveston, secretary; and R. F. Miller, Sherman, treasurer. Before adjournment, the Texas association invited the American Medical Association to hold its 1902 session in Houston.[9] The next state meeting went to El Paso, the date being set as the fourth Tuesday in April, 1902.

It soon became obvious that the choice of El Paso was unwise. A few weeks after the 1901 meeting of the state association, the

[8] *Texas Medical Journal,* IX (1893–94), 615–16.

[9] This invitation, as well as one to meet in San Antonio the next year, was declined. In fact, the only meeting of the American Medical Association ever to be held in Texas was that at Dallas in 1926.

American Medical Association had accepted the plan of organization whereby the state associations would become integral parts of the national association and the county units would assume a similar relationship to the state organization. It was realized that a large representation was desirable when such a radical change came up for discussion; it was further realized that El Paso would not attract such a representation, the distance being too great and money being too scarce because of a near-failure of crops. So on December 21, 1901, President Hudson addressed a circular to all the members explaining the situation and stating that the El Paso County Medical Society had agreed to forego its claim to the meeting. A card was enclosed, on which an alternate choice of meeting place was to be registered. Dallas was chosen. Because of a conflict of dates with the Confederate Reunion, the date of the meeting was changed to May 6–9. This matter was easily settled; but the strength of feeling on the subject of far-away meeting places may be seen in this protest by the Cass County Medical Society: "We would like affiliation with the State Medical Association if we can have a central place of meeting, at Waco, Dallas or Fort Worth; but we cannot go clear to South Africa nor to Vladivostok for a meeting place, and that for the benefit of Lord Kitchener or General Botha." [10]

Fortunately for the Association, Dr. W. B. Russ had become associate editor of the *Texas Medical Journal*. In a series of editorials, he set forth clearly the proposed plan for organized medicine throughout the nation: "First: Admission of all members of affiliating societies as members of the State Association. Second: Reduction of annual dues, probably to $3 per annum. Third: The government of the State Association to be in the hands of a House of Delegates, appointed by affiliating societies. Fourth: The adoption of a comprehensive plan of reorganization of county and district societies." [11] As time for the Dallas session neared, Dr. Russ explained what the proposed change would mean to the county society and to the individual member:

The making of membership in the county or district society an absolute prerequisite to recognition by the higher bodies will take the wind out of the sails of the fellow who now insists upon running the local society entirely his own way, or else resigns, boasting that he can hold membership in the State organization. The laity will soon learn that un-

[10] *Texas Medical News*, XII (1903), 18.
[11] *Texas Medical Journal*, XVII (1901–1902), 101.

less a physician is connected with his home society he has no standing in either the State or national associations, and, therefore, to suspect him of professional dishonesty. Men outside the organization will find it hard to make explanation, for it will be known that neither jealousy nor personal spite can succeed in excluding a reputable physician, since every one will have the right to appeal to the State society for instatement, or for reinstatement if he has been unlawfully expelled.[12]

A "good attendance" was on hand when the Association convened at City Hall in Dallas for its 1902 session. Preliminaries were few. There seemed to be an unexpressed eagerness to hear the report of the Committee on Revision of the Constitution and Bylaws. By way of anticipating favorable action on this report, delegates from thirty societies were on hand and ready to accept the plan of the American Medical Association. The report of the committee was not long in coming, and its discussion consumed the greater part of the meeting. Indeed, there were two reports. The majority report, signed by Drs. Wilson, Miller, and Gilcreest, inclined toward conservatism and recommended as few changes in the old constitution and bylaws as possible. Drs. West and Red brought in the minority report, in which all the changes recommended by the national association were embodied. In addition to several minor variations, there was one major difference, and this was all-significant. The majority report did not make membership in the county society a prerequisite for membership in the state association, as required by the American Medical Association plan.

It was generally agreed that this was the most important problem which the Association had ever been called on to solve. Certainly, the long and earnest discussion bore out this opinion. This discussion was free from bitterness. The participants were living up to the definition of a gentleman as given by former Governor John G. Pollard of Virginia: a gentleman is a man who can disagree without being disagreeable. It was obviously the desire of all to arrive at the best possible solution. Consideration of the two revisions had not gone very far before it became apparent that there was little likelihood of composing the two viewpoints. For this reason, Dr. Walter Shropshire, of Yoakum, moved that the committee be enlarged to include the president and one delegate from each affiliated society. The committee thus created had thirty-four members.

12 *Ibid.,* 292–93.

The next morning, this committee was ready with its report, which was in close agreement with the majority report. There was a decided reluctance to depart from the old constitution and by-laws. Members hesitated to give up the flimsy organization which held the medical profession of Texas together, even though they must have realized that the old plan was also holding it back. Many prominent men took part in the discussion, which occupies twelve pages of fine print in the *Transactions*. Leading the discussion for the last report were J. M. Fort, of Paris; M. M. Smith, of Austin; Bacon Saunders, of Fort Worth; and F. E. Daniel, of Austin. Those who supported the minority report and would hew to the line of recommendations of the American Medical Association were Walter Shropshire, of Yoakum; J. J. Roberts, of Hillsboro; M. L. Graves, of San Antonio; H. A. West, of Galveston; W. B. Russ, of San Antonio; John O. McReynolds, of Dallas; S. C. Red, of Houston; and Holman Taylor, of Marshall. One point of view is illustrated by these words of Dr. Saunders: "While we may have confidence in the immutable wisdom of the reorganization committee of the American Medical Association, its plan has not been tried in one iota. The Association itself does not know that it can live up to it." These words of Dr. Graves epitomize the other: "The members of the Association, it is clear, are not ready for a full and final discussion and determination of this question. Delay can hurt nobody." Dr. Russ found himself opposed to the position of his senior editor, Daniel, but this did not disturb their association as editors of the *Texas Medical Journal*. Dr. Russ felt that the majority plan meant disorganization rather than reorganization. Dr. Daniel insisted that the American Medical Association plan would be a serious blow to such groups as the North Texas Medical Society, which was reputed to be about as large as the State Medical Association of Texas.

The discussion was terminated by the adoption of a previously made motion by Dr. Shropshire to the effect that both reports be received, printed, and distributed to every member of the state association and local societies. Each society was requested to send a delegate to the next meeting with authority to decide the matter. The editor of the *Texas Medical Journal* later gave this wise counsel: "At San Antonio next April I hope a spirit of tolerance and good will, a spirit of concession and compromise, and above all, a spirit of fairness and justice will prevail, and that all sectional interests, jealousies and differences will be sunk in the larger interest of the State Association and the welfare of the whole profession of the State. We want unity and harmony. We want to organize from the ground up, and there is a way to do it. Let us be patient and careful, and find that way." [13]

The important business of reorganization did not interfere with other business and indeed nonbusiness affairs of the session. On the third night, the following program was scheduled:

PART I

President's Address	.	.	.	.	.	.	Dr. Taylor Hudson
Voice—"Villanelle"		.	.	.	.	.	*Del' Acqua*

Miss Ella Wade Pharr

Reading—"Scenes from David Copperfield"   .   .   .   Dickens
    (a) "Dora and I Are Engaged"
    (b) "Call Me Your Child Wife"
    (c) "It Is Over"

Miss Caroline Duncan

Voice—(a) "The Lorelei"   .   .   .   .   .   .   Liszt
    (b) "Spanish Love Song"   .   .   .   .   Ramalt

Miss Ethel Shepperd

PART II

Annual oration   .   .   .   .   .   .   Dr. W. H. Moore
Piano—(a) Study, C-minor   .   .   .   .   .   Chopin
    (b) Minuet, Op. 17   .   .   .   .   .   Moszkowski

Miss Maude Gillespie

Voice—(a) "May Morning"   .   .   .   .   .   Weatherly
    (b) "Irish Love Song"   .   .   .   .   .   Lang

Mrs. Jules D. Roberts

The President, Dr. Taylor Hudson, spoke rather briefly but well. In touching on human brotherhood, he quoted a line from Homer —"He was a friend to man, and he lived in a house by the side of the road"—reminding his hearers that here was to be found the inspiration of Sam Walter Foss's well-known poem, "The House by the Side of the Road." One sentence from the address shows that each succeeding generation has similar problems and, in the main, reacts in a similar manner: "The struggle for money has so taken our time and strength, has become so ceaseless and absorbing that rational leisure for thoughtful study and meditation scarcely exist."

[13] *Ibid.*, 465.

Ignorance, superstition, and a false sense of values were the order of the day. The only solution lay in the domain of education, and in this program the physician had an important role to play:

There lies before the medical profession of today a destiny compared with which all the glories of the past shall be eclipsed. We stand in the brightening dawn of possibly the greatest epoch in the history of our calling. For never in completeness, in scholarship, in patience, in great breadth of action has the profession been so well equipped. Science is advancing by leaps and bounds. In a moment unexpected she opens up a path over an untraveled country, and the advance seems so daring that we hesitate to follow lest it be upon forbidden ground. Yet she pushes on with the fervor of inspiration to sound the mighty depths of the unknown. One after another, the mighty men, the heroes of the profession, have gone forth over the seas of an ignorant past, and brought back to us from their perils and in the face of the ridicule and opposition of unbelieving men, gems from these deep soundings that have illuminated the world of thought and been the means of health and blessing to multitudes of suffering men.

The papers at this Dallas session—there were forty-eight of them—followed the usual pattern and dealt with such subjects as pneumonia, malaria, typhoid fever, tuberculosis, insanity, uterine fibroids, hemorrhoids, enlarged prostate, and glaucoma.

Even though she had entertained the Association in 1901, Galveston asked for the 1903 meeting. The invitation of Mayor Marshall Hicks of San Antonio, however, was accepted. The new officers elected were S. C. Red, Houston, president; J. E. Thompson, Galveston, first vice-president; J. E. Gilcreest, Gainesville, second vice-president; and H. K. Leake, Dallas, third vice-president. Drs. West and Miller were continued as secretary and treasurer.

As an aftermath of the Dallas meeting, Dr. F. E. Daniel made the following comments on some of the personalities involved:

Shropshire—the Sampson of Southwestern Texas. He was there, and slaughtered the Philistines—smote 'em hip and thigh. Some fellow dropped a nickel in the slot and set him to talking. He talked all the time I was there, and was talking when I left. . . . West, our handsome Secretary. Popular as he is good looking. He's a last-ditcher. Scissors if I die by it. That's the sort of man I like. . . . Dallas chuck full of people. Big Methodist Conference in session. Five hundred priests, prelates, preachers and bishops, all in black and white; solemn and serene. Three hundred doctors; medical convention. Hotels crowded. The Oriental putting cots in the corridors. Our handsome and dignified State Health Officer, George R. Tabor, came in late. Immaculate black suit, white tie, and a broad expanse of white vest spread over an aldermanic bay-window. Dignified, clean-shaven, bald and bland, he approached the hotel clerk and asked for a room. The clerk sized him up and asked: "Are you a member of the Conference?" "Am I a member of the Conference?" said the doctor, transfixing him with his eagle eye. "I'm the Bishop of the Austin Beat." "Front," said the clerk. "Show the Bishop to No. One, next to the ladies' parlor." [14]

While the State Medical Association of Texas was in the process of reorganization, the Lone Star Medical Association of Texas, composed of colored physicians, was having its sixteenth annual session in Austin, June 16–18, 1902, with President J. H. Wilkins, of Houston, in the chair. Fourteen members were present. The papers and the discussions were comparable to those presented in the association's white counterpart. Dr. M. M. Smith, editor of the *Texas Medical News,* and a Dr. Matthews, both of Austin, appeared before this meeting of their Negro brethren.[15]

When the San Antonio session convened at Turner Hall, April 28, 1903, about two hundred members were present. Those present must have been attracted to the Menger Hotel by its advertisement of rates at three dollars per day, American plan. Dr. Frank Paschal welcomed the assembly to the city where, for the first time in the history of the state, "the talented and lamented Dr. George Cupples administered chloroform; it was here that the first hysterectomy was done; that the first ovariotomy, and the first lithotomy, were performed." In referring to the plan of reorganization, he said: "Of course, the questions that will come before you will cause us to enter into the arena of debate, but let us understand that while we may differ in opinion . . . we, like knights of old, must take and give, and submit gallantly to victory or defeat. Whatever the subjects may be that we differ upon, they can have but one object—the good of the profession—therefore let us work to this end, and feel that we have done our duty to the profession and to legitimate medicine."

In his presidential message Dr. S. C. Red did not mention the reorganizational problem. Instead, he made several suggestions:

[14] *Ibid.,* 472–73.
[15] *Texas Medical News,* XI (1902), 517–19.

that a legion of honor badge or medal be designed and given to those members who had attended ten consecutive meetings of the Association; that the Association agree to defend financially its members in malpractice suits; that the Association establish a medical journal; and that a permanent home for the Association be constructed at some central point. He suggested that a certain per cent of the annual dues be set aside "until they reach such a sum as to warrant the construction of a building." The committee to which these recommendations were referred liked the legion of honor idea, but disapproved of the other three. However, while it did feel that a home was not feasible at that time, the committee did think this was a question which "should receive careful consideration of this Association, when its funds and membership would justify such an undertaking."

When the subject of reorganization came up, it was handled with surprising expedition. During the preceding year, much spadework had been done in favor of the American Medical Association plan. The time for attitudes and arguments had passed; these had had full sway at the 1902 meeting. Thus, the year 1903 became the year of decision for the State Medical Association of Texas. One potent reason for the quick decision was the address by Dr. J. N. McCormack, of Bowling Green, Kentucky, who was present as a representative of the national association. The stage had been previously set at a preliminary meeting the night before the state association convened. Prominent at this meeting was a delegation from the West Texas Medical Association, in which Dr. W. B. Russ was an influential figure. The outcome was a resolution offered at the next meeting: *"Be it resolved,* That this meeting endorses without alteration or qualification the plan of reorganization embracing County and State Associations as outlined by the Committee on Reorganization of the American Medical Association, and that the chairman of the committee be instructed to present this resolution to the State Association in session."

Dr. J. C. Loggins, of Ennis, presented this resolution as instructed and added in his motion for endorsement "that the paper of Dr. McCormack be referred to a committee of delegates, who have to report at a later meeting, in order to get it before you." The resolution, with one minor change and after very short discussion, was adopted. Doctor McCormack met with the provisional House of Delegates, and within forty-eight hours a recommendation for adoption of the constitution and bylaws, as outlined by the American Medical Association, was ready for presentation. When it came before the general session, the report of the House of Delegates received practically unanimous acceptance. Men like Dr. M. M. Smith, who had favored the majority report at Dallas, gave firm support to the new plan, which was speedily adopted. Secretary West at once telegraphed the news to Secretary Simmons of the American Medical Association. Back came this message: "Congratulations. Louisiana, Illinois and Nebraska yesterday adopted constitution practically unchanged."

The new House of Delegates was to be made up of delegates from the component county societies, the councilors, and the president and secretary of the state association. One councilor was elected from each of fifteen districts. Each county society was entitled to one delegate for each hundred members or fraction thereof. The duties of the Board of Councilors and the House of Delegates were outlined in detail. The House of Delegates became the legislative and business body of the Association. The Board of Councilors, on the state and local levels, combined the roles of organizer, peacemaker, and censor.

The personnel of the provisional House of Delegates and the local societies represented should be recorded: North Texas, C. E. Cantrell, of Greenville; Austin District, F. E. Daniel, of Austin; Smith County, T. J. Bell, of Tyler; Central Texas, J. M. Frazier, of Belton; South Texas, J. W. Scott, of Houston; West Texas, W. B. Russ, of San Antonio; Houston, J. W. Scott, of Houston; Austin Medical, M. M. Smith, of Austin; Rogers Medical Society, G. T. Thomas, of Rogers; Lavaca County Society, Walter Shropshire, of Yoakum; Kaufman County Society, James Orr, of Terrell; Williamson County Society, J. C. Anderson, of Granger; East Texas Society, E. W. Link, of Palestine; Harrison County Society, O. M. Heartsill, of Marshall; Comanche County Society, T. P. Weaver, of De Leon; San Angelo Society, Boyd Cornick, of San Angelo; Cooke County Medical Society, F. D. Garrett, of Gainesville; Brazos Valley Medical Society, I. P. Sessions, of Rockdale; and Johnson County Medical Society, J. D. Osborn, of Cleburne.

It is well to consider just what this organizational departure, as embodied in the constitution and bylaws, really meant. The most significant change was the mandatory relationship of the county societies to the state association and of the state association to the national organization. This was set down in the new constitution as one of the purposes of the state association:

The purposes of this Association shall be to federate and bring into one compact organization the entire medical profession of the State of Texas, and to unite with similar associations in other States to form the American Medical Association, with a view to the extension of medical knowledge, and to the advancement of medical science; to the elevation of the standard of medical education, and to the enactment and enforcement of just medical laws; to the promotion of friendly intercourse among physicians, and to the enlightenment and direction of public opinion in regard to the great problems of State medicine, so that the profession shall become more capable and honorable within itself, and more useful to the public in the prevention and cure of disease, and in prolonging and adding comfort to life.

These standing committees for the reorganized state association were created: Committee on Scientific Work, Committee on Public Policy and Legislation, Committee on Publication, Committee on Nominations, and Committee on Arrangements; but such other committees would be appointed as might seem desirable. State dues were set at two dollars. County societies were to receive charters from the state association as they organized and adopted constitutions and bylaws in conformity with the parent organization. Several provisions in the bylaws dealt with organization and conduct of the affairs of the county societies.

The first Board of Councilors in the order of their districts was composed of S. T. Turner, of El Paso; P. C. Coleman, of Colorado; D. R. Fly, of Amarillo; C. M. Alexander, of Coleman; W. B. Russ, of San Antonio; A. E. Spohn, of Corpus Christi; T. J. Bennett, of Austin; Walter Shropshire, of Yoakum; John T. Moore, of Galveston; B. F. Calhoun, of Beaumont; S. R. Burroughs, of Buffalo; W. R. Blailock, of McGregor; J. H. McCracken, of Mineral Wells; C. E. Cantrell, of Greenville; and Holman Taylor, of Marshall.

All in all, this epoch-making transformation was made smoothly and comfortably for all concerned. Its full significance could not have been foreseen at the time. Some enthusiasts were predicting that the Association's membership would be quadrupled in five years. Their predictions fell far short of the reality.

Other matters came up for consideration at the San Antonio meeting, but they were of secondary importance. The Board of Medical Examiners reported on its second year of work. Out of 179 applicants for examination, 28 failed to pass. A large number of physicians were issued certificates after their diplomas had been recorded with the several district clerks. Graduates of Memphis Hospital Medical College led this list with 152 names; Tulane University was second with 134. The Texas medical schools appeared in this order: University of Texas, 108; Fort Worth University, 34; University of Dallas, 6; and Texas Medical College and Hospital, 1. There was a veiled suggestion, brought out in the discussion, that the board had been too lenient in its examinations. Quick to refute this suggestion was Dr. William Keiller, professor of anatomy at Galveston. Dr. Keiller and Dr. William S. Carter, also a professor at the University of Texas, having failed to record their diplomas by the designated date, were required to take the examinations. "They kept us there for three days, writing all the time," Dr. Keiller recorded. "Both Dr. Carter and myself had writer's cramp, and I have learned something about it. I believe we had a form that is dependent upon exhaustion of the centers on the cord for the brachial plexus (where I had the pain was at the back of my neck)." The State Board of Eclectic Medical Examiners reported 42 applicants with 20 rejections. The Homeopathic Board had 15 applicants, all of whom were accepted.[16]

A few of the scientific subjects discussed at this San Antonio meeting deserve notice. Major Charles F. Mason reported a case of Malta fever in a soldier at Fort Sam Houston. This veteran of eighteen years had seen service in Cuba and the Philippines. He developed the disease at Fort Ringgold on the lower Rio Grande.[17] Fever and rheumatic pains over a period of several months were the principal symptoms. Anemia and enlargement of the spleen were present. A positive agglutination test with *Micrococcus melitensis* clinched the diagnosis. Quinine and potassium iodide did not influence the course of the disease. The patient recovered slowly. When asked by Dr. H. A. West, "Did you cure him or did he get well?" Major Mason replied frankly, "He got well."

Full discussion followed the paper of Dr. T. J. Bell, "When Is It Justifiable to Prevent Conception?" Dr. Bell approached his subject with some solicitude, recalling the Biblical injunction to Adam

[16] *Ibid.*, XII (1903), 219, 221.

[17] Ernest Gentry and T. L. Ferenbaugh, eight years later, found the disease endemic in the goat-raising section of Texas up the river from Fort Ringgold.—"Endemic Malta Fever in Texas," *Journal of the A.M.A.*, LVII (1911), 1045–48.

PAST PRESIDENTS

E. W. BERTNER, 1938   L. H. REEVES, 1939
PRESTON HUNT, 1940   N. D. BUIE, 1941

PAST PRESIDENTS

Judson L. Taylor, 1942   Charles S. Venable, 1943
H. F. Connally, 1944, 1945   Claude C. Cody, Jr., 1946

and Eve, "Be fruitful and multiply and replenish the earth." He deplored the increasing number of homes childless as the result of selfishness and lack of responsibility. And yet there were certain conditions, such as tuberculosis, syphilis, and marked pelvic contraction, which to him justified contraceptive measures. All participants in the discussion expressed a feeling of apprehension over the declining birth rate. Dr. Frank Paschal put it this way: "It behooves us, as medical men, to study this matter and educate the public to the evil of the prevention of conception, and try to prevent American born children of American parentage from being supplanted by children born of foreign parentage." More frank was a visitor, Dr. Stiles, who thought it was "better for a woman to bring only two children into the world and to train them up to be good citizens, than . . . to give birth to ten or twenty children and then die and leave the children without a mother's influence." However, none disagreed with the contention that certain conditions justified contraception.

The most notable paper at the 1903 session was given by Charles Wardell Stiles, chief of the Division of Zoology, United States Public Health and Marine Hospital Service. He spoke on "The Significance of the Recently Recognized Hookworm Disease for the Texas Practitioner," a subject that was quite new. Stiles himself, although not a physician, had almost singlehandedly impressed the physicians of the South with the prevalence of this disease. Giving Dr. Allen J. Smith, of Galveston, full credit for his pioneer work, Stiles took up the subject from every angle, using many illustrations and charts. Those who were fortunate enough to hear his eighty-seven-page paper must have realized that they were listening to a master.

President S. C. Red, in his short address, spoke on Dowieism, osteopathy, temperance, and Christian Science. J. A. Dowie, posing as "Elijah returned to earth," claimed to heal the sick by laying on of hands, grew rich, and built a town of ten thousand people in Illinois, which he called Zion City. The second subject, which Dr. Red glorified with a capital letter, he dismissed with this observation: "I think Osteopathy should be struck with the jaw bone of an ass." Temperance, he said, has much in its favor and has an important relationship to health and medicine, but "the doctor of today is not a teetotaler; he, however, condemns drunkenness wherever found, from old Noah down." Dr. Red recorded Mrs. Mary Baker Eddy as "an hysterical woman of limited intelligence, with a good heart and kindly intentions, pretty much after [the] Joan of Arc order." The Eddyites, the Dowieites, and the osteopaths, he admitted, all used certain well-known agents of cure and relieved some of their patients, but they were a menace to health and life in that they trifled with what might be serious ailments.

At the mid-point of the life of the State Medical Association of Texas, the annual oration was delivered by Dr. M. L. Graves, of San Antonio, and a most learned oration it was. It was altogether unfortunate that scholarly addresses such as this, long forgotten, cannot be made available to today's doctors. Here was a young man, out of medical school hardly more than a decade, speaking with the ease of a McReynolds and the wisdom of an Osler. Graves regretted that rarely does proper recognition come to the doctor. He could recall only three authors who had caught the spirit of the true physician: George Eliot, in *Middlemarch;* S. Weir Mitchell, in *Dr. North and His Friends;* and Ian Maclaren, in *A Doctor of the Old School.* Graves enumerated the ideals of the doctor: truth, charity, patriotism, science, home and family, and duty. The professional aims of the true doctor are high also: maintenance of public hygiene and sanitation, preservation of public and private health, development of racial and individual character, public morals, and dissemination of education. His rewards are many: consciousness of duty well done, personal and social standing, cultural development, a secure position in public esteem, and financial independence, if competency, economy, and judgment are exercised. You need no monument, said Graves to his fellow-doctors, but if you should seek one, you need "only look around you and witness the enduring memory of your labors, in the homes and hearts of your people."

San Antonio was honored when Dr. Frank Paschal was elected to the presidency of the Association. Chosen to serve with him were F. E. Daniel, Austin, first vice-president; A. L. Hathcock, Palestine, second vice-president; and Joe Becton, Greenville, third vice-president. The next meeting would be held in Austin. In accepting the high office of president, Dr. Paschal said: "We must so conduct the affairs of the Association that no man can say that this plan of reorganization was for the purpose of benefiting one man more than another, and as President of your body, I will not advocate measures that will have for their purpose the perpetuation of power or of furthering the interests of one man or one set of men."

Thus the thirty-seventh annual session of the State Medical Association of Texas began and ended on the theme of reorganization. By a happy coincidence, this radical but necessary change in the plan of organization came just fifty years from the time when that little band of ten far-seeing Austin doctors succeeded in planting the seed that was to grow into a thriving state medical association.

As a diversion, the *Texas Medical News* carried an item on "The Automobile as a Hobby," in which a spin along the countryside was recommended as a restful and exhilarating experience: the physician, besides doing a little business on his way out, "could give his family the same delightful trip if he was cocksure of getting back." [18]

It was a reawakened state medical association that convened in the University of Texas Auditorium on the morning of April 26, 1904. The addresses of welcome and the response by President Paschal consumed one hour. Then, the House of Delegates assembled in one of the classrooms, and the Section on General Medicine was opened in the auditorium. Thus, in keeping with the new constitution, the business and scientific affairs of the Association were separated. The attendance was 550, the largest in the history of the organization. It will be recalled that 500 members were present at the Dallas meeting of 1886. Since that time, the attendance had ranged between 100 and 200.

President Paschal, in his message to the House of Delegates, reported that 125 county societies had been organized with a combined state membership of 2,415. Among other recommendations, he proposed that the Association should give serious consideration to the collection of data on the history of the Association and to the establishment of a permanent home where a medical library and a museum of pathology could be maintained. In both of these ideas, he was nearly fifty years ahead of his day. To the former project he was to make an important contribution ten years later.

Dr. W. B. Russ, chairman of the Board of Councilors, made a very favorable report, and then the councilors made individual reports. From these, it was obvious that the prodigious growth of the Association was due largely to the vast amount of work which these fifteen men had done. The councilors had given freely of their time, some of them as much as a month, and had gone about their

[18] *Texas Medical News*, XII (1903), 249.

districts explaining the plan of organization to any group of doctors who would listen. The results were little short of phenomenal and gave to the Association a stability that it was never to lose.

Two of the suggestions made by Dr. Paschal at the first session of the Austin meeting received early attention by the appointment of two committees: Committee on Permanent Place of Meeting and Committee on Collection and Preservation of Records. The first committee approved the suggestion about a permanent home and advised that concessions be solicited from interested cities. The second urged that immediate steps be taken toward the collection of "all records, documents and papers, both ancient and modern," and that they be housed in some public institution. It was also recommended that portraits of all former presidents be likewise collected and cared for.

The new arrangement which gave over all business of the Association to the House of Delegates proved to be very effectual at this first trial. The business affairs were handled sanely and expeditiously in about half the usual time, as judged by the length of the minutes.

The secretarial work was done by Dr. John T. Moore, of Galveston, since death had come to Dr. H. A. West, the secretary for the past twelve years. Few had doubted Dr. West's efficiency. Sometimes he had been outspokenly blunt and, in the eyes of some, he had desired to domineer. But he had worked hard and earnestly for the Association and had made a very high contribution to its affairs. Not the least of these was the part he had played in its reorganization. Tributes of respect were paid to his memory by the Association and by several local societies. The *Texas Medical Journal* gave editorial commendation to the work of Dr. West as physician and secretary.[19] One of the former presidents of the Association, Dr. B. E. Hadra, also had died during the year. In Texas since 1872, he had been closely associated with organized medicine in Texas for more than thirty years. The recognition which came to him as a result of his method of repairing the pelvic floor has been mentioned in Chapter 7.

Two infectious diseases that had long played, and were yet to play, a serious part in the physical and economic life of Texas came up for long discussion at the Austin session. These were malaria and yellow fever. Albert Woldert, of Tyler, spoke on "Malarial

[19] *Texas Medical Journal*, XIX (1903–1904), 268–70.

Fever—Its Expense to the People of Texas." For many years he was to emphasize this topic so important in East and South Texas. In this paper, a clear description was given of the mode of transmission, diagnosis, description and life cycle of the parasite, and prevention. From a medical standpoint, the solution was simple: thorough treatment of all known cases and full use of drainage and kerosene oil. The practical management, however, offered its problems. "Texas has offered a reward of $50,000 to get rid of the boll weevil, and to save its cotton," Woldert reminded. "If it has made any appropriation to get rid of chills and fever, and thereby save the lives of 3,000 of its people annually, I have not heard of it. Human nature is a very strange thing."

Surgeon Henry R. Carter, of the United States Public Health and Marine Hospital Service, read a paper entitled "The Conveyance of Yellow Fever." His paper centered about this contention: yellow fever is conveyed from the sick to the well by a mosquito host, the *Stegomyia fasciata*, contaminated by feeding on the sick man; and, in nature it is only thus conveyed. Dr. Carter was an authority on the subject, having been with Dr. Walter Reed in Cuba and having published a contribution which suggested the presence of an intermediate host.[20] Although more than three years had passed since Reed, in his own words, had been able to lift "the impenetrable veil that has surrounded this most wonderful, dreadful pest of humanity and to put it on a rational and scientific basis," [21] Dr. Carter seemed to sense the presence of a partially skeptical audience. He gave a detailed study of the known facts of the disease, the type of mosquito involved, the period of infectivity, the period of incubation, and the experiments which had been made to uphold the mosquito theory of transmission. He cited the facts that had been advanced in support of the fomites theory of transmission and was able to nullify them completely. Control of the disease was summarized thus: keep mosquitoes from the infected patient and kill those which have access to him.

Other papers on yellow fever were presented by Dr. J. M. Reuss, of Cuero, and Dr. R. E. Dinwiddie, of San Antonio. These papers were discussed at great length, most of the discussion being directed at Dr. Carter. There were several who expressed real doubt that the

[20] "A Note on the Interval between the Infecting and Secondary Cases of Yellow Fever," *New Orleans Medical Journal*, LII (1900), 617–36.
[21] Howard A. Kelly, *Walter Reed and Yellow Fever* (New York, 1907), 152.

mosquito was the only mode of infection. Indeed, this doubt was shared by Editor F. E. Daniel.[22] Cases of yellow fever had been reported in Laredo, Minera, Cuero, and San Antonio during the year. At Laredo, between September 25 and November 30, 1903, 1,050 cases had occurred, with 102 deaths. At San Antonio a young woman had died of the disease, as had her father and mother and three neighbors. And yet there was a small group of local doctors who, with the misdirected support of one of the newspapers, contended that the fair name of San Antonio was being blackened by false reports. Dr. W. B. Russ, in his capacity as editor, reminded his readers that seventy-nine San Antonio doctors recognized the disease as yellow fever and only five opposed that diagnosis. He then exposed the shoddy tactics of the newspaper involved: "The public was solemnly warned not to patronize any physician who admitted the existence of yellow fever. Grocerymen, clerks, boarding house keepers, Tom, Dick, and Harry rushed into print to tell why they could not accept the diagnosis of yellow fever. The following headlines express alike the character of the writers, and of the paper giving them space to lay bare the poverty of their minds: 'Who's the Liar?, a Bunch of Yellow Doctors Flock around the House of Mr. W., Yellow Lie nailed.'"

In addressing the Association as president, Dr. Frank Paschal reminded his hearers that the Texas Medical Association had been organized in Austin fifty-one years before. He again affirmed that the original plan of organization was very similar to the one only recently adopted by the Association, in that county and district societies were subordinate branches of the parent organization and in that county societies were chartered by the state association. In proof of this, he submitted the charter granted in 1853 by the Texas Medical Association to the Bexar County Medical Society. Dr. Paschal recalled some of the problems that faced those early believers in organized medicine:

They were dreaming in 1853 of the things that have long since become realities. These brave patriots of medicine journeyed over long and weary miles in buggies and on horseback to meet here,—they were heedless of the dangers that beset them from wild savages then roaming over this section of the State,—they were unmindful of the inconvenience of sleeping on the ground, with a blanket for a bed, a saddle for a pillow, and a rifle for a companion, and for a canopy the limitless dome with

[22] *Texas Medical Journal*, XIX (1903–1904), 168, 206, 212.

stars, like dewdrops on the field of Heaven, keeping their vigil; the silence of the night unbroken, save by the cry of wild beasts. No selfish motives prompted them to undergo hardships and brook dangers. They were actuated, as our profession has been from the time that it broke the shackles that bound it to ignorance and superstition, by an earnest desire for the acquisition of knowledge to be used in the prevention and cure of diseases, in the amelioration of suffering, and in the prolongation of life.

All in all, the 1904 meeting in Austin was most successful. As the first meeting of the Association in its second half-century, it augured well for the future. As the members rode back and forth to the state university on the "electric cars" and as they walked to Brackenridge Hall for dinner at fifty cents,[23] a feeling of satisfaction in a job well done must have come to all of them. And the festivities must have had a deeper meaning as they sat down to the banquet, one thousand of them, and as the music in the ballroom of the Driskill Hotel "rose with its voluptuous swell," and "the soft eyes looked love all right and the lamps shown bright over fair women & brave men." [24]

Houston was to be the next meeting place. New officers elected were F. E. Daniel, Austin, president; John T. Moore, Galveston; C. E. Cantrell, Greenville; and Walter Shropshire, Yoakum, vice-presidents; Ira C. Chase, Fort Worth, secretary; and R. F. Miller, Sherman, treasurer.

The confidence which Dr. F. E. Daniel expressed in Dr. Chase was not misplaced; a young man of high promise and great energy, Chase, with laborious accuracy, piloted the Association through five eventful years, during which the *Journal* was established. His monetary reward was slight, but his accomplishments were many and important.

In retiring from the presidency, Dr. Paschal presented to the Association a gavel of historic significance, which is still in official use.[25] One part of the gavel was made from a tree near the spot where, at the siege of Bexar in 1835, Ben Milam rallied a dispirited

[23] This may not have been a bargain. Thirteen years before, sirloin steak at B. Hall was four cents, bacon three cents, pie three cents, coffee two cents.— Lane, *History of the University of Texas,* 285.

[24] *Texas Medical Journal,* XIX (1903–1904), 478. The editor was here following closely the words of Byron's *Childe Harold's Pilgrimage.*

[25] The ultimate fate of the gavel which President Coleman had given the Association in 1896 is not known. Dr. John T. Moore states in a personal communication, November 15, 1950, that it was not among the effects which came to him as temporary successor to Secretary West.

army with his words, "Who will go with old Ben Milam into San Antonio?" The other part of the gavel came from a pecan tree which had come to be known as the Sentinel Tree. On one of the two metal bands are inscribed in Latin these words: "I am the sentinel of truth, health, humanity"; on the other: "As I sheltered sentinels for Texas liberty, so will I guard this Association."

XIV

The Texas State Journal of
Medicine, 1905–1909

In his presidential message to the 1905 session at Houston, with 450 members present, Dr. F. E. Daniel recommended that the publication of the *Transactions* be continued. It was his feeling that the establishment of a journal would cause financial embarrassment to the Association. Indeed, this had been the opinion of most of his predecessors. Secretary I. C. Chase, however, brought in a strong plea for an Association-owned journal. "It will provide," he argued, "a means of intercommunication; it will publish our Transactions while fresh; it will increase our educational power among the profession and the laity; it will diminish the labor of Councilors; it will stimulate life and interest in county societies; it will affiliate more closely District Societies in complete professional unification; it will make advertisers help pay our expenses; it will furnish transportation to Councilors where now we pay their cash fares; it will enable us to hire done the clerical work of the Association; it will enable us to put by a goodly sum to expend on legislative and educational reforms, libraries, museums, hospitals and other monuments to our beloved profession." Reporting as chairman of the Board of Councilors, Dr. W. B. Russ added that survival of the smaller county societies would "absolutely depend upon the establishment of a medium of communication such as a State journal."

At this point, it will be well to survey the history of the several medical journals in Texas. Earlier mention has been made of the

245

Galveston Medical Journal, which was published as a "monthly record of medical science" from January, 1866, to April, 1871. The editor and publisher was Dr. Greensville Dowell. After 1871, a few issues of this journal appeared as the *Texas Medical Journal* and then as the *Galveston and Texas Medical Journal.* In 1880, Dr. Dowell, with Drs. J. F. Y. Paine and T. J. Heard as associate editors, revived the *Galveston Medical Journal,* but it appeared for only a few issues. Dr. Dowell's death in 1881 doubtless was the principal reason for discontinuance. It was apparently continued as the *Texas Medical and Surgical Record.*[1]

Dr. J. R. Briggs, of Dallas, edited the *Texas Health Journal* for a year from July, 1888. It was continued in Dallas by Drs. A. M. Elmore and V. P. Armstrong for nine years as the *Texas Medical Practitioner,* "a monthly magazine devoted to preventive and state medicine." The *Texas Sanitarian* appeared on the scene in 1891 as "a journal of preventive medicine and hygiene," under the editorship of Dr. T. J. Bennett, of Austin; after four years the name was changed to the *Texas Medical News,* and Dr. J. W. McLaughlin became one of the editors. Publication was continued until 1916. In its later years, Dr. M. M. Smith was managing editor with ten associate editors. The *News* absorbed the *Texas Medical Practitioner* and the *Southwestern Medical and Surgical Reporter* in 1898. The latter was a Fort Worth publication which appeared for four years under the editorial helm of Drs. E. J. Beall, F. G. Kirksey, and E. D. Capps. Another Fort Worth journal was the *Texas Medical Gazette,* which Dr. F. D. Thompson published for five years from 1901. The *Texas Clinic,* published by Dr. J. B. Shelmire in Dallas, survived only from October to December, 1898.

The most pretentious and prolonged editorial effort in medical journalism in Texas was that of Dr. F. E. Daniel. His initial venture was the *Texas Courier-Record of Medicine,* which he and Dr. W. B. Brooks edited from 1883 to 1888, first at Fort Worth and then at Dallas. Dr. Brooks seems to have taken over in 1885, for *Daniel's Texas Medical Journal* came out in Austin that year. In 1893, the "Daniel's" was dropped, and the journal was continued as the *Texas Medical Journal* until 1920.[2] This publication, which came

---

[1] See above, Chapter 9.

[2] In 1924, Miss Fannie Daniel presented a complete file of the *Texas Medical Journal* to the Medical Department of the University of Texas, in memory of her father.

to be known as the "Red Back," was the most popular state medical journal prior to the advent of the *Texas State Journal of Medicine.* It prided itself on being "down on quacks of all kinds." On its title page it carried this statement: "Independent in all things and neutral in nothing that affects the welfare of Legitimate Medicine. It is devoted to the task of organizing the Texas profession for its own safety and protection, and to acquire influence in shaping the Sanitary Laws of the State; to the advancement of Medical Science and the elevation of the Standard of Medical Education." [3]

The continued existence of all these journals depended on revenue derived from advertisements, and these were not very carefully chosen. Recognized firms such as Parke Davis & Company, Sharp & Dohme, and Phillips Chemical Company were represented. In the questionable category could be found such advertised preparations as Antiphlogistine, Listerine, and Glycothymoline. The claims of Antiphthisis for tuberculosis and Anasarcin for Bright's disease and cirrhosis of the liver put such preparations definitely in the class of nostrums. However, we should not be too hasty in condemning the advertising practices of these early journals. They had no sure standards. It was, after all, a matter of individual judgment. Even the *Journal of the American Medical Association* could not exhibit clean pages until the Council on Pharmacy and Chemistry and the Propaganda Department were created in 1905 and 1906. And, besides, much of the exposure of nostrums and patent medicines came from lay journals, such as *Collier's Weekly,* the *Ladies' Home Journal,* and *Everybody's Magazine,* and from books such as Upton Sinclair's *The Jungle* and Samuel Hopkins Adams' *The Great American Fraud.*

The impetus given to the idea of establishing an association-owned journal by Drs. Chase and Russ resulted in the appointment at the 1905 meeting of Dr. W. R. Thompson and Dr. Chase as a committee to study the idea and report their recommendations. Their report was ready the next day: "Your committee advises this *Journal* to be published under the control and direction of the Board of Trustees, that the Councilors be made associate editors, and that the efficiency of the *Journal* be further increased from year to year by the appointment of special committees, to gather facts and publish, under the direction of the editor, articles on important

[3] *Index-Catalogue of the Library of the Surgeon-General's Office,* 2nd series, XII, 973.

questions." The proposed name was the *Texas State Journal of Medicine*, each issue to contain forty-eight pages, sixteen of which would be devoted to advertisements. All advertised products would be required to state the names and quantities of the constituent ingredients, and such products were not to be advertised in the secular press. One dollar of the membership fee was to be set aside as a subscription to the journal. It was recommended that the secretary of the Association be the editor of the journal.

Discussion on this matter before the House of Delegates resulted in a motion by Dr. Holman Taylor to the effect that a monthly journal be established and that the details be left to the Board of Trustees. The motion was discussed by T. T. Jackson and W. B. Russ, of San Antonio; M. L. Weems, Jr., of Brazoria; F. E. Daniel, of Austin; John T. Moore, of Galveston; J. T. Wilson, of Sherman; I. C. Chase, of Fort Worth; R. F. Miller, of Sherman; and P. N. Self, of Cleburne. The motion carried without a dissenting vote.

Although President Daniel did not register a negative vote against establishing the journal, he did oppose it vigorously as editor of the *Texas Medical Journal*. Under the title "Rash Action of the House of Delegates," in an editorial he seriously questioned the wisdom of the step, which he thought unduly hasty. The advertisements, he predicted, would not be forthcoming, and only failure and disaster on the financial rocks could be expected.[4]

Consideration of the journal overshadowed other deliberations of the 1905 meeting in Houston. Yet, other things were accomplished. A Board of Trustees was created, to which the business affairs of the Association were assigned. The first board was composed of C. E. Cantrell, of Greenville; W. R. Thompson, of Fort Worth; J. S. Lankford, of San Antonio; W. R. Blailock, of Dallas; and S. C. Red, of Houston. In contrast to some of the earlier meetings, chairmen of committees were present with reports of their varied activities. One of the most important and active of these was the Committee on Public Policy and Legislation. It had held a called meeting in Dallas in October, 1904, with all members present and a second meeting in Austin in November, this time in conjunction with a number of the councilors. The anatomical bill, which was designed to obtain cadavers for dissection purposes, amendments to the Medical Practice Act, and the creation of an adequate board of health were discussed. In its report to the House

[4] XX (1905), 473–78.

of Delegates, this committee stated that the regular profession received no recognition from the Twenty-ninth Legislature, this despite the presence of attorneys employed by the Association. The anatomical bill withered under a flood of raillery and ridicule, the board of health bill did not come up, and no changes were made in the Board of Medical Examiners.

The chief concern of this committee was a comparatively new medical cult known as osteopathy and, to a less extent, a group of drugless healers called "physio-medicists." The three boards of medical examiners, created in 1901, were handling the situation fairly satisfactorily. But now the first school of osteopathy, established by A. T. Still at Kirksville, Missouri, was sending its graduates into Texas, and they were about to succeed in obtaining a separate board of examiners. This action was forestalled by concentrating on a one-board bill to consist of five regular physicians and one each from the homeopaths, eclectics, osteopaths, and physio-medicists. This bill, however, did not come up for legislative consideration. The osteopaths, incidentally, were quite articulate, considering their small number: at the sixth session of the Texas Osteopathic Association, held at Fort Worth in May, 1905, only fifteen persons were present. One paper presented was on "The Tubercle Bacillus—A Harmless Germ." [5]

At Houston, Dr. Daniel gave a long presidential address on "Sentiment and Science." Involved as it was in life and mind, matter and motion, the address is difficult to interpret in a small compass. Much of it concerned animal experimentation and the many scientific advancements attributable thereto. The work of Claude Bernard, Brown-Séquard, Lister, Koch, and all the others of that brilliant galaxy of experimental scientists would have gone for naught without the presence of animals in the laboratory. And, as the result of these and other workers, in a short time man's life span had been extended from thirty-three to forty-eight years.

The Association voted to hold its next meeting in Fort Worth. Incoming officers were J. E. Gilcreest, Gainesville, president; and M. B. Grace, Seguin; Thomas A. Rape, Ballinger; and O. I. Holbert, Waco, vice-presidents.

From its first issue, in July, 1905, the *Texas State Journal of Medicine* set a high standard of journalism. It was printed on good paper in double columns, was well arranged, and was altogether

[5] *Texas State Journal of Medicine*, I (1905–1906), 24.

worthy of the serious efforts of Dr. Chase and his fifteen associate editors. Their labors were lightened by Dr. Chase's secretary, Ethel Gilmore, who was later to serve Dr. Holman Taylor in the same capacity. The *Journal* contained "only helpful and ethical advertising." Not least of its virtues was a good, usable index. The first issue consisted of 3,700 copies, and a circulation of 3,000 was guaranteed to its advertisers, who responded in a surprisingly satisfactory manner. All the space in the first issue was sold, and the income derived was well above expectations. Thus from the beginning, the financial stability of the *Journal* was assured, and the security of the Association was bolstered. One potent reason for the success of the *Journal* was found in a set of rules issued by the Board of Trustees:

1. Edit all papers, reports and discussions, cutting introductions, apologies, digressions, and other matter foreign to the theme. 2. Omit all discussions of papers not corrected by authors, and returned promptly. 3. Publish first, papers read before sections. Of those read by title or previously printed in other journals, publish towards the end of the year as many as there is room for, selecting those of most scientific and general interest. 4. Request of authors of papers longer than the constitutional limit, condensation, or privilege of condensing or abstracting. In case of refusal, delay publication, and if space does not permit printing by the end of the year, return manuscripts to authors. 5. The trustees reserve the right to refuse to publish any paper previously published.

The same advice was given by the editor of the *British Medical Journal* to the editor of the *Journal of the American Medical Association* in its early days: "Better papers, more condensation, and a larger wastebasket would naturally follow an extended membership."

The editorial attitude of the *Journal* toward the other medical publications of the state was one of conciliation: "There is no wish to absorb or cripple these publications." It was but natural, however, that the existence of the other journals, never too secure, would be threatened. The *Texas Medical Gazette* ceased publication in May, 1905. The *Texas Medical News* suffered a similar fate in 1907. This left the "Red Back" *Texas Medical Journal*. Dr. F. E. Daniel, its editor, fought bitterly against the *Texas State Journal of Medicine*. The American Medical Association, he charged, would call the tune, and the new journal would have "to dance to the music of the Chicago Octopus," the journal of the national association. That great journal, it was asserted with some accuracy, could not boast of clean advertising hands in that it accepted such preparations as Campho-Phenique and Pepto-Mangan, and yet "its object is to crush out all individually owned medical journals that have the courage to criticise it." [6] The attitude of the *Texas Medical News* was about the same.[7]

The first issue of the *Texas State Journal of Medicine* contained these articles: "Intestinal Anastomosis by Intra-intestinal Ligature and Rapid Suture Forceps," by A. C. Scott; "Haab's Magnet—Its Use and Report of Cases," by E. H. Cary; and "The Value of Leucocyte Count in Appendicitis," by W. L. Brown. While the *Journal* had a policy of not printing an article that had appeared elsewhere, it early made one notable exception when it reprinted Sir William Osler's farewell address, "Unity, Peace and Concord," from the *Journal of the American Medical Association,* an address which was called "one of the noblest and most inspiring that has ever fallen from human pen, classical in diction, fervent in spirit, springing from a wealth of experience and a heart beating in sympathetic love for the profession."

A strong stimulus was given to the reorganized state association in 1905, when Dr. J. N. McCormack paid his second visit to Texas to make throughout the state his inspiring and convincing talks on the profession. He depicted the profession as it too often really was: envy, jealousy, and slander were too often present. If two physicians in a community represented each other as scoundrels often enough and viciously enough, only one conclusion could be drawn by the people of the community: they were both right. That situation had to be corrected, and Dr. McCormack thought that "a county society is the only influence that can elevate the county profession in learning, brotherly love and helpfulness." To good effect, he repeatedly stressed the desirable attributes of a physician: "The doctor, as a representative of a great charitable and learned profession, should be the cleanest man in the community—clean in speech, clean in body, and clean in morals. He should be the best dressed man, as becomes his social standing. He should be the broadest and most cultured man in literature and science. He should be public-spirited—a model citizen. He should take this vow: 'So long as God shall let me live I will never say an unkind

[6] *Texas Medical Journal*, XX (1905), 478, 497–503.
[7] XIII (1905), 532–34.

word of a fellow doctor.' If a doctor may commit an unpardonable sin, it is to mistreat a young practitioner, and it is but a little milder sin to mistreat an old one."

Using the *Journal* as its mouthpiece, the Association became increasingly articulate after the 1905 meeting. This stepped-up activity was spearheaded by the aggressive work of the Committee on Public Policy and Legislation, which had come to be known as the Legislative Committee. By the time the Fort Worth meeting convened, on April 24, at Greenwall's Opera House, full reports were ready and full discussion could be anticipated. More than 600 members registered for the meeting, and some estimates put the number in attendance as high as 800.

The report of Secretary Chase showed an admirable blending of pride and tolerance. He was proud because the Association had made exceptional advances during the year: membership had grown to 2,622, an increase of 278 in a year; the treasurer's report showed a balance of $6,716.49, an increase of $1,621.30; the advertisements in the *Journal* had carried practically the entire expense of publication; the work of the Legislative Committee, with which he had planned and worked quite closely, had borne much fruit. He gave emphasis to his pride in the *Journal*, credit for the success of which was solely his, in these words of prophecy: "The grandchildren who sit upon your knees will see the day when the Journal of this Association reaches 10,000 doctors." [8] He exhibited a spirit of tolerance toward those individuals or editors who, by bitter invective, would embroil the Association in discord and disruption. He foresaw the treacherous storm that would come to organized medicine as a result of the gross and selfish misrepresentations of the proprietary drug interests and the medical journals whose very existence was involved; he realized that in certain quarters the storm was already brewing.

Far less tolerant was Dr. W. B. Russ in his report as chairman of the Board of Councilors. "It is a well known fact," he stated, "that a very large and wealthy advertising agency is publishing regularly and distributing broadcast a journal devoted solely to the work of fighting organized medicine from top to bottom, and of vilifying

[8] Under the title "The Great Work Being Done in Texas," J. N. McCormack published an article which recommended the methods used in Texas as an example for other states.—*Journal of the A.M.A.*, XLVI (1906), 1133–35.

and misrepresenting every man and every committee placed in a position of trust and responsibility by the medical profession. It is a well known fact that some (not all by any means) privately owned journals, if forced by public opinion to drop their dirty advertising, would be practically driven out of business."

All over the land, private medical journals were quick to react. There were cries about the self-seeking politicians, the octopus, and the great medical trust. Resort to private and public defamation was the usual thing. Even the race issue was dragged in. On the local scene, the *Texas Medical Journal* took up the attack with renewed vigor—vigor born at least partially of desperation.[9] Dr. Chase wisely ignored his remaining competitive medical editor in Texas; the *Journal of the American Medical Association* was far less vulnerable, since its editorial and advertising policies were now in conformity.

Dr. J. T. Wilson, of Sherman, reported that the Legislative Committee had held an all-day session in Dallas on February 12 with all members present. The same subjects which had been in the forefront for some time were discussed again, and the outlook for legislative relief was far brighter because of the work of this committee and the editorial efforts of Dr. Chase. The anatomical bill, for instance, which had been ridiculed off the floor of the Legislature in 1905, became a law in 1906, the vote in the Senate being 19 to 5. But the real victory for this committee was the signing of the One-Board Medical Practice Act by Governor Thomas M. Campbell, April 17, 1907. The story of this important development is most significant but too long for complete telling. Here are a few of the facts.

It had become obvious that the imperfections and loopholes of the three-board plan of medical examinations were many. And besides, osteopaths and other medical groups were showing up in Texas: at Glen Rose the Texas Quadopath College of Science was advertising that "in five years' practice of these methods, it recites that they have never lost a case of pneumonia, spinal meningitis, appendicitis or any of the so-called fatal diseases," and in Dallas the Physio-Medical College of Texas had opened its doors. There was a growing feeling among the regular profession that there was no more room for "pathies" or creeds in medicine than there was in

[9] *Texas Medical Journal,* XXI (1905–1906), 361–64, 449–55; XXII (1907), 18–19, 345–47, 431–33.

geology or astronomy. But the attitude of the adherents of the minor schools was one of aloofness. The opening wedge came in the form of a scholarly letter, "Unity or Uniformity?" by a thoroughly educated homeopath, Dr. Milton J. Bliem, of San Antonio. Bliem said in part:

The keynote of modern civilization is *union*. This *zeit-geist* has finally gripped the medical profession, and under the resultant consolidation of its organized forces the status of the profession has already been revolutionized. We may well rejoice, too, that the leaders in this movement have been actuated by the loftiest motives, and that the highest ideals have been the beacon lights of guidance. The sweet-spirited Osler has spoken the typical words in his farewell address on "Unity, Peace and Concord." McCormack—that great-hearted bishop of the medical profession—is daily preaching the gospel of peace and good-will to all doctors. Under the inspiration of this fraternal spirit, factional and school lines—the heritage of misunderstanding, and enmities of historical lineage—bid fair to disappear. . . . Accepting conditions as they are, I made the heavy sacrifice of resigning from homeopathic societies in which I held lifelong memberships, and in which I cherished life-long friendships. I risked the loss of both the friendship and good-will of old friends by a seeming act of treason. But I sacrificed no iota of principle or conviction in changing my society affiliations, while I counterbalanced my loss by the hope of gaining a larger usefulness for myself and the greater good of the whole. . . . In the grand, central societies of the county, State and Nation, we would all come together to study, and to put into practice those vital truths common to us all.[10]

The *Journal* conciliated the homeopaths and eclectics by publicizing the meetings and the officials of the respective associations. It also published lists of textbooks used in the several schools, and they were practically the same.

While these developments were going on, the Legislative Committee was extending its activities to the county level. The membership was being reminded that the Association in its reorganized form had greater influence and that this influence could be best utilized when each member accepted his individual responsibility. The *Journal* gave editorial instruction. Every doctor, it contended, had a right to expect the friendship and confidence of candidates for public office. A "recipe for a political funeral" was given: "Take one full meeting of a county society. Add to it the names of the

[10] *Texas State Journal of Medicine*, I (1905–1906), 247–48.

county voters. Allot to each physician ten citizens with whom he has influence. Let the selected men be quietly informed of public health needs and the attitude of the respective candidates. While stewing avoid all political jars and the cold breath of threats and public argument. This recipe, if wisely used, will be followed on July 28th by an orderly political burial and the epitaph will read: 'Sacred to the memory of those opposed to the proper protection of human life.'"

The result of these various endeavors was what the *Journal* called a victory for public health. A governor and lieutenant-governor, both favorable to much-needed medical legislation, were elected. All but one opposition senator was defeated, and a majority favorable to the medical profession was elected in the House.

Even though the new Legislature was friendly to the wishes of the medical profession, the one-board idea did not have clear sailing. All the minor groups were openly opposed to it, principally because they feared eventual absorption by the regular profession. Editor F. E. Daniel, with disturbing consistency and relentlessness, bitterly opposed it. Association with any of these groups, in the sick room or on a board, was unthinkable. Should such a thing as passage of the bill occur, he doubted whether "any self-respecting physician will consent to affiliate with an assortment of pathies, more or less off color." [11]

Conferences were held among the various schools, and some changes in the bill were made, one at the suggestion of Governor Campbell. On February 26, 1907, the legislative committees of the physio-medical, homeopathic, osteopathic, eclectic, and regular schools of medicine signed a statement that the revised bill was "in every respect acceptable." This assured passage. The bill was signed by Governor Campbell on April 17.

Alongside the worth-while attainments in public health came a growing demand for better transportation. Dr. S. D. Bashore, of Palmyra, Pennsylvania, described his experiences as a doctor on motorcycle.[12] Editor Chase gave his approbation: "Its construction is simple; the mechanism and adjustment are easily learned; it is rarely out of order and easily repaired; when not in use it is easily stored and eats nothing. Compared with other modes of locomotion the expense is very low. If self-propulsion should fail, there is still

[11] *Texas Medical Journal*, XXI (1905–1906), 405.
[12] *Texas State Journal of Medicine*, II (1906–1907), 92–93.

a useful bicycle for reaching home. On emergency calls, a man can go and return before competitors arrive on the scene."

Getting back to the Forth Worth session, it will be seen that the research activities of the sections were overshadowed by the political activities of the House of Delegates. Even the presidential address was such as to arouse no great interest. President Gilcreest set a good example in the brevity of his message, "The Necessity for Better Reciprocal Relations Between the Medical Profession and the Public." He surveyed the accomplishments of the medical profession in controlling infectious diseases, but reminded his audience that much remained to be done. He advocated the medical inspection of school children as an aid in detection and control of these diseases. More important were better education for doctors, an improved medical-practice act, and a more understanding public. In referring to misappraisal of the profession by the general public, he used an unusual version of Alexander Pope's lines:

> At the verge of danger and not before,
> God and the doctor we do adore—
> But after the danger is over and all is arighted,
> God is forgotten and the doctor is slighted.[13]

Mineral Wells was the only city to ask for the 1907 meeting, and of course received it. Elected as new officers were G. B. Foscue, Waco, president; and E. P. Miller, El Paso; D. S. Wier, Beaumont; and A. B. Small, Waxahachie, vice-presidents.

The selection of Mineral Wells for the 1907 and Corpus Christi for the 1908 meeting served as an early reminder that the Association had grown so large that only a few cities could handle it adequately. Three factors conspired to detract from the Mineral Wells meeting: inaccessibility due to poor railroad connections, the necessity for housing the members in small hotels and boarding houses, and bad weather. It rained two out of the three days, and the unpaved streets and improvised walks became well-nigh impassable. Four hundred registrations were reported, but this figure was admittedly inaccurate. In the words of the able editor of the *Journal,*

[13] The lines as Pope wrote them:
> God and the Doctor we alike adore,
> But only when in danger, not before;
> The danger o'er, both are alike requited,
> God is forgotten, and the doctor slighted.

this was "a short enthusiastic, business session." Fewer papers were read and fewer members were in attendance on the sections than at any recent session. Rarely were more than 25 present in the sections, and in balloting for the new officers only 77 votes were cast. In the House of Delegates, 85 of the 137 county societies were represented.

This is not to conclude that the session failed to make some solid accomplishments. The Association had shown a steady growth of about 200 members a year, the treasurer was able to report a comfortable balance, and the *Journal* showed a profit of about $2,000 after paying the editor $1,200, an office assistant $1,195, and a stenographer $550. The membership was 2,910, a figure which permitted the Association to boast that over 60 per cent of the medical profession of the state were now in its fold, compared to less than 10 per cent in former years. The secretary anticipated a more rapid increase after the Association had succeeded in neutralizing the influence of a small embittered group who were endeavoring to misinterpret the purposes of the Association and to impugn the motives of its leaders.

One quite important feature of Secretary Chase's report dealt with medical economics. In great detail and by much work, he recorded on three pages of the *Journal,* facts and figures concerning Texas physicians' income. He collected data from 79 counties and 3,317 doctors. Of these, 55 per cent were making a bare living; 45 per cent were able to save something. The average income was $1,873 with the average expense $1,301, leaving a paltry $572 at the end of the year. The highest reported income was $40,000. As a rule, the doctors in the country and small towns were inclined to prosper, whereas a large majority of those practicing in the cities were struggling to get by. As in later years, the cost of living had increased about 25 per cent in ten years, while physicians' income had remained stationary. In closing, Dr. Chase expressed confidence that the State Medical Association of Texas was now sufficiently strong to guard the economic welfare of its members.

Closely involved in this subject of physicians' income was the report of the Insurance Committee, composed of Drs. C. E. Cantrell, J. W. Largent, and Holman Taylor. For several years, individual physicians had been skirmishing with life insurance companies about examination fees. Three dollars was the usual fee, and the companies insisted that some of the doctors were overpaid at that.

It seems that the "sink test" for urine was not unknown at that time. The first evidence of progress came from a visit by Secretary Chase to Chicago, where he conferred with insurance officials and doubtless with the officers of the American Medical Association. Editorials in the *Journal* kept the matter before the profession. Thousands of these editorials were printed and broadcast to doctors in and out of the state and to insurance company directors. As a result of this campaign, the committee was able to report that sixteen companies, mostly small, had agreed to pay a flat fee of five dollars for examinations; however, thirty-one companies still insisted on paying a graded fee, and among them were such companies as Metropolitan, New York Life, Union Central, and Travelers. Fifty county societies agreed not to make examinations for the lesser fees. But no great progress was made for several years, even though assistance came from the strong Insurance Committee of the American Medical Association. A powerful insurance lobby from the East took a hand in the problem in Texas and elsewhere and incurred much ill will. As a by-product and perhaps by way of retaliation, the Robertson Insurance Act was passed, requiring all out-of-state companies to invest a certain portion of their earnings in Texas, a requirement which the committee thought was just retribution for "the cold-blooded, high-handed and short-sighted business policy pursued by low fee companies."

The Committee on Public Policy and Legislation, led this year by Dr. W. B. Russ, continued its successes of the preceding year. Two measures sponsored by the Association, the Pure Food and Drug Bill and the State Board of Pharmacy Bill, were reported by the committee as having become law. Many of the scenes in the Legislature were recalled as the One-Board Medical Practice Act worked its way doubtfully through the legislative hopper. The friends of the act were applauded, and the foes were set apart. The strongest opposition came from Christian Scientists, who, with the support of the *Houston Post* and the *Austin Statesman,* sought exemption from the provisions of the act. With a tie vote in the Senate, Lieutenant-Governor A. B. Davidson raised his gavel and said, "With as much pleasure as I ever cast a vote in my life, I vote 'Aye,' and declare the amendment tabled." The act was finally passed.

To the legally qualified practitioners of medicine, whatever their school, the new medical-practice act meant very little. All they needed to do was to send to the proper authorities their diplomas, district board certificates, or suitable affidavits that they had been properly authorized to practice medicine in Texas prior to 1901, when the three-board plan was instituted. Those legalized to practice after 1901 were required to register their licenses with the district clerk. In each instance, a fee of one dollar was collected. But the real importance of the act was that new applicants were to find passing the examinations increasingly difficult. These applicants must come from reputable schools whose course of instruction embraced four terms of five months each. "Only scientific branches of medicine" were included in the examinations: anatomy, physiology, chemistry, histology, pathology, bacteriology, physical diagnosis, surgery, obstetrics, gynecology, hygiene, and medical jurisprudence. In other words, the system of treatment was left to the discretion and the ability of the applicant. The act did not assign membership on the Board of Medical Examiners on the basis of schools of medicine. It stated that there were to be eleven members, to be appointed by the governor, and that no school should have a majority representation on the board.

Representing the allopaths on the new board were E. P. Becton, of Greenville; W. B. Collins, of Lovelady; J. J. Dial, of Sulphur Springs; G. B. Foscue, of Waco; and J. D. Osborn, of Cleburne. The eclectics were M. E. Daniel, of Honey Grove, and J. P. Rice, of San Antonio. T. J. Crowe, of Dallas, and J. D. Mitchell, of Fort Worth, represented the homeopaths. J. F. Bailey, of Waco, and R. O. Braswell, of Mineral Wells, were the osteopathic and physiomedical appointees. Drs. Daniel, Crowe, and Foscue were elected president, vice-president, and secretary, respectively. The career of this board was one of confusion and courage, temporary storm and eventual success. A veritable rash of mandamus suits was filed from one end of the state to the other. Some were defended successfully, but some were lost; all were useful in bringing order out of a difficult situation. No small factor in solving the many problems that faced the board was the spirit of harmony and co-operation that pervaded its deliberations.

Closely related to the work of the Board of Medical Examiners was the matter of medical education. In 1904, the American Medical Association had created the Council on Medical Education. At its 1906 meeting, Dr. John T. Moore was the Texas representative. In his report at the Mineral Wells meeting, Dr. Moore made a plea for better medical education and pointed out the recommendations of the national council: a high-school education as a medical prerequisite, a four-year course of at least thirty weeks each year, and a satisfactory examination before a state licensing board. The new Texas Board of Medical Examiners honored these recommendations and also required that all applicants must come from schools with curricula approved by the Association of American Medical Colleges. The Council on Medical Education of the American Medical Association made a report about this time which reflected the need for better educational facilities in Texas: from 1903 to 1906, 1 applicant out of 79 from the University of Texas failed; 1 out of 27 from Fort Worth University; 8 out of 29 from Baylor University; 5 out of 9 from Gate City Medical College; 2 out of 8 from Southwestern University; and 5 out of 9 from the College of Physicians and Surgeons. Two applicants from the Physio-Medical College of Texas passed. All 1904 and 1905 graduates from the University of Texas passed the state board examinations; of those from Fort Worth, 12.5 per cent failed; from Baylor, 44.4 per cent; and from Gate City, 60 per cent. Most of the Texas schools were requiring a high-school education for admission. The University of Texas required one year of college. Nationally, only Johns Hopkins and Harvard demanded college degrees for admission.[14]

In the four years since reorganization, the members of the State Medical Association of Texas had become close and active participants in the work of the American Medical Association. At the Atlantic City meeting in 1907, 25 Texas members were present, 5 being delegates. Only five other states had a larger number of representatives in the House of Delegates. Dr. Frank Paschal served on the Committee on Legislation and Political Action, and Dr. C. E. Cantrell was honored with the chairmanship of the Judicial Council. Texas had 893 members in the American Medical Association, and 518 more were subscribers to the national journal. Two years later, Dr. Cantrell was elected as a trustee and Dr. Paschal was advanced to the chairmanship of the Committee on Amendments.

At the 1907 meeting of the state association, two significant changes were made in the Constitution. It was provided that the officers should be elected by the House of Delegates on nominations from the floor, no nominating speech to exceed two minutes; and it was required that all papers read before the sections must have been presented previously before a county society. An official but-

[14] *Journal of the A.M.A.*, XLVIII (1907), 1703–1707, 1764–77.

ton was adopted: a small red cross within a white star was surmounted on a blue ground, a gold rim surrounding the periphery. The letters "S.M.A.," standing for "State Medical Association," were inserted on the blue background.

President Foscue's address was the shortest on record up to that time, filling only one page of the *Journal*. And it was as sensible as it was short: substitute tolerance and charity for ignorance and prejudice, and the title of his paper was achieved—"Unity and Harmony in the Medical Profession."

The Mineral Wells meeting saw, too, the passing of the annual oration. This was indeed the end of an era. For a generation, the doctors of Texas had gloried in the spoken word. They had been willing to sit and listen as orators such as John O. McReynolds or Marvin L. Graves, in words befitting the occasion, recalled the medical glories of the past, emphasized the triumphs of the present, and envisaged the accomplishments of the future. Time had moved slowly then. Now the hours had grown wings. The world was moving faster. The bicycle and motorcycle had arrived, and the automobile was in sight. So, with the speeding of time, able William S. Carter, professor of physiology and dean of the medical faculty, University of Texas, became the last annual orator. Appropriately, he chose a matter-of-fact topic: "Individualism in Medicine as Influenced by Medical Education." Better preparation, better choice of students, better educational facilities—all these combined to make better doctors. The close of his oration was most apt. "Trade," he declared, "is occupation for a livelihood; profession is occupation for the service of the world. Trade is occupation where anybody may enter; profession is occupation where only those who are prepared may enter. Trade is occupation which is followed until something better presents; profession is occupation for a lifetime. Trade makes one the rival of every other trader; profession makes one the co-worker with all his colleagues. Trade knows only the ethics of success; profession is bound by the ties of sacred honor. Trade is occupation merely for the joy of the result; profession is occupation for the joy in the process."

Other papers were in keeping with the stepped-up tempo of medical progress: "Cholecystenterostomy, with Report of a Case," by John T. Moore; "The Microscopic Diagnosis of Diseases of the Uterus and Cervix Uteri from Scrapings and Sections," by James J. Terrill; "Some Remarks on Cerebro-Spinal Meningitis," by

M. L. Graves; and "Cancer of the Breast—Its Diagnosis, Prognosis, and Treatment," by Bacon Saunders.

One most unusual presentation before the Section on Medicine and Diseases of Children was made by Dr. John S. Turner. It dealt with a notorious murder trial of 1900, in which Albert T. Patrick was accused of murdering William M. Rice, an eighty-four-year-old multimillionaire of Houston. The old man's valet confessed that he administered chloroform while Rice was asleep in his New York hotel room. Rice's physician gave the causes of death as "old age, weak heart and collocratal diarrhoea with mental worry." [15] A forged will, with Patrick as beneficiary, and other convincing facts made the evidence incontrovertible. The medical testimony centered about the controversy of whether the pulmonary edema found at autopsy was due to chloroform inhalation or could have been due to embalming fluid. Following three thousand pages of testimony and ten weeks of legal battle, Patrick was condemned to die. After several stays of execution, however, his sentence was commuted to life imprisonment, which ended on November 28, 1912, when he was granted an unconditional pardon by the governor of New York. Almost on this very day, Rice Institute, the recipient of William M. Rice's residuary estate, opened its doors. Dr. Turner's purpose in bringing up the case six years after the trial was to stress the unsatisfactory state of medical testimony in general and the difficulty of reconciling the opposing testimony of Dr. John A. Wyeth and Dr. H. P. Loomis, of New York.

At the closing session of the House of Delegates at Mineral Wells, C. E. Cantrell, of Greenville, was elected president over three other nominees. H. D. Barnes, of Tulia; D. S. Wier, of Beaumont; and A. B. Small, of Waxahachie, became vice-presidents. C. A. Smith, of Texarkana, became the new treasurer. Corpus Christi, Waco, Beaumont, and Texarkana wanted the next meeting, with Corpus Christi winning over Beaumont, 41 to 39.

Recalling some of the experiences at Mineral Wells, Dr. J. S. Lankford, chairman of the Board of Trustees, and Dr. W. B. Russ, chairman of the Board of Councilors, made a visit to Corpus Christi

[15] This unclear diagnosis is taken from Edmund L. Pearson, *Five Murders* (Garden City, New York, 1928), 215. This book gives a good account of all the facts of Rice's death and Patrick's trial. Patrick attended Texas Agricultural and Mechanical College and later graduated in law from the University of Texas. Arthur Train's *True Stories of Crime* also deals with this trial.

to investigate the new meeting place. They brought back a glowing report: plenty of hotels, good railroad facilities, ample financial backing, and fine local transportation,—"thirty hacks & thirty automobiles in the public service." They predicted a large and successful meeting.

To uphold this prediction, the *Journal* of April, 1908, carried a four-page spread of description and pictures. Corpus Christi, then a city of eight thousand people, was presented as "the State's most popular tropical resort." Certainly a three-dollar rate for a double Pullman berth from Fort Worth and Dallas was an attraction.

Corpus Christi lived up to the expectations concerning her. Four hundred and twenty-five members registered, and 250 of them brought their wives. A new badge had been designed, very similar to the one now in use; it hung "from a metallic buckle, in which is space for the name and address of each wearer." Members, delegates, and guests were designated on the badges; thus "the introduction, acquaintanceship and entertainment of those present" were furthered. The setting of the meeting, in the Pavilion, was altogether different from the usual milieu. The high winds, the sea gulls, and the sound of the whitecaps under the Pavilion made hearing difficult. But this did not dampen the enthusiasm of the meeting. There were side trips to Rockport and Brownsville, dancing, a complimentary automobile ride, bathing, fishing, and a fish-fry at Epworth-by-the-Sea, served by beautiful women with "smiling grace." At this meeting, the Medical Department of the University of Texas was growing up: an alumni smoker was given at the home of Sam Rankin, and "a jolly time" was reported. The *Corpus Christi Caller* published a long poem, "When the Doctor Comes." What the poem lacked in poetic structure and medical learning may have been neutralized by the thought that the doctors at the convention would "cut all sorts of didos."

Professional and material advancement was reflected in all reports to the House of Delegates; 142 component county societies, 3,117 members, and a cash balance of $8,720.45. This last figure was possible despite the loss of more than $1,000.00 due to cancellation of advertising contracts which did not meet the new standards of the *Journal*. Secretary Chase could boast that the affairs of the Association had grown so big that the office at Fort Worth occupied a space forty-five by fifteen feet, and in this office were found "four large desks, two typewriters, vertical files, two cabinets containing a directory of State physicians, cases for the accommodation of medical publications, back numbers of our *State Journal* and a number of books." This did not mean that he was content with the Association as it was. On the contrary, he was looking far ahead.

As your Editor and Secretary, I am especially anxious that the Trustees plan wisely for the future. There should now be laid a foundation to meet the needs of the great organization which twenty or thirty years hence will form the State Medical Association of Texas. But two years ago we thought we had only 5,000 physicians in the State. After the new law goes into effect in July we will probably find some 7,000 enrolled. In twenty years there will perhaps be twice this number, with State meetings at which 1,000 to 1,400 may be in attendance. Our library will have increased to thousands of volumes; the circulation of the Journal will be 10,000. The principal committees will require a paid secretary to conduct their work. We will be compelled for reasons of economy probably to install a more or less expensive printing plant, etc. We already need room for some branches of our work. The Committees on Insurance, Railroad Contract Practice, and Legislation, already need the attention of a clerk. We should plan for a business home. This does not imply a permanent place of meeting, but merely a property, a fire-proof building and its equipment—a home like the American Medical Association. I urge the Trustees to this end to invest their funds to wisely provide for these future needs of the growing profession of Texas.

The work of the Committee on Medical Education and the Board of Medical Examiners continued to prosper, even though hindrances and handicaps were encountered. During the year, the Physio-Medical College of Dallas and the Gate City Medical College of Texarkana closed their doors as the result of "a solar plexus blow" from the Board of Medical Examiners. The board, moreover, had many other problems. A group of anonymous letters threatening harm to its members if the writers were not granted licenses to practice must have put them in a quandary. A move on the part of the board to have suits brought to revoke licenses of advertising doctors only multiplied the number of mandamus suits, which were already too plentiful. The defense of these suits entailed an outlay of funds beyond the means of the board. It appealed to the Board of Trustees of the state association for one thousand dollars to employ counsel. The Board of Trustees wisely rejected the request on the ground that this was not a fight of legalized doctors in the Association against nonlegalized doctors outside, but that it was a fight of all the people for self-protection. To complete the financial embarrassment of the Board of Medical Examiners, the attorney-general ruled that its funds were liable for the costs of unsuccessful suits, a ruling that the board felt to be obviously unfair and without legal basis.

But, withal, the Board of Medical Examiners had made a remarkable beginning. In its first eight months, it had mailed 25,000 letters and investigated 7,000 records. The only criticism leveled at the board was that it had been too lenient in its dealings with the older practitioners who had failed to register their licenses or diplomas in time to comply with the law. Since the board realized that these men would have difficulty with the examinations, it granted a credit of 1 per cent on grades for each year of practice. As a result of this ruling, some of these oldsters achieved the arithmetical feat of making over 100 per cent on the examinations.

Reverting to the custom of earlier presidents, Dr. C. E. Cantrell gave a long address. He chose to review the growth of the Association during the past ten years. A tenfold growth in membership and passage of desirable medical legislation could be reported. And yet Texas was, with Idaho, still without a board of health. This disgraceful lack had to be filled, and the need was immediate.

The trend of medical thought in Texas in 1908 can be gauged from a few of the papers read at Corpus Christi: "Toxemia of Pregnancy," by E. J. Alexander; "Diverticulosis and Diverticulitis," by James J. Terrill; "Appendicostomy," by W. B. Russ; "Acidosis," by K. Heberden Beall; "Splenic Anemia—With Report of a Case," by M. J. Bliem; "The Importance of Autopsy Work in General Practice," by J. M. Frazier; "A Case of Hypernephroma of the Kidney," by A. L. Hathcock; "Radical Operation for Inguinal Hernia," by E. J. Hamilton; and "Psychoneuroses," by Holman Taylor. Two papers on retro-displacement of the uterus, by R. R. White and Adolph Herff, reflected the inchmeal progress that was being made in that controversial subject. J. N. Mendenhall, of Plano, was seriously perturbed over the trend toward therapeutic pessimism. Medicine had not become an exact science or art, but, he insisted, he could not agree with Osler who had said that pneumonia could "neither be aborted nor cut short by any known means at our command." In other words, "a little peppermint water will do as well as anything." Even so, energy, cheerfulness, and enthusiasm are mighty factors, maintained Dr. Mendenhall. "It is told of a large, fat, jolly man, who was a good laugher, that he was employed to sit in a ward of a hospital for the insane, and laugh long and loud at certain intervals, for the benefit of a poor sufferer from melancholia, who had given up and had not been known to smile for a long time. After awhile the melancholic noticed the jolly man and ventured to laugh, and when he did so, new life and vigor came to him and he was cured. Good cheer is contagious and is good medicine. It requires neither brains, patriotism, nor religion to be a knocker, a kicker, a pessimist or an iconoclast. A mule can destroy or kick down a barn, but it takes a man to build one."

Amarillo, Dallas, Waco, and Galveston asked for the next meeting. Preferring the seashore, the Association chose Galveston. Elected to serve as officers were H. W. Cummings, Hearne, president; and J. M. Inge, Denton; A. Garwood, New Braunfels; and A. M. Wood, Galveston, vice-presidents.

The year 1908 saw the advent of chiropractors—first called "chiropractics"—who expected exemption from the Medical Practice Act on the ground that they healed by manual manipulation and hence were masseurs. Although the horse and buggy were on their way out, within a few days of each other Dr. T. A. Miller, of Corsicana, and Dr. William E. Luter, of San Antonio, were seriously injured in runaway accidents. Less fast to leave the medical scene in Texas were pus tubes, for the cure of which Dr. W. W. Samuell, of Dallas, could report sixty operations without a death. A fire in the Association office forced a move to better quarters in the basement of the Continental Bank Building. The problem of fee-splitting came in for condemnation by the Board of Councilors. Finally, the year saw no decrease in the birth rate. "Dr. Wilkins, of Wellington, in the Panhandle, reported that he and the two other doctors in his town caught three pairs of twins one night, and it was not a good night for twins, either. Dr. Holman Taylor, of Marshall, saw his ante and called him. He reported that he and his father caught six (single shots) in one night." [16]

The newspapers of the state were giving more and more space to the activities of the Association. One type of medical publicity came in the form of cartoons, which appeared in the papers of Fort Worth, Houston, and San Antonio. In December, the *Fort Worth Star* and the *Houston Post* emphasized the necessity of fighting tuberculosis through purchase of Red Cross stamps. The *Fort*

[16] *Texas Medical Journal*, XXIII (1927–28), 509.

Worth Star, the next month, depicted Doc Progress in the act of throwing baseballs at a group of dolls in a sideshow. The baseballs are labeled "clean streets" and "no spitting." The large doll in the center is named "Tuberculosis—12.08% of total annual deaths in Texas." Arrayed on each side are eight lesser diseases. The attendant is saying, "Aim at the big white one, Doc."

When the forty-third annual session [17] was called to order at the Scottish Rite Cathedral in Galveston, the glee club of the medical college provided an innovation with four vocal numbers, two of which were "Fishing" and " 'Twas a Dream." The loss of 130 members during the year did not appear to Secretary Chase to be significant and, in his eyes, was attributable to lack of industry on the part of the district councilors. As an offset to this loss, he could point to the fact that "93 per cent of the known, licensed, regular, reputable, white, medical college graduates of Texas" were enrolled in the Association, and that the mailing list of the *Journal* had grown to more than 4,000.

The Committee on Public Policy and Legislation had had another busy and profitable year, culminating in the passage by the Legislature of a bill creating a State Board of Health. Hard and persistent effort against unexpected opposition had been necessary to achieve this result. Three meetings of this committee had been called by the chairman and the secretary, Drs. H. W. Cummings and I. C. Chase. In addition, many visits had been made to Austin. A group of San Antonio physicians—Frank Paschal, J. S. Lankford, W. B. Russ, and W. A. King—with the assistance of State Health Officer W. M. Brumby, succeeded in getting the Democratic Convention in San Antonio to insert in its platform a plank favoring a board of health. Opposition came from the minor schools of medicine and, strangely, from the County Judges and Commissioners Association. When the time came to vote, however, there was no dissenting vote in the Senate and there were very few in the House. Governor Thomas M. Campbell appointed the following to the first board: W. M. Brumby, Austin, president; J. E. Gilcreest, Gainesville; H. W. Cummings, Hearne; M. H. E. Whiteside, Timpson; J. W. Burns, Cuero; Boyd Cornick, San Angelo; and Thomas F. Burnett, Seymour. In appreciation of unflagging

---

[17] It should be recalled that the two 1853 sessions were regularly overlooked, so that in the records the 1909 session is called the forty-first.

support given to the board of health bill, the *Journal* printed short biographies and pictures of the following: Senators A. J. Harper, of Mexia; J. P. Hayter, of Decatur; McDonald Meachum, of Navasota; and D. M. Alexander, of Weatherford; and Representatives J. C. Ralston, of Waller; J. P. Turner, of Slidell; W. C. Davis, of Bryan; and W. A. Tarver, of Corsicana.

Dr. J. D. Osborn presented to the House of Delegates the report of the Board of Medical Examiners. He felt that the Association should stand squarely and financially back of the board: "We have had to stand alone in our fight against judges that were Christian Scientists, judges that were osteopaths and others who would order the Board to issue certificates." And yet, fighting alone, they had fought a good fight: the Ira W. Collins case in El Paso had upheld the validity of the Medical Practice Act, as had the Stephen A. Morse case in McLennan County; but the crowning triumph came in San Antonio, when the notorious impostor, "Dr. Lafayette Berry the Phenomenal," had his license revoked. This faker, heralded by a brass band and vaudeville show, went about Texas claiming to cure gall-bladder disease, appendicitis, and cancer. But gall-stones were his specialty. A quart of olive oil, two Seidlitz powders, and a half-pound of Epsom salts comprised his treatment. Reward to the "Doctor": fifty dollars in advance. Result to the patient too weak to pursue the culprit: "half a hat full" of soap balls. The striking success of the Medical Practice Act was shown by a letter of praise from the attorneys of the American Medical Association. They suggested "that whenever legislation upon this subject is to be enacted by other States it would be well to follow the Texas statute."

After several years of quiet but effectual work, the Committee on Collection and Preservation of Records reported at the Galveston meeting. Practically all the *Proceedings* and *Transactions* of the Association were assembled, along with photographs of many of the former presidents. As a result of the interest and energy of Dr. R. H. Harrison, of Columbus, and his committee, it became possible to get together one or two complete files of these publications. From these, much of the early history of the Texas Medical Association has been garnered. It was at this meeting, and apparently using the records collected by this committee, that Dr. S. O. Young, of Galveston, presented his "History of the Early Meetings of the State Medical Association of Texas." Some of the recollections

PAST PRESIDENTS

B. E. Pickett, Sr., 1947   Tate Miller, 1948
G. V. Brindley, 1949   William M. Gambrell, 1950

PAST PRESIDENTS

Allen T. Stewart, 1951　　　　T. C. Terrell, 1952

George Turner, 1953　　　　Holman Taylor

Secretary and Editor, 1912–1947

of Dr. Young were utilized in Chapters 6 and 7 of this history. In 1909 a stimulus to the matter of collecting and preserving records came in the form of a letter in the *Journal* from the Western Association for the Preservation of Medical Records, signed by C. A. L. Reed as chairman and Otto Juettner as secretary, both of Cincinnati.[18] They urged the preservation of "anything and everything pertaining to medicine and medical men": books, journals, manuscripts, photographs, letters, and catalogues.

The running battle that had been going on between editors I. C. Chase and F. E. Daniel came to a climax in Galveston. This battle had begun when the Association had decided to establish its own journal. Dr. Daniel, in repeated editorials in his *Texas Medical Journal,* attacked the management and policy of the *Texas State Journal of Medicine.*[19] The controversy dealt with the question of proper advertisements and brought Editor Simmons of the *Journal of the American Medical Association* in for castigation, along with Dr. Chase. With admirable forbearance, Dr. Chase for the most part was content to ignore the situation. At Galveston, Dr. Daniel tried to air his presumed grievances before the general meeting of the Association but was repeatedly ruled out of order. The general membership had come to realize and appreciate what the Association and the *Journal* had accomplished and were inclined to discount the vociferous but poorly grounded onslaughts of Dr. G. Frank Lydston on the national medical level and of Daniel in Texas.

Dr. Charles H. Mayo and Dr. Isadore Dyer should be singled out from the several guests at this Galveston meeting. Dr. Dyer came as a fraternal delegate from the Louisiana Medical Society and addressed the Association on "Skin Diseases and the Public." Dr. Mayo was the first of a long line of speakers who were to come to Texas from the Mayo Clinic. His address on "Goiter with the Surgical Treatment of Hyperthyroidism" was, said the editor of the *Journal,* "an occasion to be long remembered."

"The Doctor's Duty as a Public Educator" was the subject of President Cummings' address. In developing a more enlightened public sentiment in matters of public health and preventive medicine, the medical profession would have to furnish intelligent and

[18] Reed had been president of the American Medical Association in 1901. Juettner is remembered as the author of *Daniel Drake and His Followers* (Cincinnati, 1909).
[19] *Texas Medical Journal,* XXIV (1928–29), 424–28, 515–20.

fearless leadership. The average layman was unversed in these subjects but was willing to learn. No one had a better opportunity to teach him than the doctor. The average layman, for instance, didn't know the difference between patent medicines and proprietary medicines. The difference, as Dr. Cummings saw it, was this: "The patent medicine vendor uses the distinguished Congressman and the lay press, the proprietaries use the doctor and the medical press to reach the people."

Up to this time, specific remedies for diseases were practically nonexistent. Indeed, there was much to uphold Osler's therapeutic nihilism of which Dr. J. N. Mendenhall had complained at the last meeting. So the paper by Dr. J. C. Erwin, of McKinney, "Report of Ten Cases of Epidemic Meningitis, Treated with Flexner's Anti-Meningitis Serum," was significant. It so happened that the Tarrant County Medical Society was co-operating with the Rockefeller Institute for Medical Research in the use of Flexner's serum and had a supply on hand. Early in January, 1909, Dr. Erwin had treated three cases of meningitis in one family, and all had died. In seven other cases, the diagnosis had been made by lumbar puncture, a little-used procedure at the time. The serum was administered, and five patients recovered. In the two fatal cases, the specific serum was given rather late.

Dallas was chosen over Amarillo and Marlin to entertain the Association in 1910. Dr. W. B. Russ was elected president without opposition. He was thirty-five years old, the youngest man ever to serve as president. His service as one of the architects of reorganization, the first chairman of the Board of Councilors, and chairman of the Committee on Public Health and Legislation secured his election. Chosen to serve with him as vice-presidents were C. M. Alexander, of Coleman; J. W. Largent, of McKinney; and W. W. Wardlaw, of Plainview.

The Society of Ex-Presidents of the State Medical Association of Texas was organized at Galveston with Dr. D. R. Wallace, of Waco, as president and Dr. Taylor Hudson, of Belton, as secretary. It was agreed that meetings would be held each year in conjunction with the state association, and for forty-four years this agreement has been kept. This society, under the leadership of Dr. Frank Paschal, showed an early interest in the history of the state association.

At the Galveston meeting, Dr. Chase asked to be relieved of his duties as editor of the *Texas State Journal of Medicine*. The Board of Trustees, authorized to choose his successor, took no official action. The Association in session could well have said that the unprecedented progress since reorganization could be credited more to the work of Dr. Chase than to any other factor. Of course, the contributions of many others played important parts. But month in and month out, it was Dr. Chase's energy and interest, ability to think problems through, tact in dealing with many people of many minds, and wise foresight concerning the future of the Association, that assured the success of the organization. These qualities and his achievement in establishing the *Journal*, which early became and has continued to be one of the best of the state journals, marked Dr. Ira C. Chase as a timely leader of Texas medicine. Dr. Holman Taylor was chosen to succeed Dr. Chase at a salary of $1,800 a year. In addition, he was to receive the income from 25 per cent of all new advertising above twenty-six pages. In the opinion of Dr. Chase, he was the best qualified man in the state for the position. Dr. Taylor moved to Fort Worth, where, over a period of nearly forty years, he served intelligently and efficiently as editor.

XV

Uneasy Tranquillity, 1910–14

FROM THE ELECTION of Governor O. B. Colquitt in 1910 to the impeachment of Governor James E. Ferguson in 1917 and beyond, Texas experienced some radical changes. Serious crop reverses from 1911 to 1916 became a part of the general business depression of that era. Cotton in 1914 sold for less than eight cents a pound. Repeated revolutions in Mexico involving Madero, Huerta, Carranza, and Pancho Villa reflected themselves as acts of lawlessness along the Rio Grande, so that the United States was forced to seize Vera Cruz and to send a punitive expedition into Northern Mexico under General John J. Pershing. The impeachment and conviction of Governor Ferguson, based primarily on his highhanded interference in University of Texas affairs and backed legally by his inability to distinguish state funds from his own, came within a few months of the entry of the United States into World War I.

The State Medical Association of Texas in 1910 came back to Dallas for the fifth time. As in 1874, 1886, 1895, and 1902, the attendance was the highest up to that time. This year it reached eight hundred. This excess in attendance was doubtless partly due to geographic location and concentration of medical population. Also the enthusiasm of the local medical profession was a factor; with two more than friendly rivals in control, Dr. John O. McReynolds as chairman of the Committee on Arrangements for the third time and Dr. E. H. Cary giving one of the welcoming addresses, success was a foregone conclusion.

Realizing that the meetings of the Association had become cum-

272

bersome because of its size and success, President Russ recommended that a committee on credentials and several other committees be appointed early in each session and that many of the details previously coming before the House of Delegates be handled by these committees. He touched on the financial problems of the Board of Medical Examiners, which had become quite controversial.

The monetary worries of this board had become acute. A special meeting of all groups concerned had been held at Fort Worth, and a patched-up arrangement had been agreed on. The members of the board were to contribute a part of what they received, toward employing an attorney. The minor schools offered about one hundred dollars each, and the trustees of the Association were to bring the amount up to one thousand dollars. At this special meeting, Dr. S. C. Red felt that such an arrangement was ill advised; he, as a trustee, "looked upon the fund in the treasury as a sum to be spent for the elevation of the medical profession, the providing of a permanent home for *The Journal,* of a State medical reference library, and other purposes to advance general professional interests. It might be we find ourselves required to spend something in this crisis, but in fact he and the doctors of his district considered it a misappropriation of funds to spend the doctors' money to enforce State laws."

In his recommendations to the House of Delegates, President Russ counseled a middle course. The Association should lend assistance in prosecuting violators of the Medical Practice Act; however, in cases "in which the integrity of the law is not called into question, the task, I think, should not be undertaken by the State Medical Association." The reaction of Dr. J. D. Osborn, president of the Board of Medical Examiners, was more disturbing. He felt that the board, a creature of the Association, had been treated like a step-child. He saw no reason for the Board of Trustees to abrogate the decision of the House of Delegates to allow two thousand dollars to be given to the Board of Medical Examiners. Further doubt and indecision were cast on this phase of the board's work by the attorney general when he reaffirmed his ruling that the state was in no way bound to assume financial responsibility for defending suits against the board. The upshot of the matter was that no final decision was made. However, about one thousand dollars was donated by the county societies. This did not mean that the important phases of the board's work did not continue; they did, and very acceptably. Great assistance was given to the board by J. N. Wilkerson, of Fort Worth, who without compensation had acted during the past year as general counsel for the Association. Further aid was supplied to the board by the Flexner report, made in 1910, in which the condition of the Texas medical schools was plainly stated and frankly criticized.[1] The Texas schools came in for criticism also from the Council on Medical Education of the American Medical Association.[2] In the report, only one, the University of Texas, was in Class A; three other schools were placed in Class B. Dr. N. P. Colwell, secretary of the council, had this to say about the situation in Texas: "Since the passage of the present practice act medical conditions in Texas seem to me to be very satisfactory; indeed, in comparison with most other States, I am accustomed to refer to it as ideal."[3]

Secretary-editor Chase made his final report at this meeting. He spoke with "parental pride" of the accomplishments of the Association during his six years of service: establishment of a journal, revision of the constitution, passage of the Medical Practice Act, the creation of the Board of Health, great increase in membership, and a solid financial status. He entertained a feeling of alarm that the ugly head of politics was more and more being raised in the election of officers. He favored a return to the use of a nominating committee. The plan of nominating candidates from the floor lent itself to "exchanging of influence to secure various offices" and resulted in the election of indifferent and inefficient officers. He closed his report by saying: "I wish to express my love and gratitude to those

[1] Abraham Flexner, *Medical Education in the United States and Canada* (Boston, 1910), 309–12.

[2] The complexity of medical education in Texas was reflected in the existence of nine medical schools in Dallas alone between 1900 and 1910: University of Dallas (later changed to Baylor University College of Medicine), Dallas Medical College, Physio-Medical College of Texas, Bell's Medical College (later changed to College of Physicians and Surgeons of Dallas), Southwestern University Medical Department (later changed to Southern Methodist University Medical Department), Eclectic Medical and Surgical University, University of Medicine and Surgery, Dallas Post-Graduate Medical School and Hospital, and Gate City Medical College.—Samuel Wood Geiser, *Medical Education in Dallas, 1900–1910* (Dallas, 1952), 6.

[3] Records made at the medical schools in Texas have been altogether worthy through the years: in 1925, 60 graduates from the University of Texas passed their state board examinations and none failed; from Baylor, the figures were 28 and 0. In 1940, the respective figures were 99 and 4, and 79 and 11; in 1951, the figures were 103 and 4, and 77 and 0. At Southwestern in 1951, 67 passed and none failed.

whose warm friendship has cheered my work and warmed the chills of hostile criticism. To such, our modest achievements are largely due. In laying down my work, I have the keenest pleasure in turning my editorial duties over to a capable, fearless, upright and unselfish successor, and my personal friend as well, in whose hands I have confidence that the present standards will be maintained and the work carried to a still greater success."

Dr. Chase's retirement from office was marked by the presentation of a watch, the gift of his many friends, by Dr. S. R. Burroughs, of Buffalo, who said: "We are about to give up a most valuable servant, one who has served us long and well in a most difficult position, and one who has suffered criticism patiently and kindly from many of those whom he would serve." The Board of Trustees likewise expressed appreciation of the "splendid service" and "rare devotion" which Dr. Chase had brought to the many vexing problems of his office. A dissenting opinion was expressed by Editor F. E. Daniel. With ungracious delight, he wrote: "He had a tempestuous voyage and few tears will be shed over his departure." [4]

In the matter of politics, the Board of Councilors felt that the practice of "honoring" members with office when no particular fitness existed was to be severely condemned. And the Committee on Reports of Officers and Committees, headed by Dr. Bacon Saunders, said that "the Association should select for its officers such of its members as have demonstrated their worth by their endeavors in the field of scientific or organized medicine, rather than such as have been active principally in their own behalf." This committee endorsed Dr. Chase's suggestion that the Association re-establish the committee method of nominating its officers. Despite these recommendations, however, the House of Delegates refused to make the change.

Dr. W. B. Russ, in his presidential address, stressed the significance of the Association's attainments since reorganization. Modestly, he said nothing of his part in these attainments. "Not a single law asked for since our reorganization," he said, "has failed to pass." But the battle was not yet won; ceaseless vigilance must be continued against the same desperately active enemies: the patent and proprietary medicine interests, medical journals that accepted advertisements from this group, opponents of the national Pure Food and Drug Law, low-grade medical schools, the many "isms" of medi-

[4] *Texas Medical Journal*, XXV (1909–10), 431.

cine, blatant quackery, and those chronically inclined brethren who were "agin" the Association on general principles, believing perhaps that a membership fee of two dollars was excessive. This address was printed not only in the *Texas State Journal of Medicine* but also in the June 11 issue of the *Journal of the American Medical Association*, where it attracted wide attention and favorable comment. Especially noted was his sharp attack on Governor Campbell for vetoing the tuberculosis sanatorium bill and crippling the Board of Health Law.

Many of the papers read at Dallas reflected medical progress. Dr. Bacon Saunders, talking on cancer, emphasized early diagnosis and early surgical treatment as the only hope. The first symposium to be heard before the Association was in the Section on Pathology on the subject of human and bovine tuberculosis. Participants were Drs. William S. Carter, James J. Terrill, and William R. Howard. Dr. Carter epitomized the discussion by urging pasteurization of all milk. This should be done, he thought, "by the individual consumer rather than trust to the uncertain pasteurization by dairymen."

Specific therapy was again exciting the interest of Texas doctors. This time it was the treatment of syphilis. Paul Ehrlich had just made a report on salvarsan or "606" and had hailed it as the long-sought *therapia sterilisans magna:* "One injection utterly destroys all spirochetes, but is harmless to the animal tissues." Four years before, August von Wassermann had published his sero-diagnostic test for syphilis. Editorials in the *Journal* and a paper, "Treatment of Syphilis with Ehrlich Hata Salvarsan ("606")," by Dr. M. W. Colgin, of Waco, kept the subject actively before the profession of Texas. The possibilities of the combination of such a test and such a treatment induced Dr. B. F. Stout, of San Antonio, to go to Berlin and study for two months with two of Wassermann's associates, Drs. Julius Citron and Paul Fleischmann. The crusading enthusiasm of Ehrlich had spilled over to his associates and from them to their students, so that Dr. Stout was prompted to ask, "Why spend all this time and money in learning how to do the test and how to give the treatment, when syphilis will be extinct in a short time?" Dr. Stout came back to San Antonio and made the first Wassermann tests in Texas and administered the first salvarsan in southwest Texas, at a cost of twenty-five dollars each. Editorially, the *Journal* announced in January, 1911, that Dr. J. H. Black, of Dallas, and

276

Dr. Stout were prepared to make the test. One month later, W. G. Cook and J. D. Covert, of Fort Worth; M. W. Colgin and W. S. Witte, of Waco; and Wilson's Sanitarium, at Memphis, were added to the list.

The administration of "606" was terrifically painful. Both the preparation and the administration of the solution for intravenous use were a careful ritual, in reach of laboratory directors and a few other doctors only. Often a general anesthetic was required. This meant that intravenous therapy was as new as intraspinal therapy had been a year or two earlier. The unrestrained enthusiasm over "606" could not see beyond to the many failures, a good many fatalities, and the necrotic abscesses in multiple glutei muscles of hopeful patients. But withal, this drug was one of the early steps in the chemo-therapy of syphilis.

Amarillo was selected over Waco for the 1911 session. Chosen to preside over that meeting was Dr. John T. Moore, of Houston, and with him, as vice-presidents, Dr. A. D. McReynolds, of Stamford, and Dr. W. A. Harper, of Austin. Apparently, this year only two were elected.

President Moore, characterized by Dr. F. E. Daniel as "perhaps the most popular man in the society," called the House of Delegates to order at the Grand Opera House in Amarillo on May 9, 1911. Editor Holman Taylor, with hardly warranted enthusiasm, spoke of this Amarillo gathering as one "long to be remembered." The reception, the entertainment—especially the barbecue in picturesque Palo Duro Canyon—and other features may have justified his words of praise. However, only 298 members registered, the smallest number since reorganization. The population of the city was 15,000, and the membership of the Potter County Medical Society was only 32. The loyalty of this small group was attested by the registration of all but 3 of them. But this could not make up for absent essayists and a "distressingly small" attendance at the scientific sections.

Present as guests were Drs. W. D. Haggard, of Nashville; G. H. Noble, of Atlanta; A. H. Andrews and Dean Lewis, of Chicago; and several others. Among the exhibitors were the McDermott Instrument Company, Kirby Instrument Company, Horlick's Malted Milk, and the W. B. Saunders Company. This was the first time the name of George Henser was to appear as Saunders' representative. He had formerly represented D. Appleton and Company and had only recently become a partner of J. A. Majors. For a period of forty-five years he was a welcome figure at these meetings and in the offices of doctors all over Texas.

President Moore made recommendations concerning the establishment of a permanent home for the Association, the enforcement of public health laws, closer organic union with the American Medical Association, and medical defense. As to the permanent home, he rightly felt that accumulation of funds from dues and donations could mean that realization would come in the "rather distant future." Medical defense by the state association, which today is accepted as a matter of fact, was first brought up by Dr. Moore. He realized that the general membership was not yet ready for it, since it would have to be paid for. In reality, the members could not have fully realized how much they were already getting for two dollars per year.

Reporting as secretary-editor for the first time, Dr. Holman Taylor manifested a trait that was to be a part of him for all his years of fine service, namely profuse detail and many words. It was his desire here and always to deal with his subjects in full particular and in all clarity; and as a result, he too often buried his facts in a mass of details which the ordinary reader may not care to push aside. The historian, however, can well be thankful that he set things down fully and clearly. In this report, he explored every facet of the Association's activities and manifested complete familiarity with the many phases of its work. He noted a slight falling-off in membership, which he attributed to lessened zeal on the part of the councilors, just as his predecessor had done two years before. This gave Dr. Taylor a chance to emphasize the great importance of electing councilors who would accept their assignments seriously. With this in view—and again agreeing with Dr. Ira C. Chase—he advocated resumption of nominations by committee.

The Legislative Committee reported a successful year: the enactment by the Legislature of a sanitary code and the appropriation of funds for building a tuberculosis sanatorium and a leprosarium. The latter was never built because no site for its location was available. The establishment of a hospital for indigent consumptives had received the constant attention of a committee headed by Dr. Frank Paschal, and now after eleven years, $140,000 had been appropriated for this hospital, which was built at Carlsbad and received its first patients in 1912. With patience not too much in keeping with his restless spirit, Dr. Paschal concluded his final report: "We must not be too quick to criticize or condemn, but let us be thankful that an intelligent Legislature, and a liberal and humane Governor have considered the necessity for an institution for the care of indigent consumptives."

Dr. O. L. Norsworthy and his Committee on Enforcement of Public Health Laws were back again with their financial woes multiplied. During the year, they had raised less than $300 to pay Attorney Wilkerson. The committee's report showed that its members had obligated themselves to the amount of several hundred dollars. This meant that the hat had to be passed again. The repetition of these unhappy experiences crowded on the membership the realization that the state association was not a law-enforcement agency and that even if it were, it could not stand the ever mounting cost of such enforcement. What, it was logically asked, about the damage suits against the Association to the amount of $65,000? In short, it was becoming increasingly obvious that law enforcement was everybody's business and not that of a professional association.

It will be recalled that Dr. John T. Moore had served exceptionally well as chairman of the Committee on Medical Education. He fittingly chose as the subject of his presidential address, "The Obligation of the State to the People in Securing by Education and Licensure, Good Doctors." He reviewed the work of the Council on Medical Education of the American Medical Association, with which he had been closely associated. He praised the work of Abraham Flexner, to whom part credit was given for reducing the number of medical schools in the United States from 166 to 129. He called attention to the action of the Johns Hopkins Medical School which put the heads of all departments on a full-time teaching basis. "We are coming to understand," he said, "that men who are teaching medicine must give their entire time to teaching, rather than to use their position to increase their prestige." Higher premedical requirements were essential: "I am firmly convinced that most of the states should require a full four years' course in a recognized high school and one year of college work, before permitting persons to enter upon the study of medicine." Better medical schools, better-prepared medical students, and alert boards of medical examiners would ensure to the people of Texas the type of doctors they deserved. "These are the ideals for which we stand, and thus you may see why the State Medical Association of Texas and its leaders have labored in season and out of season to secure a Medical Practice Act, a Sanitarium for Tuberculosis, and a State Board of Health, and all of the other agencies for good which are really of less personal interest to the doctor than to the people."

When Dr. Moore was speaking of better doctors, he may have had in mind one Penn B. Thornton, who had filed against him and some of his associates a suit for $25,000. Dr. Thornton alleged "that he is the owner of a sanitarium located near the one conducted by Dr. John T. Moore and run in opposition to the plaintiff; that he is not a member of any county medical society and never expects to be, as he is not in sympathy with its objects. He says he has a large and lucrative practice, and that Dr. Moore being a newcomer from Galveston, has not established a large nor a lucrative practice and is very desirous of doing so."

Chosen to preside over the 1912 session at Waco were David R. Fly, of Amarillo, and, as vice-presidents, A. L. Lincecum, of El Campo; J. H. McCracken, of Mineral Wells; and W. H. Freeman, of Lockney. When Dr. Fly died of tuberculosis on November 29, the Board of Councilors appointed Dr. McCracken to the unexpired term.

At Amarillo, the House of Delegates appointed a Transportation Committee to arrange for a special train to the American Medical Association meeting at Los Angeles. The round-trip fare of fifty dollars permitted return by way of San Francisco, Salt Lake City, Denver, and Colorado Springs. Forty-eight Texas physicians made the trip, which was altogether enjoyable. Recognition came to the delegation when Drs. W. B. Russ and Joe Becton were made chairman and secretary of a newly created Section on Hospitals.

About this time the National League for Medical Freedom had become active in Texas. This organization, with its high-sounding name, was a direct outgrowth of the curbs which had been placed on patent and proprietary medicines and was sponsored by the manufacturers of these products. It moved into Texas, opening headquarters in an expensive suite of rooms in the Wilson Building in Dallas. Money was spent lavishly on pamphlets and newspaper space to discredit the doctor and his works. The science of medicine, it was claimed, had never benefited the world in all its history. The lowered mortality in diphtheria, for instance, was attributed to the fact that the doctor had such faith in antitoxin that he allowed the patient to get well unimpeded by other treatment. Dr. Holman Taylor made this editorial comment on the activities of this organization: "Good men, to whom the world owes an unpaid debt of gratitude, are maligned; self-evident facts are denied without reason; history is sadly and maliciously warped; the American Medical Association is libelously misrepresented in its every effort, and venom of the most unaccountably vicious sort is evident throughout."

This league, which was about as sincere as its modern counterparts, was particularly violent in its attacks on Dr. Harvey W. Wiley, chief of the Bureau of Chemistry, United States Department of Agriculture, who had given the patent-medicine interests many difficulties. Likewise, it aroused nation-wide opposition to the Owen bill, which would have created a national department of health represented in the President's cabinet by a physician. The league made little headway in Texas. Many nonmedical groups favored passage of the Owen bill, and several Texas newspapers, notably the *Dallas News,* strongly supported the bill. The medical profession of Texas agreed with the Bexar County Medical Society when it reminded its congressman that "the so-called 'National League of Medical Freedom' is the source of this opposition, and that it is composed of the men who are personally interested in the adulteration of food and the manufacture of patent medicines." Nevertheless, the Owen bill did not pass. The need for it is as great today as it was in 1911.

The Waco Auditorium was the gathering place of the 1912 session of the state association. The dates were May 7, 8, and 9. The registration of 734 members was nearly double that of the last meeting. Secretary Taylor's report showed a membership of 2,924, a loss of 38 during the year. This and other slight losses were not seriously significant and were probably attributable to difficult economic conditions. While Association membership did not increase in proportion to the state's population, its growth was progressive and healthy. By 1913, the membership exceeded 3,000, and at no time did it again fall below that figure. Healthy growth, too, was reflected in a cash balance of $11,256.24.

Important reports were made by the Committee on Medical Defense, the Legislative Committee, and the Committee on Care and Treatment of the Insane. The last two committees were emphatic in their assertion that remedial legislation should be passed in the interest of "the unfortunate insane of this State, and that without delay." It was recommended that the name "Insane Asylum" be changed to "State Hospital." Dr. F. S. White, of San Antonio, pointed out for his Committee on Care and Treatment of the Insane that in 1860 there were 60 patients in the State Lunatic Asylum, or 1 to 1,007 of population. In 1890, the figure was 1,113, or 1 to 2,008. By 1910, when one million dollars was spent for their care, there were 4,808 patients in the several institutions, or 1 to 810 of population. This meant that progress was being made, but it was not enough; county jails were still filled with the insane.

The increasing prevalence of mental ailments was the cause of much concern to the medical profession. Numerous articles and editorials in the medical journals of the state were stressing the seriousness of the situation. There were advocates of vasectomy to stop "this over-production of undesirables." [5] A bill for the sterilization of defectives in state institutions passed the House of Representatives by a large majority but was killed in the Senate by a vote of 14 to 11. One writer published an article entitled "Medicine in 1950—A Look Forward." With apt prevision, he looked into the future and predicted the control of infectious diseases through the medium of specific remedies. In connection with mental disease, his prescience was uncanny:

As fevers and acute and infectious diseases become less and less, those of a neurotic trend will become more numerous. It will be an age of wits, of education, of sharp competition. Few will care to do rough work and most everybody will want to direct his work through a system. It will be a time and age that will draw heavily on our gray matter and our neurons. Mental ailments, neuroses and psychoses will be abundant, although symptoms will be named and classified differently than now. Such terms as "hysteria," "neurasthenia," "psychasthenia," "anorexia," and many others will be obsolete. The sanitariums and hospitals will nearly all be for people suffering from broken and decrepit nerves and the ailments incident to old age. It will be the endeavor of psychiatrists to cure people before they become insane, instead of after.[6]

Dr. O. L. Norsworthy and his committee continued to plug away at the problem of enforcement of public health laws. Being without funds, they made no great effort to prosecute medical quacks and

[5] *Ibid.*, XXVI (1910–11), 390–91.
[6] W. T. Marrs, *ibid.*, XXVII (1911–12), 330–36.

impostors. Their main project for the year was mailing a questionnaire to 150 secretaries of local societies in an attempt to enumerate the irregulars, "including masseurs, magnetic healers and snake charmers." From 50 replies, 421 offenders were located. Ten of these had been convicted of illegal practice. The problem was complicated by this discovery: of the district attorneys and district judges interrogated, 3 believed in quackery, 1 believed in Christian Science, 35 upheld legitimate medicine, and 13 were unconcerned.

This year the memorial services, which at times had become somewhat perfunctory, recalled the deaths of three former presidents: Drs. D. R. Wallace, H. C. Ghent, and David R. Fly; and the death of Dr. Minnie C. Archer, the first woman member of the State Medical Association of Texas. The eulogy was delivered by Dr. T. T. Jackson, one of the natural orators of the Association. In memory of these and twenty-eight other deceased members, Jackson said:

They have passed out beyond—across the divide, across the river where we cannot see and concerning which we know nothing. Of their religion, of their belief, of what they thought of the great hereafter, we know not; but we do know that they had a religion, a religion of relief, a religion that carried peace and solace as gentle and tender as the dews of the May morning to the sick and to the afflicted. I do not know and I do not care what they thought or what they believed—I believe that any man and that any woman can afford to take the chance in the hereafter that any good doctor has to take, whether they believed in this or that or the other. We know, you know, we all know that like Abou Ben Adhem, they loved their fellowman, and he who loves his fellowman cannot be forgotten by the world.

The scientific papers covered the usual subjects, along with one that appeared for the first time—pellagra. Papers on the subject were presented by Dr. K. H. Beall and Dr. M. M. Smith. The first reported death in Texas from this disease occurred in 1907. By 1911, the number of deaths from it had increased to 276; the subject had become of serious importance. Dr. Beall, one of the best clinicians of his day and treasurer of the Association from 1923 to his death, in 1946, summarized the few then known facts about the disease. He studied the various possible causes, but the mystifying and unknown factor of diet deficiency evaded him and all others of his era. He leaned to the parasitic theory of causation and, from analogy, predicted that the parasite was a protozoan.

Prominent guests of the session were Drs. C. Jeff Miller, of New Orleans; George W. Crile, of Cleveland; and Oscar Dowling, state health officer of Louisiana. Their subjects were "Indications for and Technique of Vaginal Caesarian Section," "Anociassociation— A New Principle in Operative Surgery," and "Public Sanitation."

In his presidential address, Dr. J. H. McCracken recalled the tremendous strides medicine had made in the conquest of transmissible diseases in a short quarter-century: diphtheria, malaria, yellow fever, typhoid fever, smallpox, hydrophobia, and tuberculosis—all these had yielded more or less completely. "It should be evident to any reasoning creature," he declared, "since Medical Science has plucked so much from the vegetable and mineral kingdom and from mechanical appliances, admittedly of such powerful assistance to our flesh, blood and bone in its struggles against disease, that it was in the original divine plan that we should have doctors, skilled in the science of the application of these aids to nature, to relieve the suffering, restore the sick and even where restoration is not possible, to stand over them in their passing hours, mitigating their agonies, alleviating their pain, and tenderly, affectionately, easing them into that life boat that transports them into that great beyond, where our mission ceases." Thus he summarized the mission of the physician. He closed by referring to the tomb of Sir Christopher Wren, in St. Paul's Cathedral: "No imposing monument was erected to him, but at his head a simple marble shaft was placed and upon it were inscribed these words, 'If you seek this man's monument look about you.' So I say of our noble profession, if you would seek the deeds it has done you have only to look about you at the habitable, healthy world and consider the lengthened span of life resulting from its devotion to science and humanity."

The Association decided to meet next in San Antonio, with its officers John S. Turner, of Dallas, president; and J. W. Overton, of Sweetwater; O. L. Norsworthy, of Houston; and J. B. McKnight, of Brady, vice-presidents.

In 1913 the State Medical Association of Texas met in San Antonio for the fifth time, previous sessions having been in 1878, 1889, 1899, and 1903. The general session was held in the Travis Park Methodist Church, while the House of Delegates met in the ballroom of the St. Anthony Hotel. A registered membership of 629 was on hand. The Bexar County Medical Society made a particularly good showing: out of its 150 members, all but 5 registered and 3 of these lived out of the city.

The chief result of the Legislative Committee's efforts for the year was the enactment by the Legislature of a bill authorizing the establishment of county hospitals. The act provided for voting of bonds by a county, a group of counties, or a county and a city for the purpose of hospital construction. In the discussion, it was brought out that the erection and equipment of a good hospital could not cost "much less than $1000.00 a bed," and cost of maintenance could be figured at $1.25 a day per patient.

At the memorial services, Dr. Frank Paschal made an unusual presentation. After Dr. J. J. Terrill had spoken feelingly of the thirty-four who had passed on—including Drs. Ferdinand Herff and J. F. Y. Paine—Paschal reminded his auditors that the thirty-five doctors who incorporated the Texas Medical Association in 1853 had been practically forgotten. "They left their mark upon the pages of the history of Texas, and blazed the way and today this great profession is following in their footsteps. We have let them die without memory, but from now on they should and must live amongst us." [7]

This long-delayed eulogy was followed the next day by a full discussion in the House of Delegates on the origin of the Association. Its history had been much neglected. In 1911, however, on motion of Dr. J. D. Osborn, seconded by Dr. J. E. Gilchrist, the Association recommended that writing "the history of the Texas State Medical Association from its incipiency to present date be allotted to members of this Society as follows: From 1853 to 1869, Dr. Frank Paschal of San Antonio; from 1869 to 1879, Dr. H. W. Cummings of Hearne; from 1879 to 1889, Dr. W. B. Russ of San Antonio; from 1889 to 1899, Dr. John T. Moore of Houston; from 1899 to 1909, Dr. G. B. Foscue of Waco." Nothing, however, had come of these assignments.

At the 1912 meeting of past presidents, Dr. W. B. Russ moved that Dr. Frank Paschal be requested to write a history of the Association. Paschal set to work at once and unearthed the 1853 charter and other information which has already been discussed at its proper chronological place in this history. Presenting the charter to the 1913 House of Delegates, Dr. Paschal said: "I have here a document

[7] Henry P. Howard, of Dallas, the last of this worthy group, died six months later at the age of eighty-four.

285

which shows that fifty years before the State Medical Association of Texas shaped its present plan of operations, these men were proceeding along identically the same line." Dr. Paschal's enthusiasm and sense of historical responsibility are suggested by his remarks on presenting to this same body a copy of Dr. George Cupples' presidential address of 1853—

the first annual address delivered by the President of the State Medical Association of Texas. I attach a copy ... to this report as I do not care for the original to get out of my hands until the State Medical Association of Texas has a permanent home in which such valuable documents can be kept. Indeed I believe that it would be a great loss to the profession, and of the State Medical Association of Texas to be transferred from hand to hand and from pillar to post. I prize the evidences of the splendid efforts of those who have gone before us too highly to take chances of having their labors lost or destroyed. I deem them so sacred that I keep those documents in my possession carefully guarded in safe under lock and key.

Dr. Paschal was fully aware of the value of his contribution. He proposed that "to perpetuate the organization from 1853 ... the seal that was then used take the place of the present seal." He urged the delegates, "By all means let us insist that our State Medical Association was organized in 1853 instead of 1869. Let us even 'give honor to whom honor is due' on this late date." [8]

The result of Paschal's report was the unanimous adoption of the following resolution:

WHEREAS, The State Medical Association of Texas at the present time dates its origin from the year 1869 and counts its annual meetings from that date, and

WHEREAS, There is documentary evidence that it was in fact organized in 1853, and incorporated by the State Legislature during the same year, and

WHEREAS, It has been shown that the Association was reorganized in 1869, and operated on the charter of 1853 until it was rechartered in 1889; therefore, be it

Resolved, That we acknowledge that organized medicine had its beginning in this State as early as 1853, and that it was at that time operated on precisely the same plan that it is operating upon today, the county society being the unit and the county and district societies owing

[8] For Paschal's further contribution to the history of the Association, see below, Chapter 17.

allegiance to the State Association, and in order that it shall be apparent that this is the case, be it further

Resolved, That the Board of Trustees and all other officers concerned, be and they are hereby instructed from this day to date the organization of the State Association 1853 instead of 1869, and to so number and date all annual sessions and transactions.

About this time, open surgical season was declared on the colon. Out of all proportion to its anatomical and physiological importance, the colon was emphasized as the source of multiple human ills. The work of Elie Metchnikoff, of Russia, and Sir Arbuthnot Lane, of England, stood in the forefront. "Auto-intoxication" was the word of the hour, and the colon was the scapegoat. "That the colon is functionless is the least of its evils; it is furthermore a menace to health—a murderer," wrote Dr. R. S. Loving, of Dallas, in a paper on "Colon Disharmony." Bulgarian buttermilk, as advocated by Metchnikoff, was the only medical treatment of promise. The next step was the short-circuiting operation, and, failing this, a complete colectomy, following Lane, was advocated. A paper entitled "Colonic Membranes" was presented by Dr. J. H. McLean, of Fort Worth. This unprovoked and unjustified attack on the colon in Texas seemed to center in north Texas. The next year it assumed symposiac proportions. A "Symposium on Alimentary Toxaemia" was offered by Drs. H. G. Wolcott, J. M. Martin, and A. B. Small, all of Dallas. There was much talk of Lane's kink, membranous pericolitis, and Jackson's veil, and all these had to be corrected. This surgical spree, despite formidable mortality rates, lasted several years and then gradually petered out.

Dr. John S. Turner, in his presidential address, took a backward glance at the medical history of Texas. He paid tribute to those doctors who had made conspicuous contributions to the profession and to Texas: James Long, Branch T. Archer, Jack Shackelford, William Mottley, James H. Starr, William E. Throckmorton, Anson Jones, and Ashbel Smith. On two points concerning the Association, he erred: the organizational meeting on January 17, 1853, was held in Austin and not in San Antonio; and the Association did not meet regularly up to the time of the Civil War.[9] Coming down to a later period, Dr. Turner spoke of George Cupples, Ferdinand Herff, R. M. Gano, D. R. Wallace, T. D. Wooten, J. Larendon,

[9] See above, Chapter 5.

R. M. Swearingen, and many others. And finally, he applied a group of alliterative adjectives to men of his own generation: the "Peerless and Pacific Paschal"; the "Dignified and Indefatigable Daniel"; the "Generous and Gracious Gilcreest"; the "Formidable but Friendly Foscue"; the "Crafty and Cautious Cantrell"; the "Capable and Careful Cummings"; the "Restless, Rustling Russ"; the "Magnanimous and Methodical Moore"; the "Faithful, the Fond, the Loved and Lamented Fly"; and the "Manly and Modest Mc-Cracken."

Two of the guest speakers at the 1913 meeting—Dr. William F. Braasch, of Rochester, Minnesota, and Dr. Carroll W. Allen, of New Orleans—had their papers published in the *Journal*. Their subjects were "Infections of the Renal Pelvis and Ureter" and "Local Anesthesia, with Special Reference to Hernia." Another distinguished visitor to Texas this year was Colonel William C. Gorgas, fresh from his sanitary conquest of Panama and soon to become surgeon-general of the United States Army. He spoke to the graduating class at Galveston on "The Part Doctors Have Taken in the Construction of the Panama Canal." He gave full credit to the work of Laveran, Manson, Ross, and Reed. He modestly minimized his own work, when in fact he was already being acclaimed as the world's greatest sanitarian. He touched on the French failure to dig the canal when 22,000 workmen lost their lives between 1880 and 1889. He told how his own efforts were hampered, the work delayed, and many lives needlessly sacrificed by meddling politicians in Washington and ignorant officials on the Isthmus. "In all this period of panic and oppression, not a single doctor or nurse or other member of the Sanitary Department showed the white feather or deserted their post," Gorgas testified. The results of his work were epoch-making: French mortality in 1889 was 250 per 1,000; American mortality in 1913 was 4 per 1,000.[10]

Dr. Marvin L. Graves was honored with the presidency for the year 1914, being elected without opposition. Associated with him as vice-presidents were J. H. Foster, Houston; J. C. Anderson, Plainview; and R. R. White, Temple. W. L. Allison, of Fort Worth, succeeded C. A. Smith, of Texarkana, as treasurer. The invitation to meet in Houston was accepted.

[10] A comprehensive and readable biography of this really great doctor has been published recently: John M. Gibson, *Physician to the World, the Life of General William C. Gorgas* (Durham, North Carolina, 1950).

288

With his usual dignity, Dr. Graves called the forty-eighth annual session of the Association to order in the Auditorium at Houston on May 12, 1914.[11] After a number of welcoming addresses, the House of Delegates got down to business, with not too much business to transact. There were the usual officers' and chairmen's reports, all pointing up the healthy condition of the Association. There was much discussion on revision of the constitution and bylaws, on the evils of fee-splitting, fees for life insurance examinations, and many other things.

One important accomplishment of the Houston meeting was the adoption of a plan of medical defense. This plan had first been broached by President Moore in 1911, and committees had been working on it since. The first chairman of the Committee on Medical Defense was Dr. Walter Shropshire, of Yoakum; he was succeeded by Dr. W. D. Jones, of Dallas. President Graves, in his annual message, gave both sides of the argument on the subject but made no recommendation. However, Dr. Jones and his committee brought in a highly favorable report. They submitted data from nineteen other state associations, which refuted all the arguments about loss of membership, burdensome dues, etc. After full discussion, the constitution and bylaws were amended to create a Council on Medical Defense, the vote being 52 to 12. The council was to be composed of three members, nominated by the retiring president and elected by the House of Delegates. By the change in the bylaws, the Association obligated itself to investigate and defend its members against claims of malpractice and to pay all costs of defense, but would not accept responsibility for judgments obtained against them. The dues were increased from two to three dollars to take care of the anticipated expense. The personnel of the first council was as follows: W. D. Jones, Dallas, chairman; E. F. Cooke, Houston; and W. A. King, San Antonio.

Dr. C. E. Cantrell, reporting as Texas representative of the National Council of Medical Education, brought up the subject of medical schools in Texas. The University of Texas had continued to be in Class A and Baylor in Class B. The medical departments of Texas Christian University and Southern Methodist University

[11] The session of the previous year was designated as the forty-fifth. The discrepancy was explained, in a footnote to the *Transactions,* on the basis of "documentary proof that the Association was organized in 1853 instead of 1869." Thus the two meetings of 1853 were finally added to the count.

had been placed in Class C by the Council on Medical Education of the American Medical Association. During the year, however, the rating of both schools was raised to Class B.

Chicago and New Orleans furnished important guests at the Houston meeting. The Windy City sent Drs. Truman Brophy and A. R. Craig, the latter being secretary of the American Medical Association. From the Crescent City came Drs. C. Jeff Miller, S. M. D. Clark, Isadore Dyer, E. Denegree Martin, and C. C. Bass.

In his presidential address, "The Spirit of Modern Medicine," Dr. Graves pointed to the great advances which the medical profession had made in the control of communicable diseases. Some of these had come to be considered as a stigma on a community: smallpox, malaria, typhoid fever, tuberculosis, and hookworm disease. He stressed the increasing incidence of mental diseases and quoted Karl Pearson in defense of the doctrine of sterilization of the unfit: "The humane tendency of modern medicine to preserve the diseased and deformed is not only detrimental to the human species, but can only be set off or obviated by preventing these defectives from breeding their kind." He reminded his hearers, many of whom were laymen, of the notable contributions of the medical profession in a generation: asepsis, anesthesia, serology, immunity, experimental and synthetic therapeutics, and public hygiene. For the new century that had dawned, he predicted that the shibboleth would be preventive medicine. "This," he concluded, "is the Spirit of Modern Medicine. Is it too much to expect and to request that the great lay public, vitally interested in every movement for the public health, shall join hands and hearts and brains with this unselfish public-spirited body of medical men in all their laudable efforts for the public good?"

Before adjournment a resolution was introduced by Dr. E. H. Cary inviting the Southern Medical Association to hold its 1915 meeting in Dallas. The resolution was adopted. Dr. Cary promised that Texas membership in the Southern Association would be increased to one thousand by the time of the meeting. This promise was exceeded by one hundred, thus giving Texas the largest state membership in the association, an ascendancy which has been maintained to the present time.

Fort Worth furnished the place of the next meeting and two of the new officers. These were Frank D. Boyd, president, and K. H.

Beall, vice-president. Other vice-presidents were L. H. Reeves, of Decatur, and G. T. Hall, of Big Spring.

The *Texas State Journal of Medicine* continued to play its important part in the cause of the profession in Texas. It was literally the mouthpiece of the Association. Year in and year out, only about one-fourth of the members attended the annual session; thus the *Journal* was the principal contact with the majority of the membership. The *Journal* was not, however, without its critics, notably the editor of the *Texas Medical Journal*. As an offset, Editor Holman Taylor received a pat on the back from Dr. Olin West, then editor of the *Journal of the Tennessee State Medical Association:* "You can't make a touchdown without getting a few knocks on your way to the goal line. As I see it, the score is already 40–0 in favor of the *Texas Journal.* Stiff upper lip, all sphincters tight, head up, tail over the dash-board—shoot 'em a few! Your *Journal* is all right. It does not suffer by any comparison that is fair to make." The May, 1914, issue (the first in Volume X) of the *Journal* contained the first change in its format. The twenty-two state journals had formed a co-operative advertising bureau so that uniformity in page size became desirable. The new page was six by nine inches, three-fourths of an inch smaller than the original. The *Journal* had stabilized itself in page numbers at from 450 to 500 pages per year, and here it remained for about ten years, with the exception of Volume XI, which reached 678 pages.

XVI

Preparation and War, 1915–19

As early as 1915, the state and national medical profession felt the threat of war that was hanging over the country and began seriously and sensibly to do something about it. The sinking of the British ship *Lusitania* by a German submarine in May, 1915, causing the loss of more than 100 American lives, provoked the introduction of a resolution in the Texas Senate calling on Congress to sever relations with Germany. The resolution failed: we were "too proud to fight." Once war was declared, however, Texas doctors entered the conflict with all their energy and resources. Texas became one vast training area for soldiers, sailors, and airmen. Texans to the number of 197,389 saw service in the three branches. Fourteen hundred and ninety-four doctors were in uniform and 26 failed to return.

The Fort Worth session, in advance notices, promised much. A committee, headed by Dr. I. C. Chase, vouched for entertainers from Chicago, moving pictures, and a menu served in the Coliseum running "the gastronomic gamut from roast turkey, lamb and suckling pig through salad, ice cream, coffee to a car load of fresh fruit, 2,000 bottles of grape juice—and other juices, and a fresh importation of new cigars and cigarettes from Cuba." And the pre-session promises were fulfilled. The meeting called to order in the First Baptist Church showed a registration of 1,008, the highest up to that time. One thousand and eight registrations out of 3,365 members made an interesting comparison with 2,307 registrations out of a membership of 42,956 at the American Medical Association

292

session at San Francisco in the same year: 1 out of 3 as compared with 1 out of 19.

Scientific exhibits were utilized for the first time. Pathological specimens, X-ray plates, and original research material were on display. And the commercial exhibits had increased to twenty-five. Guests at this session were many and prominent: Dr. Oscar Dowling, of New Orleans, and Dr. Seale Harris, of Birmingham, president and secretary of the Southern Medical Association, respectively; Dr. Albert H. Andrews and Joseph C. Beck, of Chicago; Dr. F. W. Parham, of New Orleans; Dr. Edward H. Skinner, of Kansas City; Dr. William C. MacCarty, of Rochester; Dr. Frank A. Jones, of Memphis; and several others. These were not all guest speakers, and in those days the guest speakers paid their own expenses. The work of the House of Delegates was perceptibly accelerated by the recently adopted committee system. All matters of importance were given over to committees which would thrash out their varying assignments and then report the findings and recommendations to the house, thus saving much time and trouble.

The first thorough revision of the constitution and bylaws was effected at this meeting. For several years, a capable and conscientious committee—Marvin L. Graves, chairman, Holman Taylor, Frank Paschal, A. C. Scott, and I. C. Chase—had been working on suggested changes. In 1914, this committee was replaced by one under the chairmanship of John S. Turner, which made a few minor changes; but the revision was largely the work of the Graves committee. Mention has already been made of the Council on Medical Defense. The Committee on Legislation and Public Policy was elevated to the position of a council and called the Council on Legislation and Public Instruction. Members of both these councils were to have seats in the House of Delegates, with the right to vote. Provision was made for the election each year of a president-elect instead of a president and, in an effort to nullify the interference of politics, it was provided that any person known to have solicited votes for any office should become ineligible for that office. A closer union with subordinate societies was assured by a requirement that district societies must confine their membership to members of their respective component county societies. And there were many minor changes in the constitution and bylaws, such as closer screening of commercial exhibits, selection of time and place of meeting, and control of social functions.

The revised constitution and bylaws avoided any reference to fee-splitting. It was content to lean on the principles of medical ethics of the American Medical Association, hoping that this long-present evil could be handled better on the county level. But the problem was the object of much concern and the occasion of much confusion. The entire subject was reviewed in four pages of editorials in the May, 1915, issue of the *Journal*. But no satisfactory solution was offered; none could be offered. Through the years, few attempts at enforcing morality by legislation have ever succeeded. To paraphrase William Alexander Percy, as long as man continues to be "that amazing alloy of the hellish and the divine," fee-splitting and kindred evils will be with us.

In 1915 the scientific sections were heavy with two subjects, cancer and pellagra. H. R. Dudgeon, of Waco, presented the "Report of the Committee on the Study of Cancer." Then William C. Mac-Carty, of Rochester, spoke on "Facts Versus Speculation in the Professional Conception of Cancer"; A. C. Scott, of Temple, on "What the Public Should Know about Cancer"; M. Smith, of Oklahoma City, on "Off Symptoms of Cancer of the Stomach"; R. R. White, of Temple, on "The Cautery in the Treatment of Cancer"; J. S. McCelvey, of Temple, on "Cancer of the Colon"; and Henry Hartman, of Temple, on "Some Rather Unusual Carcinomatous Growths." In addition, as part of an educational campaign, the *Journal* published the "Articles of Faith Concerning Cancer," by William S. Bainbridge, of New York City.

As for pellagra, papers by Seale Harris, of Birmingham, K. H. Beall, of Fort Worth, W. F. Thomson, of Beaumont, and C. A. Smith, of Texarkana, presented various aspects and opinions of the disease. For the most part, the cause of the ailment was as obscure as that of cancer. As good an observer as Dr. Beall was forced to conclude that "there are at present no known scientific facts" as to the nature of the disease, even though he was familiar with the work of Dr. J. Goldberger, of the United States Public Health Service, which was soon accepted as partial proof that pellagra is a protein-deficiency disease. Since Goldberger used a diet high in protein, it is likely that an adequate amount of vitamin B was being supplied. Editorially, Dr. Holman Taylor accepted proteins in the diet as the therapeutic solution to this baffling problem.

One feature of the 1915 session which had begun in other years was very successful this year, the public-health meeting held on the evening prior to the opening meeting. Dr. W. C. Rucker, assistant surgeon-general of the United States Public Health Service, spoke to a crowded house at the First Baptist Church on "The Geographic Distribution of Plague and Its Menace to the United States." These meetings were designed for the purpose of instructing the public in matters of health and medicine.

President Frank D. Boyd addressed the Association on a historical subject, as had many of his predecessors: "Development of American Medicine." Since Dr. Fielding H. Garrison's *History of Medicine* had come out two years before, Boyd's problem was greatly simplified, and he wove into a readable presentation such names as Rush, Shippen, McDowell, Physic, Sims, Mott, and many others. After touching on the origin of the American Medical Association, he traced the development and accomplishments of the Texas Medical Association.

For the next year's meeting place, only Galveston, "the second greatest seaport of the United States and the playground of Texas," was considered. Following the change in the constitution, a president and a president-elect were elected, these being George H. Moody, of San Antonio, and J. M. Inge, of Denton. The vice-presidents were O. H. Sholars, of Orange; J. L. Burgess, of Waco; and G. T. Thomas, of Amarillo.

In the way of general news of the profession, a dictaphone was installed in the secretary's office and a charter was issued to a chiropractic college in San Antonio, this when the practice of chiropractic transgressed the Medical Practice Act. A package library was established by the *Journal,* and the Texas Surgical Society held its first meeting at San Antonio, under the presidency of Dr. James E. Thompson, with eighteen of the twenty charter members present. From Dr. C. L. McClellan, of Farwell, came a letter to the *Journal* describing "A Simple Radiator and Garage Warmer." A detailed description was given of this early effort to deal with cold weather in the Panhandle, in which a sheet-iron hood and an oil lamp were utilized. Hazard of fire and accumulation of soot were the inventor's main problems. "In order to meet this contingency," he said, "I have placed the heater I use in a pan of water, and I have found that a very small flame will meet all requirements; the lower the flame the less likely it is that the stove will smoke. I have also resorted to the expediency of suspending an ordinary fire cracker above the stove so that should the flames get too high the consequent explosion will give me due warning. I find that this simple device will keep the water in my radiator warm for twelve hours on about 6 cents, and it is a joy to be able to step into a warm garage and crank a car without the usual cold engine difficulties."

The general meetings of the 1916 session were held in the auditorium of the Galveston City Hall, while the House of Delegates convened in the ballroom of the Tremont Hotel. Two new phases of insurance came before the House of Delegates for the first time. These were spoken of jointly as social insurance and were the outgrowth of an aroused social conscience that was abroad in state and nation. Three years before, a Workmen's Compensation Act had been passed by the Legislature. Dr. A. P. Howard brought to the delegates' attention the inadequacy and inequity of this act. Medical and hospital bills were paid for one week only. The injured employee began to receive compensation at the end of the first week. The editor of the *Journal* summarized the law thus: "The law is fine for the employer, good for the working man, questionable for the doctor and disastrous to the lawyer." This act was later amended so that the doctor's interest was better protected.

With the workingman protected from accident, the next logical step was to protect him from disease and then to extend these benefits to the general population. Dr. A. C. Scott, as secretary of the Board of Councilors, gave a complete report on health insurance. He was thoroughly familiar with the medical situation in England which had cut incomes of the physicians of that country considerably. He realized, too, that the English approach to the problem was similar to the condemned custom of contract practice. Already, two insurance companies in Dallas and one in Waco were selling health insurance, but the Board of Councilors could not recommend their methods. Dr. Scott's advice was to go slow and wait. Unfortunately, thinking on this subject on a national level was thoroughly beclouded. The *Texas State Journal of Medicine* for October, 1916, contained an article by Dr. Alexander Lambert, of New York, "Provision for Medical Care under Health Insurance." Dr. Lambert, who was chairman of the Committee on Social Insurance of the American Medical Association, had made several reports in which he opposed voluntary sickness insurance and gave tacit approval to a compulsory plan. Under such conditions, the House of Delegates could only authorize the proper committees to

296

continue their studies, fully conscious of the fact that some form of health insurance was inevitable.

The affairs of the *Journal* were aired by the editor, Holman Taylor. A deficit of $1,157.19 for the year was cause for alarm. Doubling of paper costs, with comparable increase in other expenses, reflected the war in Europe, a situation discussed in repeated editorials. There was talk of decreasing the number of pages or increasing the advertising income: "more money or less journal." Another suggestion was to increase the dues so that the *Journal* would receive $.50 or $1.00 more per member. As one thumbs through the pages year after year, it is really astounding how fine a journal was provided for the allotted $1.00 per member. This predicament of the *Texas State Journal of Medicine* was similar to that faced by practically all medical journals. The *Southern Medical Journal*, for instance, experienced a deficit of $6,500.00. And the American Medical Association in this same year showed an operating loss, though it was due in part to the high cost of defending the association in the Wine of Cardui libel suit. The editor's suggestion about increasing the dues was carried out the following year. The increase to $5.00, $2.00 of which was to go to the *Journal*, made the dues the same as they had been before the reorganization in 1903.

The Council on Legislation and Public Instruction repeated its continuing opposition to any legislation giving recognition to optometrists or chiropractors with their "nefarious practices." These two groups were incessant in their demands on the Legislature and were gaining favor with that body. The council could point with satisfaction to the passage of wholesome legislation with which the medical profession was directly concerned: passage of the Vital Statistics Bill, requiring registration of births and deaths, establishment of a training school for the adult blind, and appropriation of $400,000.00 for a new mental hospital and $70,000.00 for rural health work. In the interests of public health the Legislature passed one bill which the council did not sponsor; it limited the speed of automobiles to fifteen miles an hour on city streets, eighteen miles in the country, and six miles on "obscure roads."

At this Galveston meeting, the women medical students at the university invited all the women physicians of Texas to an open house at University Hall. The *Journal* printed forty-nine names of women eligible to accept this invitation. As further emphasis on the distaff side of medicine in Texas in 1916, the *Texas Medical Journal* devoted its April number to "a demonstration of what women are doing in the practice of medicine in this country and especially in Texas." The contributors were Mary Harper, of San Antonio; Ethel L. Heard and Violet H. Keiller, of Galveston; Minnie L. Maffett, of Dallas; and Ray K. Daily and Martha A. Wood, of Houston.

Pellagra continued to find a frequent place on the program. Typhus fever in Texas had become a real menace. Papers on this subject by Dr. C. C. Pierce, senior surgeon, United States Public Health Service, and Dr. H. L. McNeil, whose promising career at the University of Texas was cut short by his untimely death, presented the pertinent facts known at that time. And forty cases of poliomyelitis had appeared in Texas during three summer months of 1916. As to typhus, sixty-eight cases had occurred in counties near the Rio Grande. These cases were obviously traceable to Mexico, where the disease was epidemic in certain areas. The United States Public Health Service had set up delousing stations along the north bank of the river as a method of control. But it must have been recognized then, as now, that nothing short of converting the historical Rio Bravo into one vast dipping vat would contain the menace. Control was effected only after widespread and continued rat extermination was carried out.

Dr. Donald C. Balfour, of Rochester, was the most prominent guest speaker. He presented his subject, "Cancer of the Uterus: Its Surgical Treatment," in a short but complete paper. Education of the public, early recognition, and early removal were stressed. Thorough excision was his treatment in early and moderate cases. Radium, then comparatively new in therapy, might convert an advanced malignancy into an operable case.

Dr. George H. Moody, capable psychiatrist that he was, chose "Mental Health" as the subject of his presidential address. As causes of mental disease, he cited heredity, syphilis, alcoholism, drug addiction, crime, and poverty. He could not agree with Dr. Oliver Wendell Holmes when he said that "our brains are seventy-year clocks. The Angel of Life winds them up once for all, then closes the case, and gives the key into the hands of the Angel of the Resurrection." He felt that each individual had an obligation to shield himself against "the inroads of imprudence, immorality and excesses." Good mental habits, compounded of "thoughtfulness, serenity, courage, composure and generosity," were Moody's *summum bonum.*

E. H. Cary, of Dallas, became the president-elect. Elected as vice-presidents were Robert Y. Lacy, of Pittsburg; Charles R. Johnson, of Gainesville; and W. L. Brown, of El Paso. Although Dallas had entertained 1,200 members of the Southern Medical Association the previous year at a cost of $6,000, she asked for and received the 1917 session of the state association.

After two years of war in Europe, medical preparedness in the United States was making headway. In Texas, a committee was formed in April, 1916, the two chief purposes being to encourage membership in the Army Medical Reserve Corps and to co-operate with the Red Cross in the formation of base hospital units. The members of the committee were W. B. Russ, of San Antonio; J. M. Inge, of Denton; Holman Taylor, of Fort Worth; John L. Burgess, of Waco; John W. Burns, of Cuero; H. M. Doolittle, of Dallas; John H. Foster, of Houston; F. C. Beall, of Fort Worth; and J. E. Thompson, of Galveston. Editor Taylor of the *Journal* was already in service as a major and commander of the First Battalion of the Third Texas Infantry. Dr. Ira C. Chase, former editor, volunteered to step into Taylor's shoes during his absence.

As an echo of the war, there was complaint that the doctor's dollar was buying less and less. Cost of living had increased 20 per cent in a year, whereas in the preceding twenty years the increase had been only 50 per cent. It was pointed out that carpenters and painters received larger incomes than doctors. In calling attention to the fact that "the country is increasing in wealth by leaps and bounds and leaving the doctor behind," Chase urged the county societies to take whatever action was necessary to insure an adequate income to the physicians of Texas.

In keeping with the stepped-up war in Europe, the *Journal* of May, 1917, editorially announced the Dallas meeting in this fashion:

WAR ON GERM-LAND
DALLAS ÜBER ALLES!
General Advance Begins May 7th

Opening Gun
10:30 A.M., May 8th
Three Days Siege

"Dallas above all" proved true in the matter of attendance. Registrations reached 1,204—the highest to that time—more than one-third of the total membership of 3,435. This was the highest figure until the Association returned to Dallas in 1935, when the attendance reached 1,336. This is not to imply that all Dallas sessions have been fully attended; in 1921 attendance fell to 736, but stringent times played a part that year.

Since the United States had entered the World War one month before, much time at the 1917 meeting was spent on medical preparation for war. The usual reports and the usual discussions were heard. Secretary Chase pointed out the top-heaviness of the program. In 1915, 1916, and 1917, the number of papers was 118, 136, and 109, respectively. The reading of so many papers, distributed rather unevenly through eight sections, was creating a confusing situation. He felt that the House of Delegates should lessen the number of papers or the number of sections. The inclusion of these papers in the *Journal* was increasing the burden of the publication. Relief in both directions could have been obtained by complying strictly with the newly revised bylaws, which required that all papers must previously have been read before the author's county society, that papers published elsewhere could not be published in the *Journal,* and that the Board of Trustees had the authority to abstract or refuse publication of any paper.

Dr. Frank Paschal reported as chairman of the Committee on Collection and Preservation of Records and not only urged the collection and preservation of historical data but also advised strongly that the collected material then available be used. "Posterity will write our history, we should write of those who anteceded us, and in so doing let it be a history written by writers of talent and supervised by a committee that will give it a guarantee of accuracy, truthfulness and beauty. Such a history would be replete in noble deeds, unselfish acts, and bespeak the talent and character of Texas physicians, a history that would add luster to that of the Lone Star State, whose history is scarcely equaled and not excelled by the history of any State in the Union."

Dr. Chase, in editorial retrospect, saw this Dallas meeting as "rather sombre, thoughtful, earnest and patriotic." It could not have been otherwise; the United States was in the war and was unprepared medically as well as in other ways. Preparedness was the keyword in all walks of life. One wheatless meal a day and one

300

R. B. ANDERSON
Assistant Secretary and Editor
1927–1947

Headquarters of the
Texas Medical Association
1935–1948
1404 W. El Paso St.
Fort Worth

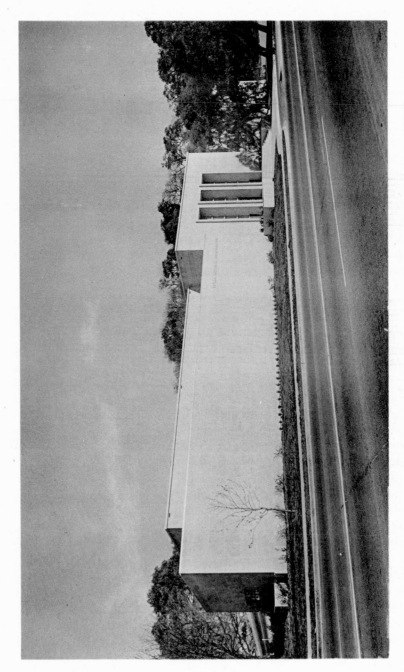

New home of the Texas Medical Association, 19th and Lamar, Austin. Dedicated 1952

meatless day a week became common practice. The surgeon-general of the army was asking for 25,000 and later 45,000 doctors to meet the needs of an ever expanding army and navy. Estimates of the number of doctors to be recruited in Texas ranged from 200 to 800. The doctors of Texas were kept informed through the *Journal;* and the Texas Committee on Medical Preparedness, headed by Dr. W. B. Russ, was given ample time at the Dallas session to present all the facts. In an effort to mobilize the medical resources of the state, this committee had sent out blanks on which were to be recorded the pertinent facts about all doctors under fifty-five years of age. Thus, the availability and eligibility of the state's physicians would be quickly and completely put on record. The annual salary of most medical officers was $2,000, the pay of a first lieutenant. A captain received $2,400 and a major $3,000. Editorially, it was explained: "Are you physically incapacitated or so burdened with dependents, institutions or debts that $2,000 a year will not meet absolute needs? If so you are excused."

The process of medical preparedness in Texas was not without its confusing aspects. Washington was lagging behind and adding to the confusion. Many physicians closed their offices and waited for weeks for the expected call. There was talk of drafting physicians; some state committees approved the idea. But despite the handicaps and delays that beset a democracy, 791 Texas doctors were commissioned in the Medical Officers Reserve Corps, National Guard, Regular Army, and Navy. This was 14.5 per cent of all licensed physicians of the state and 20 per cent of the membership of the State Medical Association of Texas. The Baylor University Base Hospital Unit, under command of Major M. E. Lott, received orders on February 19, 1918, to report to Fort McPherson, Georgia, prior to service in France.

The House of Delegates passed one resolution of serious importance. Governor Ferguson had vetoed the University of Texas appropriation bill and was demanding the dismissal of President Robert E. Vinson and several members of the faculty, including Dr. James E. Thompson. The ostensible reason was that Dr. Thompson was not an American citizen. The editor of the *Journal* interpreted this as "an unwarranted, illegal and dangerous attempt by political influences to interfere with the affairs of education." The resolution petitioned the Board of Regents to "retain the invaluable services of Dr. J. E. Thompson." The impeachment of

Governor Ferguson settled the problem, and the appointment of Dr. Ralph Steiner, of Austin, to the board gave recognition to the medical profession. Dr. Thompson became an American citizen shortly thereafter.

President Inge addressed the session on "The Relation of Medical Organization to the Commonwealth." He surveyed the success of medicine in general and of the Texas association in particular. He directed attention to medical conditions in war-torn Europe, where for the first time deaths from disease were less than those from battle. In this war, he classed medical officers with military officers. But, he argued, the results of service of the two groups were not to be compared. Did not the world place Napoleon over Pasteur, Wellington over Lister, Von Moltke over Koch? Fields of carnage and desolated ruins are the harvest of the one; whereas, healthy habitations of the happy and prosperous crown the work of the other. "These victories over the most insidious enemies of mankind," he said, "were won in silent laboratories, in bloodless battles with disease. These patriots had no selfish motives in accomplishing what they did. Their lives were consecrated to the task of unraveling the mysteries of disease. Great is victory without bloodshed."

May 14–16 was the date chosen for the next session, which was to be held in San Antonio. S. P. Rice, of Marlin, was named president-elect over James E. Thompson. Vice-presidents elected were W. P. Coyle, of Orange; F. V. Painter, of Corpus Christi; and T. K. Proctor, of Sulphur Springs.

Much discussed in 1917 and 1918 were woman suffrage and prohibition. Editor Chase disapproved of the former on idealistic grounds, at the same time admitting that women would vote for better schools, better-paid teachers, and better hospitals. As for prohibition, "We are glad," he said, "that the curse of America, the saloon, the distillers' agent to push high alcoholic beverages on and into the public, is gone. May it stay gone! The end is the same in all lands and countries, light refreshing beverages sold and taken with food." Texas cellars, he estimated, were well stocked with "three million dollars worth of booze," money which might have gone into Liberty Bonds.

The *Journal* gave editorial commendation to a doctor-hero during this war year. Although Texas doctors had already proved themselves in World War I, it chose a hero not of contemporary vintage, Dr. John Pickering. This centenarian was presented as the last survivor of the Battle of San Jacinto, as having been present when Santa Anna was captured and brought before Sam Houston, as having been with Dr. Anson Jones during the battle. Some of these claims are perhaps dubious; for instance, Alfonso Steele, who died in 1911, is considered to be the last survivor of San Jacinto. But that is unimportant. Here was a doctor-hero, who at the age of one hundred still felt capable of hitching up "Dolly" and driving over the needle-covered roads of Angelina County to treat the old residents who preferred his services, even though he charged no fees.

In anticipation, Editor Chase presented the 1918 San Antonio session as centered about "commodious hotels, intense military spirit, great army training camps, 70,000 soldiers, Base Hospital of the Southern Department, aviation fields, the Alamo." After the event, he recorded it as having been pervaded by "an air of thoughtfulness, deep feeling, quietude and unity." Patriotism and preparedness could well have been included in this characterization. On Monday night, a patriotic rally was held at Travis Park Methodist Church, at which General Henry T. Allen, commander of the Ninetieth Division, and Dr. Franklin H. Martin, member of the Council of National Defense, were the speakers. Attendance at the session of only 665 was in part due to the fact that more than 900 Texas doctors were in uniform—a fact which explains also the absence of 43 out of 84 scheduled speakers. Dr. Martin made two appearances at the session. Along with President Cary and many others, he stressed medical mobilization: the army and navy needed doctors; England and France needed doctors; and the United States was the logical source of supply.

Emphasis was given to the patriotic and military spirit of the session by several papers and demonstrations. Colonel J. B. Clayton, commanding medical officer of the South, spoke on "The Functions and Duties of the Army Medical Officer." Dr. R. W. Knox, of Houston, gave a paper on "How We Treat Wounds Today." Clinics and operations were conducted at the Fort Sam Houston Base Hospital, designed to demonstrate the latest surgical techniques, intravenous therapy, utilizing X-ray, and the treatment of wounds.

This war brought great advances in the treatment of wounds. Improvement came largely from two sources: debridement and the Carrel-Dakin method of irrigation. The practice of cutting away all dead or injured tissue from war wounds came into wide use.[1] This, combined with the complicated Carrel-Dakin system of wound irrigation with hypochlorite solutions, no doubt controlled many infections and thus saved many lives. From our viewpoint, some of the derived benefits came from leaving the wounds unsutured.

Some indirect results of the war were in evidence at the San Antonio meeting. Most county societies were paying the state dues of their members in service. The Board of Trustees voted to invest $5,000.00 in Liberty Bonds; this they could easily afford, since the treasury contained $25,284.55. And, for the first time in a generation, absorbed as the Association was in the war effort, no amendment to the constitution and bylaws was introduced. The *Texas State Journal of Medicine* was almost a casualty of war. Its editor was in uniform. Cost of labor, paper, and publishing had doubled in two years. The number of pages was reduced, and the War Industries Board demanded the use of very light paper. And yet the *Journal* continued its career of usefulness to the profession. Fortunate it was that Dr. I. C. Chase was able to replace Dr. Holman Taylor.

Dr. Frank Paschal, as chairman of the Committee on Collection and Preservation of Records, requested that the presidential address of Dr. George Cupples be reprinted. This was done.[2] Editor Chase commented, with much understatement, that after sixty-five years the address sparkled with "a diction and a style which would place him among the most scholarly of our own favored time—an address which will rarely be matched and perhaps never exceeded in our State Association."

Dr. Cary, in addressing the session as president, logically centered his theme about the war. He digressed, however, long enough to refer to socialism and paternalism, predicting that some form of government health insurance was sure to come and urging the med-

---

[1] This procedure was accepted as a product of World War I. In reality, Dominique Jean Larrey had described it over a century before: "Desault taught us, that in order to change the nature of wounds, from a complicated to a simple state, it was not sufficient to make the part bleed: that in order to attain this end, it was necessary to remove the bruised edges with a sharp knife. . . . In my campaigns in Germany and Egypt, I have profited by the practical lessons of this man of genius, who appears to have here made one of the most important discoveries in surgery."—*Memoirs of Military Surgery and Campaigns of the French Armies* (Baltimore, 1814), I, 19.

[2] *Texas State Journal of Medicine*, XIV (1918–19), 7–13.

304

ical profession to be prepared to meet or modify it. War in its essence, he thought, was both cruel and wasteful. But out of war there might come benefits to be carried over into peacetime pursuits. Dr. Cary reviewed the story of war from the time of Xenophon and showed how military skill and medical science had developed along parallel lines. He saw the acme of military and medical science in the career of Surgeon-General Gorgas. He next turned to the war then in progress and dwelt on the important parts played by the medical profession of Texas. Hopefully, he concluded: "When this war has ended, the ideals of our nation will be cherished by a mighty throng in every nation, in a world made safe for democracy. Can it not be said, now and forever that the medical profession was great in sacrifice, eager in service, unflinching in duty, their patriotism unquestioned?"

The Woman's Auxiliary to the State Medical Association of Texas was organized at this San Antonio session. In May, 1917, the first county auxiliary in the United States was formed at Dallas. Similar organizations sprang up at Waco and San Antonio within a few months. Mrs. E. H. Cary was elected the first president of the state auxiliary. For the title of her presidential address she chose "Woman—the Ideal Maker of Nations." The *Journal* for April, 1919, set down the objects of the Woman's Auxiliary: "To extend the aims of the medical profession, through the wives of the doctors, to the various women's organizations which look to advance in health and education; to assist in entertainment at State, district and county society meetings; to promote acquaintanceship among doctors' families, that local unity and harmony may be increased." In 1922, the auxiliary idea was carried to the American Medical Association, then meeting in St. Louis. Mrs. S. C. Red, president of the Texas organization, presented the plan, which was readily accepted and which has thrived beyond all expectations. Mrs. Red became the first president of the national organization.

Present as prominent guest speakers at the San Antonio meeting were Dr. A. J. Ochsner, of Chicago; Dr. R. C. Lynch, of New Orleans; and Dr. V. C. Hunt, of Rochester.

Dr. R. W. Knox, of Houston, was chosen president-elect. The vice-presidents were H. L. Moore, Dallas; H. F. Connally, Waco; and L. J. Manhoff, Aransas Pass. Waco was selected as the place of the next meeting.

During the year, the American Medical Association published

its report on the medical schools of the country. The previous year, the Fort Worth Medical College had 5.9 per cent failures on state board examinations; Baylor had 5.3 per cent; and the University of Texas had no failures. This was a good showing when compared with the average of 7.2 per cent failures from Class A medical colleges. The Fort Worth Medical College, which was the medical department of Texas Christian University, closed its doors this year. The pressures of war, increased costs, decreased registrations, and higher educational requirements were the assigned reasons. This left only the University of Texas and Baylor.

Two events of much significance occurred late in 1918: the influenza epidemic, a tragedy; and the armistice with Germany, a presumed blessing. From 30 to 40 per cent of the population were attacked by influenza, and from 5 to 10 per cent of these died. Particularly hard hit were the doctors. In the November issue of the *Texas State Journal of Medicine,* there were notices of 11 deaths, all due to influenza. In two issues of the *Journal of the American Medical Association,* there were 255 notices, and influenza was the cause of death in at least 154. Churches, schools, and theaters were closed. Business was at a standstill. The war effort faltered.

As for the armistice, it was no more than the word implied—a temporary cessation of hostilities. With hopeful hearts but with short memories, we hailed the end of the war that was to have made the world safe for democracy. The world was not safe, but the armistice was most welcome, nonetheless. To the soldier-doctors of Texas, it meant a return, sooner or later, to their homes and to civilian practice.

The fifty-third annual session of the Association convened in the Waco Auditorium on May 13, 1919. Waco had entertained the Association forty-six years before, and sessions had been held in this middle-Texas city, which had meant so much to organized medicine, in 1881, 1891, 1900, and 1912. Waco had furnished six presidents to the Association—more than any other city. Houston and San Antonio could claim five; Austin, Fort Worth, and Galveston, three each; strangely, only two had come from Dallas.

The Waco sessions were designated editorially as a victory meeting, "commemorating the greatest victory the world has ever known and the most necessary." Dr. T. T. Jackson, who was to become president-elect, addressed the general session on "The Part of the

Texas Doctor in the War." He reminded his hearers that the Texas doctors in uniform were following the example of their forebears in the Mexican, Civil, and Spanish-American wars—always on a volunteer basis, never by drafting or compulsion. He said that 929 Texas doctors were in the Army, Navy, or National Guard.[3] This number represented approximately one-third of the members of the Association, or one-fifth of all Texas doctors. In addition, 750 medical men served on various medical boards. Within six months of the armistice, fortunately, about half of the Texas medical officers had been discharged.

But words of praise were not enough. Depression and discouragement were the lot of too many of these soldier-doctors of Texas. Some were disabled; some returned to find their practices dissipated or taken over by others; all had difficult adjustments to make in an era of changed medical and economic conditions. This situation was well presented by Dr. A. C. Scott in his report to the 1919 session as chairman of the Board of Councilors. He realized the difficulties of the problem. The suggestions he made centered about factors of gratitude and fair play. Dissensions, he thought, had best be quickly resolved, for on the medical horizon was becoming visible the specter of socialized medicine such as had already overtaken England.

The subject of venereal diseases was emphasized at this session. As far back as 1903, the American Medical Association had had a committee to study this question, but little progress had been made. The impact of war was needed to accent the importance of the subject. Prudery of the public and the doctor's desire to protect his patient kept these diseases in the background. Now, with the coming of war, the public press could call syphilis and gonorrhea by their rightful names. Dr. A. I. Folson, of Dallas, ably headed a committee which made two constructive reports. Frequent and extensive editorials by Dr. Chase kept the profession advised. Surgeon-General Rupert Blue of the United States Public Health Service contributed two articles on the subject to the *Journal*. The need for action was increased by reports from the draft boards of the state. An alarming number of draftees were found to be infected: from San Antonio, 12 per cent; from Dallas, 14 per cent; from Galveston, 15 per cent; from Houston, 17 per cent; and from Fort

[3] The correct total was 1,494, and the armistice prevented the commissioning of 142 more.

Worth, 19 per cent. The upshot of the matter was the passage of laws prohibiting the advertisement of so-called cures, regulating prostitution, making venereal diseases reportable, and giving public-health officials the authority to ferret out the sources of infection, prescribe treatment, and if necessary resort to quarantine. But the principal benefit came about as the result of publicity. These diseases were smoked out into the open, where all could see: they were diseases to be treated and cured, not concealed.

Chairman John T. Moore of the Board of Trustees reviewed the financial status of the Association. He recommended that dues be raised from $5.00 to $10.00. The carpenters paid $24.00 as their dues; certainly the doctors should do half as well. The accumulation of $31,525.99 was to him insignificant. His ambition was to see $200,000.00 to the credit of the Association, so that a permanent home could be built. For the realization of this dream, the profession had to wait thirty-four years. To further strengthen the *Journal*, the trustees authorized the employment of Mr. Ford Alcus, of Fort Worth, on a half-time basis as advertising manager, at a salary of $75.00 per month.

Always at these sessions there were distinguished guests. This year they were Drs. Dean Lewis, of Chicago; Fred H. Albee, of New York; and James T. Case, of Battle Creek.

One persistent group with which the Association had to contend, through its Committee on Optometry Legislation, were the optometrists. Year in and year out for the better part of a decade, the Association had thwarted the efforts of this group to gain recognition for its own board of examiners. Just a few months earlier, the House of Representatives had badly defeated a bill to regulate optometry. As a result of Association activities on this bill, G. H. Aronsfeld, of Galveston, brought suit for $15,000.00 against the Association, alleging injury to his reputation and business. The language used in an editorial in the March, 1919, issue of the *Journal*, which was the real basis of the suit, was not especially severe. However, the Association seemed shy of damage suits. In the *Journal* for April, 1920, there appeared "A Disclaimer," which was in reality an apology more humble than can be readily understood at this distance. Aronsfeld accepted the apology in apparent good faith, but did not fail to utilize it fully in his presidential address before the Texas Optometrical Association.

As published in the *Journal*, the presidential address of Dr. S. P. Rice, "Some Quotations on History of Medicine," is an enigma. On the first page, there are six quotations, properly enclosed in the usual marks and credited to the authors by initials only. Most of these quotations and initials would be unknown to the average medical reader. The last is credited to "E. S." This should have been attributed to Fielding H. Garrison, for it is the opening paragraph of his remarkable chapter on "The Identity of All Forms of Ancient and Primitive Medicine," in his *History of Medicine*. And then the next five pages are taken from Garrison verbatim, word by word, paragraph by paragraph. And at no place in the address is the name of Garrison mentioned. This profundity of knowledge of primitive medicine must have impressed the president's auditors. Charitably, we might reason that the printer ran short of quotation marks. The end of Dr. Rice's address was the end of Dr. Garrison's chapter, except that Rice added this observation of Sir Thomas Clifford Allbutt: "To folk-medicine, doubt is unknown; it brings the peace of security."

The delegation from Mineral Wells came armed with telegrams from the mayor, Rotary Club, and Chamber of Commerce urging that their city be selected for the 1920 session, but Houston was the victor. T. T. Jackson, of San Antonio, was chosen president-elect. The new vice-presidents were George H. Lee, Galveston; Martin E. Taber, Dallas; and W. L. Crosthwaite, Waco. When Jackson died, December 12, 1919, I. C. Chase was elected to complete his term of office.

On the general medical scene, the high cost of living was much to the forefront. Editor Chase advised against hoping that living costs would come down. Everything was going up: food, clothing, rent, drugs, automobiles—everything. Carpenters and brickmasons were receiving $8.00 to $11.00 a day—more than the average doctor was collecting. The only recourse was an increase in charges for services. A McLennan County fee schedule was published as a sample. This society had increased its charge for a visit up to 9 P.M. to $3.50 and its obstetrical fee to $35.00. These figures were suggested as a working basis and not to be considered as a violation of the Sherman Anti-Trust Law.

This year, tragedy struck Dallas and set back diphtheria immunization in Texas and elsewhere. Toxin-antitoxin was just being popularized. It so happened that a lot was sent to Dallas which was fifty times as strong in free diphtheria toxin as it should have been. More than fifty severe reactions were encountered, and there were six deaths. At least fifteen damage suits were brought against H. K. Mulford Company, most of which were settled out of court.

XVII

The Aftermath of War, 1920–24

WITH THE WAR OVER, a new era seemed to have begun. The short-lived depression of 1920 was erased as soon as the wheels of industry were geared to civilian production. There was expansion of business in every direction. Prosperity came to Texas during the "mad decade," and little heed was given to those unwelcome prophets who saw the lean years ahead. Governor Pat M. Neff had this word of warning for the Legislature in 1921: "We are pioneering today amid the rocks and reefs and whirlpools of the most disturbed and uncertain financial ocean the world has ever known. These are testing times. The affairs of men are shifting. Things are abnormal. The world is at a turning-point in civilization."

The Houston meeting of the Association was scheduled for April 22 to 24, about two weeks early. The change was made so that the members could attend the seventy-third session of the American Medical Association at New Orleans from April 26 to 30. Texas doctors to the number of 394 availed themselves of this opportunity.

After an absence of four years, Dr. Holman Taylor was present at this Houston meeting. As secretary-editor, his salary was increased to $5,000. More welcome than this, however, was the opportunity to doff his uniform so that he could again resume the duties which Dr. Chase had ably performed during his absence.

The Committee on Hospital Standardization, which had functioned for two or three years under the chairmanship of Dr. A. C. Scott, reported commendable progress on work done in conjunction with the Council on Medical Education of the American Medical Association. Staff organization and adequate records were stressed.

311

The plan backfired at Amarillo, however; when the staff at St. Anthony's Sanitarium was organized, an osteopathic physician was excluded. The resultant damage suit for $11,000 against eleven members of the Potter County Medical Society was taken seriously by the entire membership. Dr. A. F. Lumpkin took the lead in the fight.[1] Four firms of lawyers were employed at a cost of $3,200, and the suit was won. Dr. Lumpkin brought the matter before the House of Delegates and asked that the state association accept responsibility for half the cost of the suit. After three pages of contradictory discussion, it was agreed to contribute $500.

The Association, through its Council on Legislation and Public Instruction, kept in close touch with political developments in the state and showed no hesitancy in speaking out in behalf of those candidates who were favorable to public health and the general welfare of medicine in Texas. This was election year, and two friends of the medical profession were candidates for governor: B. F. Looney, of Greenville, and Robert E. Thomason, of Dallas. Other candidates were Pat M. Neff and Joseph W. Bailey, former United States senator. A questionnaire sent out by the Dallas County Medical Society, sounding out the attitudes of the candidates, was given wide publicity in the *Journal*. On paper, all the replies were satisfactory. But the McLennan County Society was at odds with Pat Neff, charging general unfriendliness in that he had represented the chiropractors before a Senate committee and had defended a chiropractor in the courts. This, too, was given editorial comment by Dr. Holman Taylor. The influence of the Association in behalf of its known friends, however, was not enough. Neff defeated Bailey in the run-off primary. Any apprehension the profession may have had toward Governor Neff was soon dissipated. The new governor was an invited guest of the Association at its next meeting, and his subsequent words and acts proved him to be in sympathy with the aims and ambitions of legitimate medicine.

The Council on Legislation and Public Instruction was busy in another direction. The Legislature was in session, and the Association was sponsoring some corrective amendments to the Medical Practice Act. In familiar alignment, the Association, the osteopaths, homeopaths and the eclectics were arrayed against the chiropractors, the optometrists, and the Christian Scientists; on the sidelines stood

[1] Lumpkin had gone a long way since he refused to don cap and gown on that graduating night in 1896. See above, Chapter 12, n. 10.

the chiropodists. A bitter fight ended in defeat of the amendments. The committee could take heart in that several worthy public health measures were passed: persons with communicable diseases were forbidden to work as food-handlers, the sanitation of barber shops was safeguarded, and the prophylactic use of silver nitrate in the eyes of the newborn was required.

President R. W. Knox, a surgeon, chose to address the session on "Public Health Education." He surveyed the advances in public health through the years. The surface, however, had hardly been scratched. In substantiation, he pointed to the large number (about one-third) of rejections for military service in World War I because of physical defects. Universal military training for all young men between the ages of eighteen and twenty-one was advocated as one means of correcting this problem. The health of a people, he said, is paramount. "The time is near and in fact now at hand, when the health of a state, city or county, will be a matter of public record and general information, and a high mark will not only speak volumes from a humanitarian standpoint, but will also be of economic value beyond the dreams of the present generation."

With persistence akin to obsession, year after year, Dr. Frank Paschal was on hand to plead the cause of a history of the Association. Facts and figures should be collected and preserved; and the written record should be set down. "In justice to those who have made history we should by some means perpetuate their names and make the record so indelible that time shall not fade nor age erase it from the memory of those who follow." So far he had found no one who would undertake the actual writing. "We do not despair, however, of finding a historian and believe that as Texans have always met conditions and have been able to successfully cope with them, it is only a matter of patience and time." Editorially, the project was commended and encouraged. Two names mentioned as authors were Drs. I. C. Chase and Holman Taylor; and as seen in retrospect, either could have done a splendid job. They could have written the history more accurately and more acceptably than anyone before or after them, for they were there when much of the history was made. Dr. Paschal's persistence resulted in the appropriation of $2,500 in 1923 to be used in collecting historical data of medical significance. He had previously enlisted the interest and co-operation of Dr. Eugene C. Barker, professor of history at the University of Texas. Miss Winnie Allen, archivist of the University, agreed to supervise the undertaking, which was carried out with thoroughness but not to completion. A vast amount of valuable data, from newspaper files and other sources, was discovered and preserved in sixteen bound volumes.[2] Only recently have further funds been allotted to complete this worthy project.

The claim of Dallas to the 1921 session of the Association, so eloquently presented by C. M. Rosser, went uncontested. T. J. Bennett, of Austin, became the new president-elect; and W. S. Miller, of Estelline; W. J. Pollard, of Kaufman; and Walter Shropshire, of Yoakum, became the vice-presidents.

The Medical Department of the University of Texas came in for some criticism in the public press, and there was talk of moving it to some other city. The Legislature appointed a committee to investigate. Since a vote of the people would have been necessary to change the location, nothing came of the investigation except that Galveston was stimulated to give greater local support to the institution.

And to the doctors of Texas of that time, came a new and woeful experience: the filling out of income tax returns. There was much discussion about Forms 1040 and 1040A. But the experiences of that day were not too disagreeable in comparison with those which were to come.

The state association gathered in the City Temple of Dallas for its fifty-fifth annual session. There was more fanfare than usual, more welcoming addresses, more music. The members were obviously more carefree with the war well behind them. Optimism was stimulated by the secretary's report of 3,674 members and by the treasurer's report of a balance of $42,722.93, nearly half of which was in Liberty Bonds.

The Council on Legislation and Public Instruction and the Committee on Optometry Legislation saw their hopes fade in 1921. Strong efforts over a period of several years failed to lessen the growing support for a bill to license optometrists. The bill passed the Legislature by a wide margin. The proponents of the bill aided their cause tremendously by exhibiting large bundles of prescriptions on which rebates had been paid to doctors by optical firms.

[2] This material assisted Paschal to the facts about the founding fathers of the Association which he contributed the year before his death. See above, Chapter 4.

314

Some of the most prominent ophthalmologists of the state were thus involved in this evil practice of modified fee-splitting, a situation which has only recently been corrected, not on a voluntary basis, unfortunately, but by pressure from the federal government.

Another legislative defeat came to the medical profession this year, this time on the federal level. The passage of the Sheppard-Towner Bill amounted to partial socialization of the obstetrical branch of medicine. The fact that the name of Senator Morris Sheppard of Texas appeared on the bill gave it support locally. College professors such as Dr. J. Whitridge Williams, of Johns Hopkins, influenced many legislators in its favor. Logically, the State Medical Association of Texas, which incidentally was not consulted, contended that such matters should be handled on a state and local basis.

With the optometrists legalized, the Council on Legislation did not have to look far to find other claimants for legislative recognition: the chiropractors were becoming very articulate. But their progress was comparatively slow. They received some free publicity when the medical students at the University of Texas protested that the University publication, the *Texan,* was carrying chiropractic advertisements. The *Journal* gave further publicity by publishing the report that veterinary chiropractors were being turned out: now mules could be adjusted as well as men. But this warning was given: "That men, ignorant of the body and its processes, should treat the ailments of men, women and children is apparently a small thing; human life is the only thing involved. But that ignoramuses should trifle with the health of a horse or a hog is an outrage; that is property. If chiropractors are wise they will confine their malpractice to humans; it is safer."

"The Manhood of Medicine" was the title of Dr. Chase's presidential address. The "boyhood of medicine," he said, was that phase of medicine which began in primitive times and extended to the present, in which the effort of the individual doctor was the important factor. This period he considered significant. "There's nothing so cheap," he quoted Abe Martin as saying, "as a good doctor." But the day of individual medical effort was over. Now, co-ordinated action through the media of state, county, and local health organizations had become imperative. The task would not be easy. Public apathy and ignorance must be overcome. "You can shake the average layman's teeth out," Chase said, "before you can get the health nonsense out of his head. He still believes boils come from the blood, teething gives babies fever and fits, and that he catches influenza from a raised window." But the urge of necessity and the promised rewards made the task worthy of all effort. Professional activity and an aroused public would bring accomplishment. "Then shall we lay at the feet of humanity our gifts of social medicine, more precious than our personal ministrations. Then shall we have come into the Manhood of Medicine."

Most elections in the Association were quiet affairs; at least, on the surface everything was sweetness and light. In most instances, there probably had been some horse-trading behind the scenes. But at this 1921 session at Dallas, all pretense was quickly dispelled. Dr. J. J. Terrill, of Dallas, had just nominated Dr. C. M. Rosser, of Dallas, for president-elect in a long and flowery speech. Dr. B. J. Hubbard, of Kaufman, then bluntly explained that he had had two ambitions in life: to reward his friends and to fight his enemies. The second ambition had ended since he had outlived all his enemies. So now he wanted to reward a friend by nominating Dr. Joe Becton, of Greenville. And besides, he had just driven over in "the best car that was ever made, a 1916 Ford." East Texas demanded recognition, and the president-elect should come from a small town. The large cities had had the office beyond their deserts. Becton was elected, the vote being 58 to 32. Dr. Becton's father, E. P. Becton, had been president of the Association in 1885. C. E. Durham, of Hico; William Myers, of Seguin; and S. J. Wilson, of Fort Worth, became the vice-presidents.

When it came to selecting the place for the 1922 session of the Association, distance seemed to lend enchantment. El Paso, Fort Worth, and Galveston were in the running. The invitations from Galveston and Fort Worth, especially the latter, seem to have been prompted by desire rather than duty. And yet El Paso del Norte was chosen, by the one-sided count of 60 to 6.

In Dallas, during the year, announcement was made that contracts had been let for the erection of the Medical Arts Building at a cost of $1,000,000, Dr. E. H. Cary lending the guiding hand. In Fort Worth, too, there was medical progress. The Association offices were moved from the basement of the Texas State Bank Building to the second floor of the Newby Building, at Throckmorton and West Eleventh streets. Here, in conjunction with the Tarrant County Medical Society, were provided ample quarters for the state association and a meeting place for the local society. Particularly proud was Editor Taylor of the room set apart for the accumulating library. A new employee, Vivian Irvin, was added to work half time in the library and half time for the Tarrant County Medical Society.

"The El Paso meeting was a wonder," in the opinion of Editor Taylor. The proximity of Juárez to dry Texas was doubtless a factor in this judgment. Very definitely the members had a good time; it was even moved that El Paso be made a permanent meeting place. As a matter of fact, however, the 1922 attendance of 565 was the lowest since the Association had journeyed to faraway Amarillo in 1911. The Woman's Auxiliary was on hand with 214 members. President Bennett was absent, as were also the chairman and secretary of the Section on Surgery. Dr. C. E. Durham, of Hico, was chosen by the Board of Councilors to preside. The meetings were held in the courthouse. One prominent visitor, Dr. Joseph C. Bloodgood, of Baltimore, who spoke on "What Every Doctor Should Know about Cancer," had the opportunity to discover that when he had crossed the eastern boundary of Texas, after passing through six states, he was hardly more than halfway to El Paso.

The Council on Legislation and Public Instruction brought its problems before the House of Delegates year after year. At El Paso, Dr. John T. Moore, speaking as chairman of the Board of Trustees, relaxed his usually well-controlled inhibitions and spoke out in these words: "Some of us are beginning to get tired of going before the Legislature and making fights for what we consider the interests of the people, only to have them say, 'To hell with you.'" The council, however, was not discouraged. It reaffirmed its stand on optometry, paid its respects to the resurging chiropractors, and presented plans for some much needed amendments to the Medical Practice Act. These amendments were passed by the Legislature early the next year. One provision made it possible for third-year medical students to take examinations in the basic sciences. More important was the injunction feature which made a second offense grounds of suit for injunction. Possible penalty for transgressing the act was extended to six months in jail, and it was provided that the attorney general could act where local authorities failed or refused to prosecute.

One amusing facet of this legislative success is found in the phrase which dealt with revocation of licenses for "grossly unprofessional and unethical conduct of such a nature as to deceive and defraud the public." The osteopaths, who were supporting the amendments, expressed fear that this provision was aimed at some of their number who were using the "oscilloclast" of Dr. Albert Abrams of San Francisco.[3] They were reassured, however, and their support was retained.

A committee composed of Marvin L. Graves, E. H. Cary, Bacon Saunders, and John T. Moore could be counted on to come up with something of value to the medical profession. This was the Committee on Medical Education. For some years, the matter of postgraduate medical study in Texas had been under discussion. This committee recommended and the House of Delegates approved the arrangement which had been made with Baylor and the University of Texas for short courses after the regular session. They were held from June 5 to 10 and from June 26 to July 1. The plan was a success, and similar courses were continued for many years. At Baylor, eighteen doctors were in attendance; at Galveston, forty-seven. It was editorially hoped that "perhaps our dream of re-educating the medical profession will come true."

As the practice of medicine became more and more involved in an increasingly complex civilization, solutions to problems were sought in various directions. One of these was health insurance. Another was group practice. The increasing cost of medical care was much discussed. Group medicine was advanced as one of the answers by those who believed that through this means better medical care could be provided. With this opinion, Dr. H. L. Hilgartner was in disagreement. He argued, in his paper on "A Criticism of Group Medicine": "The worst fate that could befall our profession would be its evolution into narrow specialists the practitioners of which had lost contact with the foundations they possessed at graduation. . . . Specialization in the practice of medicine is necessary, but it must be guarded against its two besetting dangers—excessive narrowness and the tendency to fall away from the foundations

[3] Abrams, M.A., M.D., LL.D., F.R.M.S., was one of those convincing medical posturers who had a large lay following; and some physicians had faith in "E. R. A.," the electronic reaction of Abrams. A series of articles in *Pearson's Magazine*, by two physicians, one preacher, and Upton Sinclair, led the publicity parade. Five notices in the *Journal of the American Medical Association* and a five-page editorial in the *Texas State Journal of Medicine* gave the medical profession the facts. Abrams claimed that his oscilloclast could diagnose disease from a drop of blood or even a person's autograph.

318

upon which it should ever stand in structural unity." Dr. Hilgartner felt that there was, and always would be, "a paramount need for highly competent general practitioners," and about them the practice of medicine should be centered. Editor Taylor, in an accompanying editorial, was favorable to the group idea. The association of physicians and surgeons into groups or clinics offered certain obvious advantages in efficiency and in economy. He quoted Dr. Arthur Dean Bevan, however, in defense of the general practitioner: "It is in the personal element that the art of medicine comes and it is something we cannot get away from."

In the absence of President Bennett, his address, "A Plea for the Establishment of a State Psychopathic Hospital," was read by title and later published in the *Journal*. Dr. Bennett called attention to the progress already made in this field. Michigan had established the first state psychopathic hospital in 1906. Then came the Boston Psychopathic Hospital and the Phipps Psychiatric Clinic, at Baltimore. He urged the establishment of a state hospital for the diagnosis and treatment "of incipient mental diseases as well as of the mildly psychopathic conditions which do not come strictly within the domain of legislative enactments relating to the insane." Such a hospital would become the psychiatric division of the state's public health agencies. Texas belatedly established the Galveston State Psychopathic Hospital in connection with the University of Texas in 1931.

Chosen as leaders for 1923 were A. C. Scott, of Temple, president-elect; and F. R. Winn, of Alvin; C. P. Yeager, of Kingsville; and J. A. Daniels, of Carthage, vice-presidents. K. H. Beall, of Fort Worth, was selected to serve as treasurer in place of W. L. Allison. The next session was assigned to Fort Worth.

Fort Worth was proud to welcome the Association to the Crystal Ballroom of the new Texas Hotel on May 8, 1923. The editor of the *Journal* remarked on the prevailing good humor and cordiality of those in attendance. In addition, it can be said that at this meeting the Association perhaps reached its most aggressive attitude toward public health, enforcement of laws of a medical nature, and allied subjects. The Medical Practice Act had been suitably amended the year before, and the medical profession was highly pleased.

Those in attendance were stimulated by addresses by Dr. Oscar

Dowling, chairman of the Board of Trustees of the American Medical Association and president of the Louisiana State Board of Health, and Lieutenant-Governor T. W. Davidson, their subjects being "The Work of the American Medical Association" and "Responsibility of the State for the Health of Its Citizens." Dr. Dowling devoted most of his time to the official and physical make-up of the American Medical Association, although he did digress long enough to declare that Texas should pay its state health officer six thousand dollars instead of three thousand dollars. Davidson, always a friend of the medical profession, referred to the accomplished facts of health legislation in Texas and gave the doctors full credit. But lassitude or indifference on the part of the profession, he warned, might prove ruinous. "Members of the medical profession—men who are trained to think—should not hesitate to exercise the right of suffrage and make their voices heard and felt in the affairs of State, not alone in the interest of public health, but there particularly, because that is the subject to which they have given most consideration."

Following the lead of these keynote speeches, addresses were made by Drs. W. B. Thorning, T. J. Crowe, W. B. Russ, and A. C. Scott. Dr. Russ was asked to repeat his address before a second group. All these speakers dealt with the relationship of the medical profession to the public. On this subject the Council on Legislation and Public Instruction secured the passage of the following resolution: "That a campaign of public education be conducted on the whole problem of the practice of medicine, the status of the cults and sects in medicine, and the effect on the public health of quackery and medical incompetence, whether through ignorance or desire to defraud." To pay for this campaign, an educational and publicity fund was set up on a voluntary basis; the desire was to collect ten dollars from each member. About one-fourth of the members had responded by February, 1924. The two principal concerns of the Association had to do with strengthening the State Health Department and with controlling the increasingly powerful chiropractors. Anticipating an increase in work in the Association office, the Board of Trustees employed Dr. D. R. Venable as assistant to Dr. Taylor. Bonnie Collins was employed as secretary to the new secretary-editor. At this time, also, a new accounting system was installed and Anna Keith charged with the dual responsibility of the ledger and the advertising in the *Journal*. By 1953 the accounting department was to include three other employees —Mildred Whiteman, Eula Lea Holmberg, and Martha Lambert —Miss Keith, after thirty years' faithful service, continuing to guard the Association's funds.

In connection with the public-education and publicity campaign, the *Journal* of July, 1923, contained an editorial of gratitude to friends of the medical profession in the Legislature. The exact record of each legislator had been kept in the office of the Association, so that identification was easy. Following the editorial were four full pages of photographs of sixteen senators and sixty-one representatives.

One method of promoting good public relations had been in use for several years; this was to have doctors make addresses on public health in the various churches on Sunday preceding the session. At Fort Worth, twelve outstanding physicians were thus in the pulpit.

Dr. Joe Becton, eloquent son of an eloquent father and former president, chose to speak on "The Doctor." His father, thirty-seven years before him, had spoken in praise of "American Medicine." He quoted from his father's address in defense of the doctor, praised the work of doctors through the ages, remarked on the epochal progress of public health, and pointed out those who would betray the health of the people. "How long," he asked, "would you live in a city where the health officer was a chiropractor and the food inspector a christian scientist?" In retrospective sentiment, more befitting the generation of his father, he declared:

The one fact of which I am the proudest of all, is that God never made a coward and a true doctor in the same man. There is no record in present or past history where any people, of any nation, clime or country, where disease, plague or pestilence stalked by day and night, claiming its victims by the tens of thousands, but some good doctor went fighting, fighting, until perhaps like our own brave Dr. Manning of Austin, in 1878, went to Holly Springs, Miss., during the yellow fever scourge, and remained at his post of duty until that bright life, from exposure and self-denial, like an untended flower, withered, drooped and died. Such acts will not soon fade from the memory of men. That star shed a lustre that will forever shine through the labyrinth of years, until methinks the reflection shall be caught and cast upon the throne of God.

When it came to choosing a president-elect, it was obvious that no horse-trading or back-scratching had been done. Dr. Marvin

L. Graves, in a laudatory address, put in nomination the name of Dr. M. F. Bledsoe, of Port Arthur. With equal enthusiasm, Dr. A. B. Small proposed Dr. C. M. Rosser, of Dallas; and then, for nearly four pages of fine print in the *Transactions*, seven succeeding speeches were made; it was North Texas versus South Texas, for the most part. When the oratorical smoke had cleared away and the votes were counted, Dr. Bledsoe was elected by the narrow margin of one vote. Without opposition Drs. J. W. Torbett, of Marlin; A. A. Ross, of Lockhart; and J. N. White, of Texarkana, were elected vice-presidents. Amarillo, Mineral Wells, and San Antonio were bidders for the 1924 session. Colonel E. A. Thompson came down to plead the cause of Amarillo, reminding his listeners that they could expect a repetition of the barbecue with son-of-a-gun sauce in Palo Duro Canyon. The counted ballots showed San Antonio, 44; Amarillo, 11; and Mineral Wells, 4.

Following the lead of Harvard, Pennsylvania, Yale, and Stanford, the University of Texas decided to limit its freshman class in medicine to sixty. Previously, an attempt had been made to accept all qualified applicants. The need for the reduction was found in the lack of clinical facilities at Galveston, only three hundred beds being available for teaching purposes.

In 1923, Editor Taylor wrote at length on medical economics. Although the cost of living had increased 72 per cent in twelve years, doctors' fees had remained unchanged and often uncollected. The doctor should be a good enough businessman to send bills regularly and should show reasonable expectation of making fair collections. And having made these collections, he should learn early the difference between investments, speculation, and gambling: the doctor "should first make himself reasonably secure by well selected investments, and then seek by approved speculation to increase his financial status beyond that. Any gambling he desires to do should be done with surplus money."

Editor Holman Taylor defined the 1924 San Antonio session as most delightful and pleasing. "There was so much genuine, personal hospitality, and so much opportunity for play, that we found it difficult to get down to work and stick to it." In these words, one finds a description of a situation which has long concerned medical meetings, ancient and modern. It will be recalled that in 1870 the bylaws of the Association had been amended so that no member in attendance could absent himself from the meetings without permission of the president. The problem was and is difficult; it is beyond solution except as making the programs so interesting as to command the presence of all members may be a solution. Given a group of tired doctors, free and foot-loose in the midst of extraneous attractions, it is not unnatural that some should desert the god of medicine in pursuit of pleasure and relaxation.

Two of the three general meetings were poorly attended, so much so that the programs were curtailed. This San Antonio session should have been quite attractive to those in attendance because of the visiting guests. Among these were Drs. W. A. Pusey, of Chicago, president-elect of the American Medical Association; Stewart Roberts, of Atlanta; E. Starr Judd, of Rochester; C. Jeff Miller and L. R. DeBuys, of New Orleans; and H. B. Matthews, of Brooklyn.

The campaign to collect ten dollars from each member for the creation of an educational fund was not successful, only about one-third responding to the call. This led to the necessity of raising the dues from five to fifteen dollars, the increase being allotted to the educational fund. This increase was opposed by many on the ground that it would mean a falling-off in membership. This contention was not baseless, for there was a drop from 3,766 in 1924 to 3,403 in 1925. The highest membership up to this time had been 3,766 in 1924.

The Council on Legislation and Public Instruction, with Dr. A. C. Scott as chairman, reported to the session on its plans for spending this money on publicity and lay education. The council was very active during the year. Jeff Reese was employed as legislative counsel and was active in this educational work. The idea was to "sell scientific medicine to the public." A reliable advertising agency was employed to plan the newspaper publicity. A speakers' bureau was established, and by September, thirty-one doctors had spoken in eighty-two places. Prior to the addresses, half-page announcements would appear in the local newspapers. These announcements appeared in eighty newspapers and accounted for a large part of the sixteen thousand dollars that was expended. The results of the plan, while not measurable, must have been considerable. Many favorable comments—Dr. Taylor collected a drawerful of them—appeared in the lay press. Typical of these announcements was one in the *Temple Telegram* which spoke of "the high purpose and broad humanitarianism of the campaign."

"The Prevention of Disease and the Safe Treatment of the Sick" was the subject of Dr. Scott's presidential address. He recommended better-trained doctors, an efficient and adequately staffed Board of Health, and public enlightenment. Thirty thousand people in Texas died annually from preventable diseases. Doctors must accept their obligations frankly and seriously. The Legislature must not be content to spend twice as much on the Livestock Sanitary Commission as on the Board of Health. And complacency on the part of the public, born of ignorance, must give way to enlightenment. Education of the people, Dr. Scott thought, is "the profoundest duty ever faced by the medical profession, and I have the utmost confidence in the ability and willingness of our doctors to perform this duty when the way becomes clear to them."

A heated contest for the office of president-elect took place among C. M. Rosser, of Dallas; William Keiller, of Galveston; and John H. Burleson, of San Antonio. Rosser was the winner. Vice-presidents for the next year were S. J. Alexander, of Hearne; J. W. Gidney, of West; and P. H. Chilton, of Comanche. Austin was chosen over Galveston and Mineral Wells to entertain the next session.

Two news items of interest appeared in the *Journal* for August, 1924. Ten thousand dollars' worth of radium was lost down the drainpipe at St. Paul's Sanitarium in Dallas. A destructive plumber failed to recover the capsule, so an insurance company came to the rescue. The other item was a picture of Dr. and Mrs. J. M. Boyd, of Palacios, with their eight attractive children. The legend implied a challenge to any Texas doctor who could top this record. There were no takers. Hearty congratulations were extended to the docfor who could "feed, clothe and educate such a large and healthy family."

XVIII

Reckless Plenty, 1925–29

THE LATTER PART of the twenties saw Miriam A. Ferguson supplanted as governor by Dan Moody, always a friend of the medical profession. This change projected Texas into the most prosperous era the state ever knew. Efficiency and needed reforms in government were effected. In three years, more than $70,000,000 was spent on highway construction. Oil and gas production expanded enormously; in 1928, Texas led the nation with 257,320,-000 barrels of oil.

This period of prosperity and plenty, however, was not an unmixed blessing. A wave of speculation overtook the people of Texas, and the doctors were engulfed along with their patients. The doctors of Texas bought farms, business property, and all kinds of stocks; they bought everything that held out a promise of profit, and they bought at high prices. Later, when the day of reckoning came, this collective experience would be looked back upon as an economic debauch.

The fifty-ninth annual session convened in the Senate Chamber at Austin on May 5, 1925. The several addresses of welcome were permeated with a note of optimism. President W. M. W. Splawn of the University of Texas spoke at length on the progress of science and medicine. He commended his medical department on how much it had been able to do with $200,000 a year, when comparable schools were spending twice that amount.

A periodic revamping of the constitution and bylaws took place at this session. As on other occasions, it was mostly a matter of clarification and simplification. One change set the annual dues at $10, but back of this change lay some developments of the preceding year. When the dues had been raised to $15, there had been considerable dissatisfaction. Among the dissenters was the Harris County Medical Society, which not only objected to increasing the dues but also disclaimed any responsibility for the educational campaign. Editor C. C. Cody, in the *Medical Record and Annals*, published for the "Medical Societies of the south half of Texas," wrote a series of protests in which the parent organization was taken severely to task, and predicted a possible schism in the Association. Some county societies did threaten to withdraw. The matter came before the House of Delegates in the form of a resolution by the Board of Councilors, which in part resolved "That the Board of Councilors call upon the various societies represented by the organ to either control its editorial policy or take steps to sever their relations with the publication."

This resolution provoked a long and heated debate. Freedom of the press was invoked in defense of Dr. Cody: "It would be a mell of a hess if an editor could not express some of his views on the policies of the State Association." In reply, several of the editorials were read in full to support a charge of insubordination on the part of Dr. Cody and the Harris County Medical Society. Cody denied any charge of disloyalty and then asked, "Do you mean to tell me that this House, the legislative body of the State Medical Association of Texas, is going to throttle conscientious criticism of its policies?" When the argument was at white heat, Dr. Marvin L. Graves, with exquisite finesse, asked the secretary whether charters had been issued to these dissenting district societies as required by the constitution and bylaws. After receiving a negative reply, he continued, "Then if that be true, these district societies are not component parts of the State Association." A final vote carried the matter back to the Board of Councilors for action. Here it came to a quiet end.

The financial status of the Association had improved with the years. Treasurer Beall reported $77,128.87 in cash, bonds, and mortgage notes. All this was needed. The expenses for the year were $39,212.83, about 10 per cent of which went for attorneys' fees. This revealed that emphasis had shifted from publicity and education to law enforcement. The main effort centered about enforcing the provisions of the Medical Practice Act. Since the chiropractors were the chief offenders, their activities were much

326

in the news; this group became the main target. One issue of the *Journal* reported the arrest or conviction of seven chiropractors; and in Dallas, ten were indicted in one day. This work had been inherited from the abolished Council on Legislation and Public Instruction by the Executive Council, which was composed of the officers of the Association, the Board of Trustees, the Board of Councilors, and the Legislative Committee. The Executive Council assumed a crusading spirit. Every doctor was urged to use his individual influence with his patients. The Woman's Auxiliary was enlisted. "The idea of protecting the public against ignorance and imposition in the practice of medicine," Dr. Taylor declared, was of paramount importance.

The aggressive plan was not without its critics. It was argued that when one group of quacks was eliminated—should that be possible—another would spring up to take its place. Too often prosecution was interpreted by the public as persecution. And the publicity which a transgressor received in a court trial was an asset in some neighborhoods. Then, too, there were those who logically contended that law enforcement was the job of all the people and should not be paid for by any one group. At any rate, enthusiasm lagged, despite the active support of the attorney-general, until in March, 1926, Dr. Taylor saw fit to ask editorially, "Shall We Persist in our Publicity and Enforcement Campaign?" His conclusion was in the affirmative. And there can be little doubting that much of value was attained, even though the cost in time, effort, and money was high.

In his address on "An Epitome of Organized Medicine; Its Purpose and Duty," Dr. Murff F. Bledsoe spoke of early attempts at organization in Europe. Organized in 1735, the first medical group in America was the Boston Medical Society. But no real progress was made until the American Medical Association came into being in 1847. Six years later, the Texas Medical Association was organized, and since that time the two associations had made parallel progress. Dr. Bledsoe praised the recent work of the Association, including the education and law-enforcement campaign. Of the future, he felt secure: "I feel encouraged and have every incentive to be confident that we will never falter or tire, since, after all, I agree, as all true physicians do, with Pasteur of old, who said that he held the unconquerable belief that the future belongs to those who serve humanity best."

The Dallas County Medical Society asked the state association to join in the invitation to the American Medical Association to hold its 1926 session in Dallas. This was done, and the invitation was accepted. One inducement was the promise of seven tons of barbecued beef for the expected 10,000 visitors. This meeting was held in April and was altogether successful. It added much to the medical prestige of Dallas, especially since the Southern Medical Association had convened there four months earlier. At the regional meeting, there were 2,042 registrants, of whom 1,205 were Texans. At the national meeting, there were 4,179 in attendance; of these, Texas claimed 1,829. As a compliment to Dallas and in recognition of his inherent worth, Dr. John O. McReynolds was elected vice-president of the national organization.

The new officers of the Texas association were William Keiller, of Galveston, president-elect; and Minnie O'Brien, of San Antonio; C. A. Gray, of Bonham; and G. B. Taylor, of Cameron, vice-presidents. Dr. Keiller was elected over Dr. John Burleson, of San Antonio. Houston was chosen over Galveston for the next session.

From what has gone before, it will be seen that by 1925 the Association had established itself on an even keel. Its activities obviously varied in some particulars from year to year. But, for the most part, the goals of achievement were the same. The narration of the routine affairs of the Association, year after year, cannot fail to approach the dullness of monotony. The deliberations of the 1926 session at Houston were not greatly different from those of 1925 or 1927. So it might be well, as a diversion, to take a look at the mechanics of this session and follow through on the transactions as recorded in the *Journal*.

The House of Delegates was called to order by President Rosser on Monday, May 24, 1926, at 1:00 P.M., in the Rice Hotel. The meeting of the House of Delegates on the day preceding the opening session was an innovation which has been continued to the present. Secretary Taylor called the roll, and 57 delegates were properly accredited. A quorum having been declared, the Secretary was asked to read the minutes of the previous meeting. Since these minutes had been printed in the *Journal*, the reading was dispensed with and the minutes accepted with a few minor corrections. The president then appointed the following reference committees: on credentials, reports of officers and committees, memorials and resolutions, finance, amendments to constitution and bylaws, and scientific work. Each of these committees received from the House of Delegates such resolutions or assignments as fell in its particular field. According to custom, next should have followed the president's message, but this was omitted. The secretary's report was long and comprehensive in scope, dealing with routine matters, making suggestions for ease of operation, and calling attention to various committee vacancies. This report was referred to the Reference Committee on Reports of Officers and Committees. Treasurer Beall's good report was received and turned over to the Reference Committee on Finance.

Dr. W. B. Thorning, of Houston, read the report of the Board of Councilors. He dealt with postgraduate medicine, the educational campaign, socialized medicine, and the *Journal*. Then Dr. Felix Miller, of El Paso, reported for the Council on Medical Defense. These reports were sent to the proper reference committees. The report of the Committee on Collection and Preservation of Records, for so long and with such ardor presented by Dr. Paschal in other years, came from Dr. J. D. Osborn, of Cleburne. Dr. Paschal had died during the year, but not before he had sent Osborn some valuable documents pertaining to Dr. Ashbel Smith and Dr. George Cupples—"in the event anything happens to me." The revised bylaws had provided for the election of honorary members; Dr. Thorning's committee nominated the following men: I. L. Van Zandt, of Fort Worth; J. B. Chapman, of Paris; M. H. Maness, of Roxton; G. Graham Watts, Sigmund Burg, F. M. Hicks, and John V. Spring, of San Antonio; H. B. Tanner, of Eastland; T. L. Pierce, S. P. Rumph, and T. L. Wilson, of Carbon; W. E. Mancil, Alf Irby, and D. S. Rumph, of Cisco; T. E. Duffer, of Ranger; and E. W. Kimble, of Gorman.

Dr. Marvin L. Graves, perennial chairman of the Committee on Medical Education, referred to medical colleges in the United States, postgraduate study, the technic of medical education, and hospitals. Then, successively, came reports of the Committee on Transportation, by Holman Taylor; the Committee on Hospital Standardization, by Charles H. Harris, of Fort Worth; and the Committee on Health Problems in Education by C. W. Goddard, of Austin. Dr. W. B. Russ having been absent in Europe, Secretary Taylor reported as the Texas member of the National Legislative Council. Dr. W. H. Moursund, of Dallas, appeared as Texas delegate to the Association of American Medical Colleges. The closing item at this Monday afternoon meeting of the House of Delegates was the reading of communications by the secretary. These, along with all reports, were sent to the proper reference committees.

On Monday night there was a joint meeting of the House of Delegates and the Texas Federation for Health Education. The occasion was the presentation of a medal to the Association by Dr. Max Handman, of the University of Texas, who represented the National Committee on Prisons and Prison Labor. The medal was given in recognition of the service which the Association had performed in behalf of the prison system of Texas. Dr. A. C. Scott, during whose regime the work was done, accepted the medal for the Association in an appropriate speech.

The opening exercises of the Association were called to order at 10:30 A.M. on Tuesday by Dr. E. W. Bertner, chairman of the Committee on Arrangements. Dr. Bertner welcomed the Association and made the necessary announcements. The invocation was given by the Rev. G. E. Wiley, of the First Baptist Church. Welcoming addresses were made by Mayor Oscar F. Holcombe in behalf of the city of Houston and by President James Greenwood of the Harris County Medical Society. The final item was the address of President Rosser, which will be considered later.

The House of Delegates assembled on Tuesday at 1:30. Dr. Holman Taylor read the exhaustive report of the Executive Committee, which treated law enforcement, publicity, legislative matters, and care of the insane. Five recommendations closed the report. Then came Dr. John T. Moore, for the Board of Trustees. Year after year, as chairman, he had brought in a constructive report, as he did this year. He praised the "inbred conservatism" of the board and warned against undue enthusiasm in expending the funds of the Association. He announced the removal of Association offices to the Medical Arts Building in Fort Worth. He submitted the auditor's report, which reflected a healthy condition of the treasury. He submitted also a tentative budget of $54,000, based on probable income of the same amount. The largest item, $24,490, went to the *Journal*. This report of the Board of Trustees was sent to the appropriate reference committee, as were all subsequent reports and resolutions.

The Council on Scientific Work, with A. C. Scott, of Temple, as chairman; the Committee on Scientific Exhibits, with H. O. Knight, of Galveston, as chairman; the Committee on Cancer, with J. M. Martin, of Dallas, as chairman; the Committee on Revision of Constitution and Bylaws, with H. W. Cummings, of Hearne, as chairman; and the Committee on Publicity, with O. L. Norsworthy, of Houston, as chairman, all submitted well-prepared reports. After a telegram of greetings from the Southern Medical Association had been read, and after Dr. I. L. McGlasson, of San Antonio, had reported as delegate to the Texas Dental Society, the meeting adjourned.

At 8:00 P.M., memorial exercises were held in the First Presbyterian Church, with Dr. W. N. Wardlaw, of Childress, in the chair. Dr. A. W. Carnes, of Hutchins, gave the invocation. Handel's "Largo" was rendered by the Kiwanis glee club. Dr. Wardlaw then read the names of the thirty-five members deceased during the year, sixty-eight deceased nonmembers, and eleven deceased members of the Woman's Auxiliary. The passing of so many nonmembers showed that the work of organization was only partly done. Of the deceased members, four were former presidents of the Association: J. E. Gilcreest, J. M. Inge, Frank Paschal, and Bacon Saunders. Following three vocal numbers, special tribute was paid to Dr. Gilcreest by Dr. A. W. Carnes; to Dr. Inge by Dr. Joe Becton; to Dr. Paschal by Dr. Thomas Dorbandt, of San Antonio; and to Dr. Saunders by Dr. I. C. Chase. Mrs. Joe Gilbert, of Austin, spoke in memory of the doctors' wives. Chairman Wardlaw delivered the memorial address, and Dr. R. E. Bowen, of San Antonio, pronounced the benediction.

Particularly felt was the loss of Dr. Frank Paschal, for the Association has had few more devoted leaders than he. President of the Association in 1903, he continued as past president to work until his death to record its history and to secure a home for the relics on which its history rests.

In him, honor, chivalry, virtue, good manners—all the qualities of the gracious gentleman—were inbred and ineradicable. He had known George Cupples, second president of the Association, and entertained for him a feeling closely akin to hero worship. "The mantle of George Cupples fell definitely and fittingly on the shoulders of Frank Paschal. They were the Elijah and Elisha of the medical profession of Bexar County" [1] and, to be sure, of Texas.

When the general session of the Association was called to order

[1] Nixon, *A Century of Medicine in San Antonio,* 241.

by Secretary Taylor on Wednesday at 4:00 P.M., it was for the purpose of hearing Dr. William Seaman Bainbridge, of New York, deliver his address on "Review of Recent Investigations into the Causation of Cancer and the Outlook for Prevention and Treatment." The attendance was disappointing, but the address was later published in the *Journal*. This short general meeting was the only gathering on Wednesday except the usual sectional groups. This was an intentional arrangement, so that the delegates could attend the scientific sessions.

The House of Delegates got off to an early start Thursday morning by assembling at 8:30. President Rosser, in calling the meeting to order, took occasion to remark on the courtesy and concord that had permeated the session. Very quickly Dr. Joe Dildy, of Brownwood, was on his feet, rising to a point of personal privilege. This being granted, he spoke of one of the fruits of the publicity campaign:

I am a life-long Democrat. I am a Baptist since 1900. I am a prohibitionist, spanked into line by the Baptists in 1902. . . . I then learned to love, to honor and to respect Baylor Medical College, the professors of that institution, and all the nurses. I helped the Baptists endow Baylor University Medical College, through the $5,000,000.00 campaign put on by the Baptists. I love the Baptist religion, and have tried it and can stand anything. . . . Therefore, I rise to a point of personal privilege, having been reliably informed that a very influential ex-Governor of this state, who is a Christian and who is the chairman of the Board of Trustees of Baylor Medical College, has been taking chiropractic adjustments recently. I refer to the Honorable Pat Neff and Chiropractor Lemly, both of Waco, Texas, both of whom are fully informed of this campaign. I offer the following motion for your careful consideration. I move that this House of Delegates request of the Honorable Pat Neff a public denial of this accusation, or that he resign from the Board of Trustees of Baylor Medical College. [Applause.]

This resolution was freely debated, but prudence prevailed and no action was taken. These doctors, like their predecessors and successors, were striving toward the ideal of retaining something of the rare and subtle qualities of the doctor of old without seriously sacrificing any modern scientific niceties. Whether this was a hopeless ambition, only time will tell.

Then followed reports from the several reference committees. Their recommendations, for the most part, were in accord with

332

those of the original committees. One notable exception was the report of the Reference Committee on Amendments to the Constitution and Bylaws. This report contained some suggested amendments coming from Harris County, over the signatures of C. C. Cody, E. F. Cooke, and C. C. Green, looking toward "emphasizing the importance of the County Medical Society, and decentralizing the government of the State Medical Association of Texas." These suggested changes stemmed from the disagreement which Harris County members had had with the state association two years before. There were pages of discussion but no final action except to refer the matter to the Standing Committee on Revision.

The last item of business at this Thursday morning meeting was the election of officers and the selection of a place of meeting. Dr. Marvin L. Graves, now of Houston, who had perhaps nominated more presidents than any other one man, presented the name of Dr. Joe Gilbert, of Austin, as a candidate for president-elect. A seconding speech by Dr. A. F. Beverly, of Austin, and an accepted motion that the nominations be closed led to casting a unanimous ballot for Dr. Gilbert. As vice-presidents, C. R. Hannah, of Dallas; Malone Duggan, of La Feria; and J. M. Greenwood, of Houston, were elected. The nominating speeches were made by R. S. Killough, of Amarillo; Dudley Jackson, of San Antonio; and H. W. Cummings, of Hearne. Dr. John T. Moore had been elected to the Board of Trustees so often that his re-election was a mere formality. This time it was suggested that he serve "for life or during good behavior." Then came the election of councilors, delegates to the American Medical Association, and members to fill vacancies on several councils and committees. Brownsville and El Paso were contestants for the 1927 session. The claims of the Magic Valley were presented by Dr. W. E. Spivey, of Brownsville. El Paso came up with a long list of telegrams from a group of organizations, including the Juárez Chamber of Commerce. The vote was El Paso, 41; Brownsville, 22.

The final meeting of the sixtieth session convened at 4:00 P.M., Thursday. Following an address on "The Romance of Medicine," by Dr. I. L. McGlasson, of San Antonio, each newly elected officer was presented at some length, and each replied at greater length. The final scene of this final meeting found retiring President Rosser presenting the incoming president as "a conscientious, capable man, a scientist of international fame, a friend to all mankind, the

333

illustrious and beloved Dr. William Keiller, your President." In a few gracious words, Dr. Keiller expressed his gratitude and then declared the session adjourned sine die.

Of course, it is understood that the six scientific sections were in session, many of them simultaneously, during Tuesday, Wednesday, and Thursday. These were sections on medicine and diseases of children; surgery; eye, ear, nose and throat; public health; radiology and physiotherapy; and gynecology and obstetrics. In all, there were 110 papers on the program. On Monday, the Texas Radiological Society, the Texas Railway Association, and the Texas Federation for Health Education had held their meetings.

The Woman's Auxiliary met daily and, according to the *Journal*, "accomplished much." A golf tournament was an event of Monday afternoon. The Houston Country Club was the scene of a reception Tuesday from five to seven in the evening. The alumni banquets were held Tuesday night. The president's ball and reception were scheduled for nine on Wednesday night; there were dancing, a vaudeville show, and a buffet dinner. For those who had the time and inclination, seventeen scientific exhibits and eleven commercial exhibits were available.

During the Association's campaigns for publicity and law enforcement, Dr. C. M. Rosser had taken a major part, making many speeches over the state. It was but natural, then, that he should have chosen as president to speak on "The Crime of Quackery." He expressed confidence in the adequacy of the Medical Practice Act as passed in 1907 and amended in 1923. All that was needed was proper but aggressive enforcement of that act. In this, the medical profession must accept its responsibility. The real answer was publicity through the media of the public press and the radio, which had become available. The public had to be convinced that "what these quacks do is against the law," but also that "they offend the common decency of our country and constitute a public menace." In this fight against quackery, Dr. Rosser asked the aid of all worthy allies. "The truly scientific medical profession preoccupies the medical field, and invites to its honorable friendship and alliance, sincere and intelligent practitioners who, having equipped themselves for successful service to the sick, will devote to this undertaking their energies and talents, having at all times a due regard for the sacredness of their calling and its matchless mission among our fellow men."

334

Sad news came to the medical profession of Texas in 1926. This was the death of Dr. Allen J. Smith, who had done much for medicine in Texas and the United States. From 1891 to 1903, he had occupied the chair of pathology at Galveston and for ten years was dean there. Dr. Smith was a member of that famous first faculty, of whom only Drs. William Keiller and Edward Randall still survived.

In connection with the Medical Department of the University of Texas and all medical schools, there was great concern about the rising cost of medical education. In 1910, the average tuition fee per student was $118 a year. By 1926, the figure had risen to $274. Some schools were charging as much as $525. The day of the medical school maintained solely by tuition fees had long passed; the average expenditure by the schools per student was about three times the average fee paid by the student.

As was to be expected, the attendance at the 1927 El Paso meeting was disappointing; it was 522 as against 565 at the previous meeting in El Paso, in 1922. The session, however, was considered satisfactory, and the attendance at the general meetings was especially gratifying. The presence of such speakers as Drs. Donald C. Balfour, of Rochester; Karl A. Menninger, of Topeka; and W. A. Evans, of the *Chicago Tribune,* were obvious attractions. The membership of the Association had grown to 3,642. Of the 131 component county societies, the Committee on Credentials disclosed that 65 were represented.

It was clear at El Paso that the activities of the Association were being grouped more and more about the powerful Executive Council. Its report took up in great detail the publicity and enforcement campaign and the various phases of legislative action such as that having to do with chiropractors, Christian Scientists, the State Health Department, the Workman's Compensation Act, and many others. The council considered the chiropractors the chief "enemies of scientific medicine," and it was to them that its main efforts were addressed. A typical case was that of S. T. McMurrain, a chiropractor of Dallas. He was on trial for practicing medicine without a license. He carried a big advertisement in a Dallas paper under the caption "Faith Has Moved Mountains. Faith Will Bring Chiropractic Legislation." Beneath was a full-length picture of the great man standing behind a large loving cup, donated presumably by two hundred pleased patients. Then came this solemn pledge, "Humbly invoking the blessings of an all-wise God, we give this token of our faith in you and your cause. Long Live Chiropractic." In commenting on the antics of this hero and martyr, Editor Taylor observed, "With the blessings of God, this man proposes to continue to violate the law because he does not believe that the law should apply to him."

One new idea was injected by the Executive Council: the annual registration of all physicians of Texas. This, of course, could be accomplished only by act of the Legislature. This proposal was motivated by the factor of cost. New and increasing demands were being made on the treasury, and publicity and law enforcement were quite costly. In 1925, they amounted to $20,128.96; in 1926, $6,388.96. For the year just ahead, the Board of Trustees advised the expenditure of $8,000.00 to $10,000.00 "in an effort to educate the public on the subject of scientific medicine, and secure the enforcement of our very excellent Medical Practice Act." To this the Executive Council, realizing that law enforcement was a dubious function of the state association, added the following: "It is becoming more and more evident that the State Medical Association is going out of its way in actively promoting the prosecution of alleged violators of the medical practice act." An annual registration fee from all the doctors, it reasoned, would rightfully lighten the burden on members of the Association and shift some responsibility to nonmembers, who were still in the majority. There was some opposition, which it took a good deal of talking and doing to overcome. The minor schools of medicine supported the plan. The Medical Practice Act was amended, and on January 1, 1932, the amendment became effective. The principal provision empowered the Board of Medical Examiners with enforcement authority, and the annual fee was set at $2.00. Thus the state association, which had assumed responsibility for law enforcement in the absence of any other practicable agency, was relieved, and the Board of Examiners was provided with about $15,000.00 a year.

The Executive Council, which had practically usurped the authority of the Committee on Legislation, saw two of its important projects become law. For several years, plans looking toward reorganization of the State Board of Health had been in the making. The American Public Health Association and the United States Public Health Service had lent assistance. This year, legislation was passed, the main feature of which gave the Board of Health power to select the state health officer and to reorganize the State Health Department so as to insure both economy and efficiency. As a corollary of this legislation, a Vital Statistics Law was passed, thus belatedly placing Texas in the registration area of the United States.

Thirty-six names of deceased members were read at the memorial services. Among them were those of former President T. J. Bennett and Dr. James E. Thompson, who had played a major role in Texas surgery for more than a quarter of a century. Another loss to the Association, but not by death, was announced at this session; Dr. D. R. Venable resigned as assistant to Dr. Holman Taylor, Dr. R. B. Anderson, of Thorndale, being selected as his successor.

President Keiller spoke wisely on the subject "A Bit of Introspection." Officially, he felt constrained to take up some of the problems that beset the medical profession of Texas, but he was at his best when he spelled out the virtues of the true physician. Self-examination, correction of his own remediable faults, patience, honesty, "the divine gift of sympathy"—these are the indispensable ingredients. "The public loves comforting, pleasant lies, especially the sick public," but the true doctor cannot offer great and unbounded promises of cure. "If we could only have the Christlike word *service* written large in our subconsciousness all the time, and see in every case, even in appearance the most trivial, another great opportunity to give the *best* that is in us, it would be so much easier to save our patients from the pleasant paths of deceptive promises of speedy relief."

As president-elect, Dr. Felix P. Miller was put forward by his fellow-townsmen Drs. R. L. Ramey, T. J. McCamant, and W. L. Brown, and was elected without opposition. The new vice-presidents were H. R. Link, Palestine; Arthur Flickwir, Houston; and W. N. Wardlaw, Childress. As a place of meeting, Galveston was selected over Fort Worth, Amarillo, and Havana, Cuba.

During the year 1927, the medical profession of Texas saw something of the old and the new in medicine. In the first six months, 2,059 cases of smallpox were reported to State Health Officer J. C. Anderson—this, when vaccination had been introduced into Texas 121 years before.[2] The new and mysterious ailment, poliomyelitis, became prevalent in Texas, especially in Fort Worth, where 49 cases occurred. The etiology and treatment were no less obscure then

[2] Nixon, *Medical Story of Early Texas*, 57.

than they are today. Allergy was much in the medical news, and Editor Taylor leaned to that explanation.

On the economic side, the *Journal* dilated on the distribution of physicians in the state. Good roads and automobiles brought the average serious ailment within reach of some town or city. This had led to a scarcity of physicians in the rural areas and the overcrowding of physicians in urban areas. That early the situation was serious, and no solution was in sight. The *Journal* quoted the *Galveston News* pertinently: "Is there any life harder than that of the country doctor who treats all diseases; who is expected to be omnipresent, but has leagues to go in all weathers and at all hours; who is specialist as well as general practitioner; who brings everybody into the world, and must be surgeon and dentist as well as diagnostician; who has scant time to study his books, such as he owns, because he is on the road so much; whose patients are poor; who must be philosopher and friend as well as physician, and whose best friend is the Recording Angel!"[3]

The sixty-second session of the Association, convened in the Garden of Tokio on May 8, 1928, opened with the usual welcoming speeches. In a different vein were the remarks of Dr. Alex W. Acheson, of Denison, presented by Dr. Holman Taylor as "the dean of chronic attendants on medical association meetings." Then eighty-six years of age, Dr. Acheson told of attending the first meeting ever held in Galveston. The date was 1877, and the attendance was seventy-four. He remembered Galveston as "a collection of cypress water tanks, because they had no water works." He recalled amid applause the medical era in Texas "before sugar coated pills were known, before the inventor of capsules was born, before hypodermic syringes were in use and before thermometers were introduced." An interesting coincidence is that in 1877 a paper on "Preventive Medicine" was read by Dr. R. H. L. Bibb, of Austin, and that a

[3] Times and conditions had changed, but some of the basic problems remained the same. The following was written nearly a hundred years earlier: "The physician is subjected to great fatigue both of body and mind. He has no time that he can call his own. That regularity of life, which is so essential to comfort as well as to health, he must in a great measure abandon, especially if he practice in a scattered population. . . . And for all this generally the medical man gets comparatively a small compensation."—Worthington Hooker, *Physician and Patient* (New York, 1849), 404–405.

338

paper on the same subject was read in 1928 by Dr. Charles H. Mayo.

Amid the many topics presented in its report, the Executive Council called attention to a new aspect of the chiropractic threat. A bill had been introduced into the Legislature providing for an appropriation of $2,000.00 to be used for employing a chiropractor in the San Antonio Hospital for the Insane. The bill was at first thought to be a joke, but this idea was soon dispelled. The council was tortured by the thought of a chiropractor treating patients mentally incompetent to choose a physician, forgetting perhaps that such incompetency was not and is not confined to institutions. Their anxiety, however, was relieved when the Legislature rejected the bill, but it did receive 24 favorable votes.

The Executive Council advised the formation of a committee to plan and co-ordinate the dissemination of medical information and news over the radio. Some of the broadcasting stations, notably KRLD of Dallas, had co-operated with the medical association in the venture. The council added a word of warning: the radio "is just as dangerous as it is powerful." Already, the Chiropractic College of Davenport, Iowa, operated its own station, WOC, and Chiropractor Allison, of Fort Worth, owned station KFJZ. Editor Taylor echoed his alarm over the situation in two editorials, "Rotten Radio" and "Wholesome Radio." The whole situation was new; the radio commission was new; and progress came slowly. The Association formed no committee, and the radio stations of Texas continued to advertise the Magic Horse Collar or any other quackish product, just as the newspapers were doing, until the factor of conscience entered in or until legal barriers were established.

From time to time, the problem of alcohol and prohibition came up on the floor of the House of Delegates. The Federal Prohibition Act, popularly known as the Volstead Act, had been in effect since 1919. In other years, since the subject was quite controversial, it had been handled with caution. This year Dr. W. B. Russ, as the Texas member of the National Legislative Council, brought in a strong resolution condemning the Volstead Act for making hypocrites out of doctors who prescribed liquor: if liquor was a medicine, laymen were not the ones to dictate the amount and the manner of its prescription; if, on the contrary, much of the alcohol prescribed by doctors was used as a beverage, then the doctors and druggists should not be the dispensers. In other words, the whole approach to the problem was wrong. Heated debate followed, and the resolution was rejected. The next day, however, a similar resolution, urging Congress "to relieve the medical profession of the burden and responsibility of prescribing liquor as a medicine," was passed without opposition.

As Dr. Holman Taylor closed his sixth three-year term as secretary-editor, he was able to report an improved *Journal,* which had made a profit of $1,078.88 for the year. Income from advertisements amounted to $17,414.56, and subscriptions, at $3.00 per year, added $10,831.50 to the income of the *Journal.* The printed pages of the *Journal* had increased to about 850 a year. In his editorial capacity, Dr. Taylor continued to be a man of many words. Each month there would be about ten pages of editorials, some of them three and four pages long. This meant that about one-fourth of the pages of the *Journal* were editorial in content. All organizations are likely to contain some members who claim they do not know what is going on. No malcontents in the State Medical Association of Texas could advance such a claim if they read carefully the editorials and the transactions in the *Journal.*

The 1928 presidential address was Dr. Joe Gilbert's "Looking Backward and Forward in Public Health." He indicated a trend in Association activities when he said: "With many of you, I feel that the time has come when we should place the major responsibility for health administration where it properly belongs, namely, in the state departments established for that purpose, thereby to a certain extent relieving a scientific organization of the burden—financial, mental and moral, which it has dutifully borne throughout the past many years." Already the State Department of Health had been reorganized, and thus a great forward step was taken. Now Dr. Gilbert was advocating a plan to empower the State Board of Medical Examiners with the authority of medical law enforcement and to furnish the board with funds from an annual registration fee from all physicians. This plan, as already mentioned, went into effect in 1932. The security of the medical profession of Texas, in Dr. Gilbert's mind, was in no doubt: "Though charlatans may come and charlatans may go, the true physician remains the court of last resort with the greatest majority of the laity."

In the election of officers, Dr. Joe Dildy, of Brownwood, was the choice for president-elect. The new vice-presidents were D. H. Hudgins, of Kaufman; S. D. Naylor, of Stephenville; and J. L.

Howard, of Paris. As for a meeting place, the choices were many: Fort Worth, Greenville, Brownsville, Mineral Wells, and Amarillo. Brownsville was the selection.

During the summer of 1928, Texas was in the doldrums. It was a time of chain letters and diaper rodeos. In keeping with this spirit, the *Journal* of May, 1928, printed an X-ray picture of Rip Van Winkle, the horned toad which reputedly had spent thirty-one very peaceful years in the cornerstone of the Eastland County Courthouse. Rip having missed two wars, the fracture in his left ankle may have been indicative of the rough times ahead for him and the men about him.

The meetings in Brownsville were held in the Junior College Building. Southernmost point of Texas that Brownsville is, the attendance was only average. The Magic Valley was in glorious bloom. Members came from the far corners of Texas: eight from El Paso County and seven each from Potter and Bowie. But their interests were not all seriously scientific; these 695 physicians plus 327 auxiliary members were lured by the transformed valley and fascinated by the carefree land across the Rio Bravo. The meetings were poorly attended, and in the House of Delegates only 72 county societies were represented. A free airplane ride, offered to each visitor, a boxing match at Fort Brown, and a dinner in Matamoros were listed attractions.

The annual registration of physicians had become the chief legislative concern of the Association. At Galveston, the previous year, the subject had evoked some harsh words, principally from the Harris County delegation, spearheaded by Drs. S. C. Red and C. C. Cody and tempered by Dr. John T. Moore. This delegation was referred to as "a bunch of insurgents." At Galveston, after eight pages of discussion, the Association had taken no decisive action. It was agreed at the Brownsville session, but not without opposition, that the Association should use its influence in promoting the legislation necessary to require annual registration of doctors. When the discussion was at its hottest, Dr. W. B. Russ told of a woman who found two boys fighting and said to them, "You boys stop that, both of you on one side won't be too many." That he was in part correct is verified by an unexpected opponent, former Governor Jim Ferguson, who said: "Now brother, ain't things coming to a hell of a pass. Last week I showed where these medical trust doctors want to set themselves to tell people how to run the plumbing business and how to milk cows, and now they want to go further and abolish the right of local self-government and tell the county and district attorneys, elected by the people, where to head in." [4]

For eleven years the Woman's Auxiliary of the Association had gradually grown in numbers and in usefulness. From Texas, where the idea originated in 1918, the plan had spread to other states, and a national auxiliary came into being in 1922. Each year meetings had been held, and each month the *Journal* had devoted a column or a page to "Auxiliary Notes." At Brownsville, full recognition was granted to this loyal ally of organized medicine in Texas. The auxiliary asked that a liaison committee be appointed to coordinate the activities of the two groups. This committee was appointed. The transactions of the Auxiliary were printed in full in the June *Journal*. Meetings were held on Tuesday, Wednesday, and Thursday. Full reports and free discussion filled twenty-eight pages of the *Journal*. Forty county auxiliaries were represented, comprising a membership of approximately 1,300. Two past national presidents were in attendance: Mrs. S. C. Red, of Houston, and Mrs. John O. McReynolds, of Dallas, first and fourth presidents respectively. The submitted reports dealt with many subjects, such as tuberculosis, child health, publicity, legislation, and *Hygeia* subscriptions. Interspersed through these transactions are verses which might or might not appeal to the husbands. For example, the following was offered by Mrs. Dru McMickin, recording secretary of the Jefferson County Auxiliary:

> Some folks are natural-born speakers,
> Many others have learned to be
> But I could never be one
> So you will not hear much from me.
>
> When my name is called on a program
> The folks begin to grin,
> For my head always quits working
> And both my knees begin.
>
> I enjoyed rocking my baby,
> And I usually bake good bread,

[4] *Ferguson Forum,* February 28, 1929.

> But when I rise and say, "Madam President"
> Every thought just leaves my head.
>
> Just to read a report makes me nervous,
> So I know you will agree
> It is better to hear a speaker
> Than to have to suffer with me.

Focal infection was much to the forefront at this time in medical circles. The Council on Scientific Work emphasized it by having seventeen papers on the subject at the Brownsville session. One of these was a paper on "A Concept of Arthritis," by Dr. Lawrence H. Mayers, of Chicago. And President Felix P. Miller chose to speak on "Focal Infections, a Major Subject for Study." He discussed the question of cause and effect in disease and fully accepted the principle of focal infection. He went further by speculating on its relationship to malignant disease. Chronic infection caused chronic irritation, and prolonged irritation could be a cause of cancer. Every physician should be on the alert in this matter. Some Texas doctor, he thought, might become the author of a profound contribution to our knowledge of this subject. "To the end that we may enlarge our general knowledge of this puzzling disorder, and that our profession may advance toward that goal of usefulness that was visualized by our first [5] President, Dr. Cupples, this meeting is dedicated."

After an eloquent nomination by Dr. A. A. Ross, of Lockhart, Dr. John W. Burns, of Cuero, was elected president-elect without opposition. Drs. B. O. Works, of Brownsville; B. T. Vanzant, of Houston; and D. J. Jenkins, of Daingerfield were the new vice-presidents. Mineral Wells was selected over Waco, Fort Worth, and Dallas as the next place of meeting.

Great loss came to the official family of the Association in the death of President Joe Dildy, on November 5, 1929.[6] The Board of Councilors chose Dr. D. J. Jenkins his successor. When inducted into office, Dr. Dildy had explained that periodic physical examinations would be the theme of his administration, and in this direc-

---

[5] George Cupples was, of course, the second president. See above, Chapter 3.

[6] Dr. Dildy was the second president to die in office; David R. Fly, of Amarillo, had died in 1911 and had been succeeded by Dr. J. H. McCracken, of Mineral Wells.

tion he had made a good start. The *Journal* of December carried an editorial in furtherance of the plan, as well as a twenty-page article which had been written by Dr. Haven Emerson, of New York, for the American Medical Association and had been distributed in pamphlet form, the title being "Periodic Examinations of Apparently Healthy Persons."

This year teaching clinics were emphasized in Texas. For some time, Fort Worth had promoted a one-day meeting. The Dallas Southern Clinical Society announced through the *Journal* a three-day session of postgraduate teaching. Similar assemblies were initiated in Houston in 1932 and in San Antonio in 1933. These affairs, as successful as they were worthy, have continued to the present. With the ceaseless multiplication of local and state medical meetings, however, it can hardly be doubted that the sessions of the state association have been adversely affected.

Praise for the medical profession of Texas came from an unexpected source. The Central Texas Conference of the Methodist Episcopal Church unanimously adopted by a rising vote a laudatory resolution. It spoke of the doctor's unmeasured beneficence, his kindness and good will, his generosity, his unselfishness. Because of these, after pledging "loyal co-operation with them in programs and labors which look to the common good of our people," the resolution concluded: "We pledge ourselves to earnest prayers for the doctors, nurses and their co-workers, for the success of their labors, that the healing and keeping power of the Great Physician may minister through them to the health of our people, and that His spirit may so live in their lives as to enable them to minister in His name, not only to the bodies, but also to the souls of men." [7] This resolution bore the signature of the Rev. T. Edgar Neal, pastor of the First Methodist Church of Temple, but it may well have reflected the influence of his fellow-townsman, Dr. A. C. Scott, physician and Presbyterian elder.

[7] This mutually beneficial association of pastor and physician has grown from year to year, with the patient as the chief beneficiary. For its modern adaptation, see *The Ethical Basis of Medical Practice* (New York, 1950), by Willard L. Sperry, dean of the Harvard Divinity School.

XIX

Depression, 1930–34

THE EFFECTS of the business depression were not so severe in Texas as they were in the nation as a whole, but they were nonetheless very obvious. Five-cent cotton had very little buying power. Many banks failed, and much money was lost in the stock market. At one time, 267,000 persons in the state were unemployed. State and local relief agencies spent $80,268,595, and the federal government $351,023,546, over a four-year period. In this economic predicament, the doctors of Texas were firmly enmeshed. Their work went on as usual, but their collections were naturally much lighter.

It was an ambitious undertaking for the Palo Pinto County Medical Society to entertain the state association at Mineral Wells, since the society had only 20 members. The Association had met at Mineral Wells once before, in 1907. In both years, the attendance was well down. In 1930, however, the number of registrations was above that of the preceding two years at Galveston and Brownsville and above that of the subsequent two years at Beaumont and Waco. While Mineral Wells had a population of less than 10,000, it could claim 600 hotel rooms for its expected 150,000 visitors each year.

At Mineral Wells, the general meetings were more than ever neglected, though, in the words of Editor Taylor, "the programs ... were of such importance that it would seem that the halls would have been crowded each day." Visiting speakers at the general meetings were Homer N. Calver, secretary of the American Public Health Association; Dr. W. J. Bell, deputy minister of health of Canada; Dr. Aristides Agramonte; and Dr. Benjamin T. Terry, of

Rochester. Especially honored was the Association by the presence of Dr. Agramonte, whose renown had not lessened since he was a member of the United States Army Yellow Fever Commission thirty years before. At the time of his Texas visit, he was professor of bacteriology at the University of Havana. Dr. John O. McReynolds was at his best when he presented the distinguished Cuban as "the only surviving member of the most epoch-making commission ever appointed in the history of the race. . . . We are bound by indissoluble bonds, geographically, with our neighbors on the north and with our neighbors on the south. The black wings of pestilence and the radiant wings of healing know no national boundaries." Dr. Agramonte's address on "Looking Back upon Cuban Sanitary Progress" was a firsthand account of the definitive work on yellow fever which has added much to the honor of American medicine.

The work of the House of Delegates for the past two years had been expedited by furnishing the delegates ahead of time with the *Handbook,* in which the various reports and other pertinent data were printed. This year, Treasurer Beall was able to give the delegates a preview of a healthy financial condition: the total assets of the Association amounted to $101,446.90. Of this, $68,547.71 was invested in first mortgage loans, stocks, and bonds.

Following the trend of the preceding several years, the Executive Council assumed responsibility for the major portion of the work of the Association. As secretary of the council, Dr. Holman Taylor read, and probably had written, its report. He explained, in defense of its length, that "it takes words to convey ideas; lots of them, when ideas are so varied as they are here." Detailed facts were given on cooperation with the State Health Department and the State Board of Medical Examiners, on legislation, politics, annual physical examinations, radio broadcasting, and newspaper publicity. Years ago, the Association had invoked a time limit on scientific papers. Before this report of nearly ten thousand words was concluded, some of the somnolent delegates might have wished for brevity in reports to the House of Delegates.

One part of Dr. Marvin L. Graves's report for the Committee on Medical Education dealt with the number and distribution of physicians in Texas. According to the figures of Dr. T. J. Crowe, secretary of the State Board of Medical Examiners, there were 11,000 regular physicians and 200 each claiming allegiance to the eclectic, homeopathic, and osteopathic schools. He made allowance for certain factors, such as death and retirement, and concluded that there were around 10,000 legal practitioners in the state, or 1 physician to 500 people. New doctors were coming in at the rate of about 300 a year, and death was claiming about half that number.

President Jenkins, in addressing the session on "A Useful Medical Profession," paid high tribute to Dr. Joe Dildy, whose unexpected death had elevated Dr. Jenkins to the presidency. A general practitioner from a small town, Dr. Jenkins made a short commendable address. Tact and honest dealing must be used in the various contacts with the public, he said. Profound scholarship and professional prominence cannot come to all. Sincerity and honesty must characterize the country doctor and the specialist alike. Honest effort will bring adequate reward. "The great joy of our professional relationships must reside in the confidence and affection of our colleagues," he admonished, "in the consciousness that the guiding star of our ambitions has been to make brighter the pathway of others, and to bring help and hope and courage to the unfortunate fellows of our race."

The nominating speeches, a little longer and more eloquent than usual perhaps, presented the unusual circumstance of having two nominees for president-elect from the same city: Drs. W. D. Jones and John O. McReynolds, of Dallas. Dr. McReynolds received the nomination by a margin of 10 votes. Drs. W. L. Baugh, of Lubbock; C. W. Stephenson, of Wichita Falls; and R. B. Bledsoe, of Angelina, were unanimous choices for vice-presidents. Beaumont received just twice as many votes as Fort Worth in balloting for the meeting place in 1931.

The American Public Health Association met in Fort Worth in October, 1930, this being the first time this organization had met in the Southwest. Good attendance and prominent speakers made the meeting a success.

The subject of a medical history of Texas or a history of the State Medical Association of Texas had appeared in Association records for many years. A committee had been in existence for several years, and considerable material had been assembled. But no beginning had ever been made toward actually writing the history. In the meantime, Mrs. S. C. Red, of Houston, had been at work. She excited the interest of the auxiliary, urging the various county groups to send in data concerning the early doctors of their respective areas. Some of the material which the Association had collected at the

347

University of Texas was utilized. The result was the publication at Houston in 1930 of a creditable volume of 344 pages, *The Medicine Man in Texas*. It sold for three dollars, and the profits for the first two years went to the Woman's Auxiliary. The first part of the book, which deals with the early medical history of Texas, was derived principally from the Bexar Archives.[1] Then comes the period of the Texas Revolution and the Republic of Texas. The final two-thirds of the book is biographical, and herein lies its greatest value.

At the opening meeting of the House of Delegates at Beaumont, President-Elect McReynolds made a statement that had a sobering effect on the delegates. He saw well into the future and realized that organized medicine would soon be sorely beset from without and that minor dissensions within must be forgotten. "We have before us," he said, "some very vital problems—problems that will require the very best that we can give in the way of broad toleration, cool and dispassionate judgment and the most complete co-operation within our power." He was of course referring to the threat of socialized medicine, which was far more than a cloud on the medical horizon.

Later in the session, in line with this thought, the Council on Medical Economics was created to take the place of the Committee on Compensation and Health Insurance. Of economic significance was the reduction of dues from $10 to $8, this change to be made when the law requiring an annual registration fee of $2 went into effect in 1932. Then the Association would cease to pay $250 per month to the Board of Medical Examiners. As an offset to this decrease in expenditures, the salary of Dr. Taylor was increased to $10,000.

The *Journal* commented editorially on the Beaumont program thus: "Perhaps previously there has never been a better group of scientific programs than presented by our scientific sections this year, and the lantern exhibits, including motion pictures, both talkie and silent would have done credit to the American Medical Association." The Association had just purchased four new projection lanterns. All of these were used by Dr. Joseph C. Bloodgood, of Baltimore, projecting pictures and charts on four screens simultaneously. Dr. Bloodgood's subject was "Borderline Tumors, Types Difficult to Distinguish the Benign from the Malignant in the Mi-

[1] On loan to the Library of the University of Texas, Austin.

croscopic Section." This address was delivered on Wednesday before a full auditorium of laymen and doctors. The following day, Dr. William C. MacCarty, of Rochester, spoke on another phase of the cancer problem.

The House of Delegates adopted unanimously a resolution endorsing Dr. E. H. Cary for the office of president of the American Medical Association and instructing the Texas delegates to present his name and vote for him as long as his name was under consideration. Dr. Cary was elected national president-elect in 1931. His election was "in recognition of his accomplishments in the field of medical education, administration and eminence in the field of ophthalmology, as a builder of medical institutions, and particularly of his genius for friendship and service." [2] Something of the boundless energy and ceaseless drive of this man can be shown by the fact that during his term of office he traveled nearly 100,000 miles and was away from home 340 days.

When Chairman S. E. Thompson, of Kerrville, read the 63 names of deceased members and 65 names of deceased nonmembers at the memorial exercises, two former presidents stood out as grievous losses: Drs. J. D. Osborn, of Cleburne, and William Keiller, of Galveston. Here were two wheel horses of organized medicine, two men wholly different in their backgrounds, who yet fitted themselves into their fields of service with equal ease and dignity. As Dr. Holman Taylor spoke in tribute to the memory of Dr. Osborn, some of his auditors must have recalled how much of medical concern had happened between the time of his arrival in Texas and the day when he was laid to rest in his Confederate uniform fifty-six years later. This surgeon in General Nathan Bedford Forrest's cavalry had been signally honored eight years before by the publication of a booklet in recognition of his faithful service as secretary of the Society of Ex-Presidents of the Association since its inception. Dr. Edward Randall, his colleague of many years, paid worthy tribute to Dr. Keiller, speaking of his "rare enthusiasm and indomitable courage." Despite the handicap of semi-invalidism, he had exerted an impressive influence on medical teaching in Texas over a period of forty years. "Few are the men," Dr. Randall affirmed, "of this or any other generation who fold their wings so quietly and go down into the dusk out of the sunshine of happy labor, of many honors, of much love."

[2] Fishbein, *A History of the A.M.A.*, 785.

President Burns's address on "Progress of Modern Medicine" made a sensible survey of the course of medicine through the years and pointed out the many mileposts of progress. He found a happy summary of what he had in mind in these words of Sir George Newman: "Mighty have been the victories of this lap in the long journey from Hippocrates, and the spacious days of the fifth century before Christ, in the sunny islands of the Aegean. Today they are yours. Life is longer for mankind now; death has been, though not defeated, at least postponed; plague and pestilence have been stayed; human capacity has been enlarged and its opportunities extended. We are the heirs of the ages; and to us have come the fruits of other men's labors. Shall we idly eat, drink, and be merry before we die, or shall we accept our legacy, and by high endeavor and honest service transmute it into a further extension of the frontiers of life?"

The new president-elect was Dr. John H. Foster, of Houston. As vice-presidents, the Association chose Drs. C. H. Harris, of Fort Worth; A. C. DeLong, of San Angelo; and J. W. Torbett, of Marlin. Amarillo was selected as the site of the 1932 session. Other invitations came from Galveston, Waco, Fort Worth, and San Angelo.

But the 1932 session was not to be held in Amarillo. "Remoteness from the centers of medical population" was mentioned as the question of meeting places was discussed editorially. The main reason for the change was the subsequent decision of the American Medical Association to hold its 1932 session in New Orleans. So that both sessions might be available to a larger number, the Executive Council moved the session of the state association to Waco and set the dates for Thursday, Friday, and Saturday, May 5–7. This change in meeting place hastened a conclusion which was becoming increasingly apparent to the leaders: the smaller cities of the state were not adequate to the needs of the Association. This conviction was emphasized by constantly decreased attendance. The presence of 742 at Waco was about average for the smaller places. Since 1932, all meetings have been held in Houston, Dallas, San Antonio, Fort Worth, or Galveston, and at no time has the attendance fallen under 1,000.

The *Journal* announced that a library package service had been made available to the doctors of Texas. The American Medical Association had installed a similar service seven years before. At that time, dependence was placed principally on the 23,401 reprints which had been assembled at Fort Worth. A charge of twenty-five

cents per package was made, and a time-limit of two weeks was enforced.

Except for the president's reception, all the meetings of the sixty-
sixth session of the Association of Texas were held in the Austin
Avenue Methodist Church, in Waco. By the spring of 1932 the
medical profession of Texas was in mid-stream of the depression.
There was a general feeling of unrest; naturally, much was said
about medical economics and state medicine. Dr. R. G. Leland,
director of the Bureau of Medical Economics of the American Medical Association, spoke at one of the general sessions. He pointed out
that medical attitudes must change with changing economic conditions. "We recognize it not only a part of medicine to discuss economics, but we have discarded that old idea that it is unethical to
consider the business side of the profession." The newly created
Council on Medical Economics, under the able and alert leadership
of Dr. W. F. Starley, of Galveston, made a comprehensive report.
During the year, Dr. Starley had prepared two articles dealing with
economic matters: "The New Era in Medical Economics" and "The
Inadequacy of Socialism." These were for distribution to the doctors of Texas. This council based its report on such solid statements
as these: "There is no general panacea for our economic ills—only
hard work and study and faithful adherence to ideals. . . . The atmosphere is tense with the feeling that important changes, possibly
revolutionary in character, are in the making, in the pattern of medical practice. . . . Character, chiseled like a statue out of the past,
is the triumphant torch-bearer of medicine; taking form in a far-
removed day, it has been the guide and monitor of the doctor of
medicine. This dominant, spiritual force, be it recorded to our
great honor, almost alone correlates the diverse and conflicting
agencies that distribute medical service."

Much more was said about this dominant subject of economics.
President McReynolds, in his opening remarks, pointed the way:
"The creed of the Texas profession may well become the creed of
the world. Our conceptions of duty and high standards of thought
and conduct, like our form of National Government, may just as
well lead other peoples of the earth, rather than follow them into
the quicksands of indescribable confusion and futile regret." Dr.
John H. Burleson, of San Antonio, reporting as chairman of the
Board of Councilors, added this warning: "Let us see to it that eco-

nomic conditions do not produce bad ethics as well as bad morals. The counsel of the older men in the practice is invaluable at this time." In his report for the Reference Committee on Reports of Officers and Committees, Dr. D. H. Hudgins, of Kaufman, wisely advised that "we must steer further from commercialism during these depressed times, and manifest a greater fellow feeling for our fellow man." Dr. Holman Taylor referred to state medicine as a "menace to the health and welfare of our people and to the practice of scientific medicine."

Contract practice was not truly a by-product of the depression, but certainly hard times accentuated it. In other years, it had been accepted as ethical for railroads, traction companies, and kindred public-service corporations to employ physicians by the month. When ready cash was hard to come by, there was a strong tendency to extend the practice to other groups. Highlighting this trend was the case of the Dallas Medical and Surgical Clinic. This clinic made a contract with the Federal Land Bank and the Dallas Railway Benefit Association. The Dallas County Medical Society held that these contracts were detrimental to organized medicine and suspended indefinitely the members of this clinic. The matter came before the Board of Councilors. This body ruled that the contracts should be abandoned as soon "as possible not to work an injustice on the several parties involved" and that the suspended members should be reinstated thereafter. The decision was appealed to the Judicial Council of the American Medical Association, which sustained the Dallas County Medical Society in its suspension of the staff of the clinic. The matter was then settled on the basis suggested by the Board of Councilors.

The Association found itself involved in some practical and personal economics. Membership was 570 below the high point of 3,777 in 1930, and no provision had been made for making up for the loss in income from recently reduced dues. As a consequence, there was a shrinkage in assets of $3,529.82. The advertising income of the *Journal* diminished by $3,100. In meeting this situation, the Board of Trustees did what was obviously right in their judgment: they made a 10 per cent reduction in the salary of all employees. It is recorded that the secretary and his co-workers accepted the reduction cheerfully. This lowering of income was not a reflection on the financial status of the Association, which was sound. Investments in stocks, bonds, and loans added up to $80,338.46, on which 6 per cent interest was received.

At this Waco meeting, a radical innovation was tried in an effort to stimulate attendance. Five hours were set aside on the second and third afternoons for hearing a large number of guest speakers. The speakers on Friday were Drs. G. D. Royston, of St. Louis; A. E. Bulson, of Fort Wayne; J. W. Gray, of Newark; Alfred W. Adson, of Rochester; Albert Soiland, of Los Angeles; and R. G. Leland, of Chicago. The next afternoon seven guests were presented, including Drs. C. H. Best, of Toronto; W. Wayne Babcock, of Philadelphia; and F. M. Pottenger, of Los Angeles. The program closed at 6:00 P.M. Very few heard these papers. It must have been an exhausting experience. Someone must have concluded that glory would redound to the man who could devise a plan to do away with the front seat in a church and the last meeting of a medical assembly. Despite this unhappy and overdone initiation, the plan was worthy and was continued in modified form, the main alterations being a reduction in the number of speakers to two or three and the placing of a limitation on each speaker's time.

There could have been no apathy or drowsiness when President McReynolds delivered his address on "The Medical Profession— Its Composite Character and Relationships." Violent storms were passing, he said, over the medical profession of Texas and the nation. There was much agitation over the cost of medical care. In this connection, he wisely observed that "the cheapest thing on earth is a good doctor." In dealing with this and other problems that perplexed the medical profession, "we must hold fast forever to the imperishable principles of correct living, high ideals and scientific achievement. . . . We must fight the ravages of false philosophies from without and sinister influences within." The fight was not for one generation; for "it is the clear and imperative duty of this generation to transmit to those who follow along with our unfinished work an atmosphere of goodwill and co-operation, of kindness and of courage. This atmosphere should be unclouded by prejudice or inherited animosities. It should give to the rising generations its splendid assets without its worn and tattered liabilities."

Dr. Alonzo A. Ross, of Lockhart, in a close race, defeated Dr. J. W. E. H. Beck, of De Kalb, for president-elect. Dr. Beck for many years had carried the banner of organized medicine in the state legislature. Drs. A. D. Nelson, of San Saba; H. F. Connally, of Waco; and R. Y. Lacy, of Pittsburg, were the three new vice-presidents. Fort Worth and Dallas were claimants for the 1933 session; the former was chosen.

The American Medical Association met at New Orleans two days after the Texas association adjourned. Here Texas doctors were well represented: one, J. H. Black, of Dallas, was chairman of the Section on Pathology and Physiology; six read papers; and twenty opened the discussion on other papers.

In these days of depression, the doctors of Texas apparently had some money left. The *Journal*, as it had done for several years, published an editorial on "European Tours." These were sponsored by the *Journal* and other state journals and combined sight-seeing and clinical study. The rates ranged from $849 to $1,215.

In the field of economy and finance, the courts of Texas handed down an important decision. Dr. John R. Caulk, of St. Louis, did a prostatectomy on Colonel George W. Brackenridge, of San Antonio, and made a charge of $10,000. The executor of the estate refused to pay the fee, which he considered excessive. The case was taken to court and Caulk was upheld. The court ruled that it was entirely proper to consider a patient's financial condition in determining a reasonable value for a physician's service.

When Chairman L. H. Reeves of the Committee on Arrangements called the Association to order at the Texas Hotel in Fort Worth, there was an air of expectancy. For the better part of a year the members had heard of prosperity being right around the corner, but it had never come close. A few months before, Franklin D. Roosevelt had become president, and changes—political, economic, and social—were in order. Doctors were drawn into the New Deal program through the Federal Emergency Relief Administration, approved on May 12, 1933, to administer direct federal relief to the needy in co-operation with the various states. Doctors would be expected to contribute their share by furnishing medical service to indigents at reduced fees. In Texas the program was greeted with mixed feelings, the Executive Council of the Association expressing perhaps the immediate majority reaction to the agency by calling it a "laudable endeavor of relieving want and suffering among our people."

When the relief program, along with extended medical benefits, was enlarged by the establishment of the Civil Works Administration the following winter, Dr. Holman Taylor decided it was time to issue a warning: "We have entered upon a course which is gravely dangerous, in that it is a distinct step toward the socialization of medicine." Dr. Taylor's statement would be echoed and re-echoed with increasing frequency in the two decades ahead.

All this and much more agitated the Fort Worth session. The frequently berated Committee on the Costs of Medical Care to the American People had made its report, and the lines were partially drawn. The majority of the committee leaned toward a tax-supported program. The minority report recommended methods which could be "fitted into our present institutions and agencies without interfering with the fundamentals of medical practice." The Executive Council of the state association vigorously supported the minority report. The Board of Councilors felt that the report of the Committee on Costs of Medical Care had demoralized the public and discouraged the profession: "Its recommendations, if followed, would destroy the personal relationship existing, and which must exist, between the physician and his patient." All believed that a militant economic consciousness must be maintained and that much could be done by county committees on medical economics. Chairman W. F. Starley of the Council on Medical Economics put it this way in his talk, "At the Crossroads": "After a long journey of countless generations of doctors along a path strewn with the roses of mercy we have come at last to the sign of the crossroads. Which way will we travel now? One way leads up to the rugged path of private practice. Over the hilltops is the star of—you may call it 'medieval ethics' if you like! The other way leads down into the shadows of the valley of state medicine to reach the mausoleum of the independent, individualistic practice of medicine."

While the dominant note of this sixty-seventh session of the Association was economic, the regular work of the Association went on as usual, and the various councils and committees made their reports. Two of the Mayo Clinic's best ambassadors were on hand: Drs. F. A. Willius and Albert C. Broders. The latter, as he read his epochal paper on "The Grading of Cancer: Its Relationship to Metastasis and Prognosis," doubtless did not dream that a few years later he would become a member of the profession in Texas.

The Executive Council had its routine problems relating to publicity, the work of the Board of Health, the work of the State Board of Medical Examiners, and medical legislation. In the last category, in addition to the expected clashes with chiropractors and Christian Scientists, it met something quite different. A bill was introduced into the House of Representatives providing that a doctor could not "recover by law for services rendered, fees in excess of the following: Major operations, $100; minor operations, $10; house calls, $2.00; office consultation, $1.00, and hospital visits, 50¢." The House killed the bill by a vote of 102 to 19.

Dr. John H. Foster chose the unusual title "The Blind Men and the Elephant" for his presidential address. He based his theme on the fable in which six blind beggars attempted to tell what an elephant was like by feeling of one part of the animal's body. Members of the Association were inclined to emphasize different phases of its work: Some would like to see the Association as a purely scientific organization; some would stress its educational and sociological aspects; many would keep the political activity of organized medicine to the forefront; others would build the Association into a meeting place of friendly intercourse, common interests, and congenial tastes; and a few would devote the major part of the best thought and energy of the Association to combating the economic ills that threatened. In all these attitudes Dr. Foster saw merit, but only the full co-operation of all concerned could bring to organized medicine the support it deserved. Eternal vigilance was the price of survival: "The fact that we cannot see clearly ahead makes it all the more important that we be alert, lest we drift like sheep over a precipice."

Dr. S. E. Thompson, of Kerrville, was chosen president-elect without opposition. Here, as always, three nominations were made for vice-presidents and three were elected: R. H. McLeod, of Palestine; B. C. Smith, of Hillsboro; and N. D. Buie, of Marlin. San Antonio was the unanimous selection for the next session.

In calling attention to the problems arising from lessened membership and diminished income from advertising, the *Journal* set down for its readers exactly what the member received for eight dollars. It was a real bargain: a militant state organization, proper listing in the *Directory* of the American Medical Association, twelve issues of the *Journal*, medical and public health legislation, package library service, protection in case of lawsuits, prerequisite to membership in the American Medical Association, attendance at

356

medical association meetings, public relations, and medical economics.

In San Antonio, in 1934, the Association was again disturbed by the specter of socialization, a many-sided and difficult problem. Because of the depression, certain lay humanitarian groups, such as the Milbank Fund and the Julius Rosenwald Fund, were pleading the cause of greater medical socialization, using well-known teachers who, doctors felt, knew little or nothing about the real problems of medicine. Nor did President Roosevelt, who may have meant to be reassuring, bring any comfort when he said: "Whether we come to this form of insurance soon or later on I am confident that we can devise a system which will enhance and not hinder the remarkable progress which has been made and is being made in the practice of the professions of medicine and surgery in the United States."

Texas doctors were as uncertain about how they should feel as were doctors and laymen all over the country. Dr. Holman Taylor, in his secretary's report, went so far as to say, "If, following close study and mature deliberation, the medical profession of Texas decides upon some system of socialized medicine, all well and good." In commenting on a contract which the Association had made with the Texas Relief Commission, the Executive Council clearly recognized "the undeniable fact that in making this contract we have taken a definite step towards socialized medicine; that to this extent, at least, we are practicing panel medicine." The ordinary doctor could only be confused. This attitude was well expressed by Dr. Charles T. Stone, of Galveston, in his paper "A Physician Views the Changing Era." The average doctor, Stone said, would do the best he could and leave "the rest to the politicians and philanthropists who will most probably dominate the remainder of his existence anyway." The Council on Medical Economics, which had reflected good solid thinking, saw the situation as it was: "We see many ramifications of socialization—the greatest threat to time-crystalized principles that surely should not be swept aside by a wave of ill-considered or maudlin sentimentalism on the part of social welfare enthusiasts inside or outside of the profession. Here we should stand pat."

This council considered the subject of health insurance in its report. The American Medical Association had furnished rather inept leadership in this direction. The matter had been before the national organization for many years, but little progress had been made. In 1934, the Michigan State delegation introduced a resolution advising that powerful forces were working toward health insurance and urging the medical profession to do something about the situation in its own way. The resolution was unduly zealous and did not meet with official favor, even though it was based on first-hand knowledge of what was going on in Europe. That some form of health insurance was necessary, there was no doubt. The state Council on Medical Economics realized "that a long disability impoverishes the poor, pinches the ordinary worker, embarrasses the well-to-do, and that only the wealthy can afford a long illness." Violent disagreement arose, however, as to whether health insurance should be voluntary or compulsory. Dr. Claude C. Cody, of Houston, epitomized the problem thus: "It is a question whether the further development of our system of medical practice shall be evolutionary under the auspices of organized medicine, or revolutionary, engendered by socialistic agitators." The whole subject was difficult and complicated. In the opinion of Dr. Stone, "government care for the indigent, sickness savings accounts, and voluntary health insurance for the wage earners, offer the best solution to the pressing need of adequate medical care for all the people." The state association profited indirectly from all this agitation. The contract which the Association had made with the Relief Commission specified that all work should be handled through the channels of organized medicine. This requirement prompted the organization of new county societies and stimulated growth of the old. As a result, membership increased from 2,947 to 3,451.

The Association needed some such stimulus. Interest in organized medicine was lagging. Particularly noticeable was the decline in attendance at county medical meetings. This fact was influenced by the multiplied meetings in the larger cities. But the thing which the Association eyed with particular alarm was the growing prestige of the several postgraduate assemblies over the state. The programs of these groups were altogether excellent and were put on by distinguished speakers, whose expenses were paid. The Association saw itself being overshadowed, and a committee appointed for the purpose studied the situation carefully but found no solution. It was suggested that the assemblies might limit their activities to local areas and discontinue the practice of paying their guest speakers. But these assemblies have continued influential and excellent up to the present. It is now recognized, however, that they are worthy rivals and healthy stimuli to the sessions of the Texas Medical Association.

The suggestion about pay for guest speakers was futile. The question of paying its own visiting speakers was already under consideration by the Association. It had first come up at a called meeting of the Council on Scientific Work in March, 1934. Under the prodding of Dr. Dudley Jackson, of San Antonio, chairman of the Section on Surgery, this subject was thoroughly discussed, and a motion was passed urging the House of Delegates to provide funds for the payment of the expenses of guest speakers. The house approved the idea, but it was not until 1938 that the Board of Trustees, always watchful of the treasury, was willing to admit the wisdom and the necessity of this investment.

This year saw the passing of Dr. I. C. Chase. As secretary-editor and as president, he was one of those who had piloted the Association through troublous times. Two years before, Dr. Chase had presided over the memorial exercises when Dr. A. B. Small, of Dallas, had spoken thus of another former president, Dr. Joe Becton: "He often with his genius, like a bright jewel with many facets, illuminated dull moments in medical meetings." These words, with equal accuracy, could have been applied to Dr. Chase.

President Ross's address on "Stepping Stones in the Scientific and Social Progress of Medicine in Texas" was in high praise of organized medicine in the state. Pridefully and nostalgically, he recounted the accomplishments of the Texas Medical Association over a period of eighty-one years. Accurately, he traced the story of state medical legislation and pointed out the leading part which the Association had played. He deplored the economic trends of his day. He could not understand "how we can get out of debt by borrowing money, feed the hungry by limiting production, and clothe the naked by plowing up cotton." But when it came to his inbred loyalty to the medical profession of Texas, all doubt and uncertainty disappeared. In words reminiscent of an earlier generation, he expressed his instinctive fidelity to his profession: "The doctor needs no eulogy before this group or any other. His years in training are hard, a marathon of work; his years in practice are hard, a marathon of service. In the country or the city, a physician, a surgeon or a specialist, his days and nights are threaded with responsibility, physical, mental, and emotional. His compensation is this, that his work is actual and immediate, that with his own hands he practices his own theories, and himself observes their success or failure. Is this not the full flavor of human dignity—to solve in the degree that science and humanity may, the manifold problems of mortality?"

New officers chosen were John H. Burleson, of San Antonio, president-elect; and J. M. Travis, of Jacksonville; A. L. Ridings, of Sherman; and J. H. Caton, of Eastland, vice-presidents. Dallas, El Paso, and Houston asked for the next meeting, with Dallas the choice.

XX

Search for Survival, 1935–39

In 1936, TEXAS CELEBRATED the one-hundredth anniversary of her independence. In that year organized medicine in Texas encountered a new and serious threat when the United States Department of Justice brought an antitrust suit against the American Medical Association, the District of Columbia Medical Society, and the Harris County Medical Society of Texas. The trial resulted in a fine for the American Medical Association and the District of Columbia society. The board of trustees of the American Medical Association interpreted the suit as an "attempt to convict the American Medical Association in the eyes of the people of being a predatory, antisocial monopoly." Many laymen, as well as doctors, were considerably troubled by the outcome of the suit.

In Dallas the well-attended 1935 sessions of the Association heard much discussion about socialized medicine and compulsory health insurance, which to them were one and the same thing. The fact of the continuing economic depression and general social unrest would naturally have kept these subjects to the forefront. The Executive Council saw the situation as "the legitimate offspring of an illegitimate obsession," while the Council on Medical Economics declared that compulsory health insurance meant regimentation of the medical profession. But because the doctors were uncertain what would be done next in Washington, they were equally uncertain how to proceed to combat what they considered the inroads on their profession. In Texas they had abrogated their contract with the Texas Relief Commission, but this was scant progress when the

361

federal government was creating such vast agencies as the Works Progress Administration.

Various plans for checkmating the social reformers were advanced at the Association's annual meeting. Receiving particular attention was one procedure already in effect in Bexar County.[1] Morris Fishbein was on hand to participate in the discussion, but the Texas association was already beyond the American Medical Association in its planning for a counterattack. Except to discuss the situation thoroughly, little was done beyond naming a Committee on Distribution of Medical Service. In the October *Journal* this committee made a full report, with elaborate charts, which looked impressive and complicated. After assuming the Association presidency, Dr. John H. Burleson made a series of talks throughout the state, in which he urged the seriousness of the government's program. Always Dr. Burleson closed as follows: "It is for the next generation of doctors that I speak. If some reform is not made, medicine will cease to be a profession and degenerate into a trade." Doctors, aware of the implications of the Wagner Bill, then before Congress, invariably agreed.

Not all questions before the Dallas session, however, were economic. Bickering over routine matters had ceased as the doctors solidified their position to meet the thrusts of the government. One question which had concerned the Association for some years was the growing expense of the annual meetings. Then, too, each session tended to compete with its predecessors in elaborateness of entertainment. To solve this problem, the Board of Trustees took the income from the technical exhibits to pay the expenses of the meeting, including all entertainment. Thus the Association took over complete charge of convention arrangements, controlling expense and paying bills directly.

This year, the Texas Pathological Society awarded its first certificates for meritorious research. They went to Dr. R. M. Moore, of the University of Texas, for his paper on "Investigation of Chemical Changes Which May Excite Pain, With a Note on Distribution of Pain Fibers to Visceral Organs," and to Dr. Hardy A. Kemp, of Baylor, for his work on "Relapsing Fever in Texas." Also for the first time, the Association, through its newly created Committee on Scientific Awards, issued awards of excellence in the field of scien-

[1] Nearly two hundred programs for action in this controversy had been submitted to the American Medical Association.

tific exhibits. For their display of photomicrographs of peripheral nerve tumors, W. W. Brandes and Lewis Waters, of Baylor, received one of the awards; for their exhibit on nephritis, a similar award was given to J. M. Horn, C. N. Hamlin, and J. F. Pilcher, of the University of Texas.

The presidential address of Dr. S. E. Thompson properly had to do with economics. His subject was "Can Our Present System of Medicine Survive?" In short, sharp sentences, he developed the economic background of the depression. Poor foresight, bad judgment, and unsound thinking played their part: "we did not know the difference between what we needed and what we wanted." The result was "chaos, the night, and the New Deal." In the field of medicine, various harebrained schemes were coming out of Washington, he said, fathered by "professors" who wouldn't know "the difference between quinine and condition powders, botts and boils, spavin and sprue." The people were panicky, money was being spent lavishly, and a cry for security was heard over the land. If the medical profession did not act with assurance and dispatch, he warned, the social planners would take over. The way out for the patient and the doctor was becoming clear: it was voluntary health insurance, approved by the medical profession and not controlled and directed by politicians or laymen on the government payroll. Some adjustments in the field of medical ethics might have to be made, but if properly set up and properly directed, the plan would work.

In balloting for president-elect, Dr. Howard R. Dudgeon, of Waco, was chosen over Dr. A. O. Singleton, of Galveston. In the past, the election of vice-presidents had been a dull formality: three men were nominated and three men were elected. This year, however, there were a dozen or so nominations, and several ballots were required to elect Drs. O. F. Gober, of Temple; O. M. Marchman, of Dallas; and Thomas Dorbandt, of San Antonio. The delegates picked Houston over El Paso and Austin as the meeting place for 1936.

Two veterans of the medical profession had died during the year: Drs. Alex W. Acheson, of Denison, and Isaac Lycurgus Van Zandt, of Fort Worth, at the respective ages of ninety-one and ninety-five —one a wearer of the blue uniform of the North in the Civil War, the other a wearer of the gray of the South. Both had been officers in the army; both became privates in organized medicine in Texas. It is stated that Dr. Van Zandt brought the first microscope to Texas.

Members of organized medicine in Texas for sixty-three years, these two pioneers, in the words of Kipling, lived "in simpleness and gentleness and honour and clean mirth."

In editorial retrospect, Dr. Holman Taylor stated that the 1936 meeting in Houston "was characterized by a smoothness, deliberation and efficient operation rather exceptional in meetings of the sort. This very wholesome and satisfactory state of affairs was incident, no doubt, to the efficiency which comes of experience, both as relates to the central organization and the local setup." In other words, good arrangements and good meetings were taken for granted, and the office force of the Association, along with the official family, could accept for itself due credit and real pride. Greater pride, no doubt, came to Dr. Taylor when he reported the membership to be above 4,000. The presence of 1,124 members bore out a rough ratio which had existed for many years and which still exists: one-fourth of the members attend the annual sessions.

Recalling that the Board of Trustees had assumed responsibility for all arrangements of the meetings, Dr. Taylor was a little concerned because the Harris County Medical Society put on a floor show and dinner dance on Monday night at one of the night clubs. To use a mixed Latin phrase, he thought "there was something doing all of the time, mostly unofficial and extra cathedral." As an offset, he was able to report a profit of $179.35 for the *Journal*, when a loss had been the rule for many years. Incidentally, the net earnings of the *Journal of the American Medical Association* that year were $604,672.69.

The subject of state medicine received less attention than usual. The Council on Medical Economics did not mention it. There was a feeling that perhaps the medico-political clash was less violent. How far wrong such an opinion was is illustrated by the remarks of Dr. Charles T. Stone, professor of medicine at the University of Texas, to the Medical Auxiliary in 1951. After reviewing the tactics which New Deal enthusiasts had pursued so persistently, he told this story:

All these political machinations leave average citizens a bit bewildered. They recall the story of revenge in the Blue Ridge Mountains told by Bennett Cerf in his book "Try and Stop Me." An ornery sprout of the McGregor family plugged a member of the Larrabee family in the

364

back. One old Larrabee buck pointed out that a simple killing was too merciful for the varmint. His ingenious suggestion, promptly adopted unanimously, was that once every day a shot that would just miss him should be fired at McGregor. When Don Marquis, who originally told the story, saw the victim twenty years later, his hair was snow white, his face and hands twitched continuously, and his glance darted madly from side to side. As he was reaching for a bottle of soda pop, a shot rang out. The bottle was shattered into a thousand fragments. McGregor howled like a coyote. "They'll do it every day to him," commented a villager dispassionately, "till the poor so-and-so hangs hisself."

In like manner, the protagonists of socialized medicine and the multitude of related welfare state measures, so inimical to the American way of life, are employing near-miss methods in their effort to disconcert and disrupt our solid front against them.

For half a century or more, hopes had been expressed that the Association would someday occupy its own home. The Board of Trustees was happy to announce that this dream was now an accomplished fact. Various locations in several cities had been considered. A two-story brick residence at 1404 West El Paso Street in Fort Worth was decided on and bought, for $10,000, of which the local chamber of commerce paid $1,500. The building was large and roomy and adequate for the needs of the Association for many years. At the same time, the staff of the central office was expanded by the addition of Mildred Thomas, Hope Chase, and Marjorie Lee Thomas.

The constitution and bylaws had been amended the previous year, creating the status of "member emeritus." Nomination by the Board of Councilors and approval by the local county society brought the candidate before the House of Delegates, where a two-thirds majority was required for election. This honor was reserved for those who had rendered "exceptional and distinguished service to scientific or organized medicine, or both." The first two members to be so honored were from Houston: Drs. John T. Moore and Marvin L. Graves. Two additional members received this honor a year later: Drs. Edward Randall, of Galveston, and John W. Burns, of Cuero.

With less emphasis on economics, the scientific sections became more active. The papers presented by the members were of a high order, and the following list of guest speakers added luster to the program: Drs. Edward H. Rynearson, Lawrence M. Randall, Eugene T. Leddy, and G. J. Thompson, of Rochester; M. P. Neal, of Columbia, Missouri; Alton Ochsner and Charles J. Bloom, of New Orleans; and Oscar B. Nugent, of Chicago.

Dr. John H. Burleson chose for the subject of his presidential address, not the battle of the medical profession against the government reformers, on which subject he had spoken all over the state during his year as president, but "The Evolution of Medicine." He set down the accomplishments of medicine from the earliest time. He emphasized the conquest of infectious diseases, in which he had played a part. Medical progress was desirable, said Dr. Burleson, and was inevitable, if not impeded by selfish politicians; but the family doctor, the real source of strength of the medical profession, should be constantly recalled: "Medicine has advanced the happiness and well-being of mankind more than all other sciences. . . . What has become of the clinician, the man who looked at the tongue, counted the pulse, was skilled in the art of auscultation and percussion, and who could make a diagnosis of a chest condition without a stethoscope? . . . I sometimes wonder if the passing of the family doctor is not the tragedy of the medicine of today."

Dr. Calvin R. Hannah, of Dallas, was elevated to the office of president-elect over Dr. E. W. Bertner, of Houston. Elected as vice-presidents were Drs. W. C. Williams, of San Marcos; S. D. Whitten, of Greenville; and R. S. Wood, of Waco. Without opposition, Fort Worth received the 1937 session of the Association. As a matter of fact, the Association had begun, and would continue, to make the circuit of the five major cities of Texas.

The Board of Trustees, of which Dr. John T. Moore was chairman for many years, closed its report at the Fort Worth meeting by observing that in 1937 "the return of prosperity was definitely a fact." There was a modicum of optimism in this observation. The Association closed the year with a deficit of $365.63, and the proposed budget for the next year anticipated a deficit of $1,800.00. With a view to taking care of this deficit, dues were raised from $8.00 to $9.00, the vote in the House of Delegates being unanimous for the increase. Another reason for this increase was the decision, at last, by the Board of Trustees, in answer to a continued and persistent demand of the membership, to pay the expenses of invited guests.

The trustees included in their report an important announcement: former president S. E. Thompson, of Kerrville, had made a provision in his will whereby the library of the Association would receive $50,000.00 at his death. This proposed gift lent encouragement to the oft-expressed hope of the trustees to accumulate a reserve of $100,000.00. They were really beginning to anticipate the time when the Association would construct a building as a permanent home, an ambition fully realized in 1952.

Over a period of many years, indeed since its organization, the Association had manifested deep interest in the State Board of Health. The creation of such a board had been one of the chief concerns of the Association, and, after it was once established, the Association exercised a zealous interest in its welfare. In 1932, the Board of Health elected Dr. John W. Brown state health officer. Dr. Brown brought to his new position a certificate of public health from Johns Hopkins University, thus becoming the first trained state health officer of Texas. Over a period of four years, Dr. Brown did excellent work in advancing the cause of public health in Texas. At two sessions of the Association the House of Delegates warmly commended his work. When James V. Allred was re-elected governor in 1936, several changes were made in the membership of the State Board of Health. The Executive Council asked the board to reappoint Dr. Brown. Instead, however, it appointed Dr. George W. Cox, a practicing physician of Del Rio.

The Committee on Collection and Preservation of Records, of which Dr. W. B. Russ had become chairman, had been rather inactive for several years; the zeal of Dr. Frank Paschal was missing. This year, however, the committee presented to the House of Delegates some important data collected by the Committee on Archives of the Woman's Auxiliary, under the chairmanship of Mrs. W. A. Wood, of Waco. This material consisted of an accurate statistical table showing the presidents of the Association, the places of meeting, the attendance when available, and much other pertinent data. This table has been constantly used in the preparation of the present history of the Association.

Visiting speakers included Dr. Lewis J. Moorman, of Oklahoma City; Drs. Rigney D'Aunoy and Francis E. LeJeune, of New Orleans; Dr. Virgil S. Counseller, of Rochester; Professor Fred Hale, of College Station; Dr. Thomas Parran, of Washington, D.C.; Dr. Walter E. Dandy, of Baltimore; Dr. Edward C. Mitchell, of Memphis; and Dr. W. Warner Watkins, of Phoenix. The title of Dr. Watkins' paper, "Halisteresis as a Medical Problem," must have sent his auditors scurrying to their dictionaries.

In discussing the topic of his presidential address, "Has the Private Practice of Medicine Failed?" Dr. H. R. Dudgeon compared the practice of medicine in the United States with that in those European countries which had state medicine. From every angle, his comparison favored the private plan, which time and experience had developed. The practice of medicine in this country, he freely admitted, had its defects. The expense of prolonged illness did fall with crushing effect at times, but other misfortunes had a way of doing the same thing. The main strength of private practice lay in the personal relationship between patient and doctor: "Sympathy, kindness, pity, and cheerful hope—no amount of scientific efficiency can take the place of these in the dark hours of sorrow and trouble so common in the experience of all."

Immediately following this address came one by Dr. Charles Gordon Heyd, president of the American Medical Association, who bolstered Dr. Dudgeon's contentions. The 103,000 members of organized medicine in the United States were bound together in a plan to give to the people good medical care at reasonable cost. The American Medical Association, as shown by this quotation of Dr. Heyd, was still accenting what it opposed rather than what it proposed along the line of health insurance: "The insurance principle as applied to human sickness is acceptable only in buying hospital lodging and accommodations, food and general nursing care. The insurance principle applied to the employment of professional services will fail because there are inherent in it defects that depend upon the variability of human beings."

Officers of the Association were elected on the third day of the 1937 sessions. Usually by that time the delegates had begun to move homeward, but this year was an exception. Of the 108 delegates, 106 were present; and of these 58 cast their votes for Dr. E. W. Bertner, of Houston, and 48 for Dr. Preston Hunt, of Texarkana, in the race for president-elect. Without opposition, Drs. Craig Munter, of Fort Worth; R. B. Touchstone, of Lytle; and H. L. Locker, of Brownwood, were nominated for the offices of vice-president. Galveston, El Paso, Abilene, and San Antonio asked for the 1938 session. It was given to Galveston. Something new was introduced at the final meeting of this session when the proceedings were broadcast over radio station KTAT. New, too, was the frank discussion by Surgeon-General Parran of "The Public Health Control of Syphilis," a subject heretofore taboo on the air.

There was one doctor in Texas who was not disturbed about socialized medicine. He was John F. Brinkley, of Del Rio. His income in 1937 was $1,300,000, and he was seeking to add to this amount by selling Formula 1020 in six-ampule lots for $100. Formula 1020, according to the American Medical Association Clinical Laboratory, was prepared by dissolving 1 part of indigo in 100,000 parts of water. Dr. Brinkley has been characterized as the greatest medical charlatan of all time.

As described in the report of the Board of Trustees at Galveston, the educational activities of the Association were grouped around the *Journal* and the library. The *Journal* was at once the spokesman and the teacher of the medical profession of Texas. It gave full publicity to the projects set by the Association and kept its readers posted on political and economic developments. It published practically all the papers read at the sessions, carried the transactions of the Association and the auxiliary, gave space to the activities of the county societies, reviewed books, and devoted a few pages to personal and medical news. The reading matter ran to about nine hundred pages each year, with the advertising pages running about half that number. Altogether, its twelve monthly issues had come to be a welcome visitor to the desks of the doctors of Texas. But it was not a cheap undertaking: the expenses of the *Journal* for 1937 were $29,645.76. Few if any of the 4,148 members of the Association doubted that this money was well spent. The library had increased in importance. In four years, members saw the number of books grow from 3,824 to 4,232, the periodicals from 142 to 155, and the reprints from 40,202 to 79,224. The chief utility of the library lay in the library package service. In five years, 2,589 packages, comprising 28,076 items, had been mailed.

The topics discussed in the scientific sessions were changing with the times. Sulfanilamide, antipneumococcic serum, and air-conditioning, for instance, were on the 1938 program. And to emphasize the trends of modern medicine, an array of prominent visitors were on hand as the first group to have their expenses paid: Drs. Reed M. Nesbit, of Ann Arbor; Wendell G. Scott, of St. Louis; Emil Novak, of Baltimore; Edwin L. Osgood, of Portland; Waltman Walters, of

Rochester; John A. Kolmer, of Philadelphia; John J. Shea, of Memphis; A. T. McCormack, of Louisville; and J. H. J. Upham, of Columbus, president of the American Medical Association.

Economics and state medicine took a partial vacation at Galveston. The important developments were on a national level. The Wagner National Health Bill had been introduced in the Senate. It looked innocent enough at first, and Senator Wagner wrote to Dr. Holman Taylor: "Under no circumstances will the Federal Government undertake to furnish medical care." But there were many doubters. Their champion and spokesman was Dr. W. B. Russ, who had much to say in his paper on "The New Deal and the Socialization of Medicine." He paid his most acrid respects to the New Deal, the Congress of Industrial Organizations, the Association for the Advancement of Colored People, Dr. Hugh Cabot, and the other "emotionally drunk radicals" who had just completed a conference in Washington called by the Interdepartmental Committee to Co-ordinate Health and Welfare Activities of the Government. Its purposes, he said, were clear: "Blessed by the President, dominated by the C.I.O. and all the Reds, pinks, and yellows, this so-called conference resolved itself into a grand rally in which the self-righteous fanatics proclaimed on behalf of themselves and the New Deal an absolute monopoly of all the human virtues, including honesty, justice, fairness, kindness, and sympathy for the poor." And on and on he went, mingling sarcasm with fact. Which of these elements predominates in the following comparison, the reader must decide: "Man is supposed to have the advantage of intelligence, memory, and a social heritage, and therefore ought to profit by the experience of the race. The monkey, unable to profit by lessons of history, is a great social planner. Like the New Dealer, he plans often and always without regard to the experience and lessons of history. He plans a new world every morning. Unlike the New Dealer, however, the monkey does not organize the mob and get himself elected to office, for which we should be thankful."

When Dr. Calvin R. Hannah read his presidential address, "The Responsibility of the Physician," he took a general look at the practice of medicine, referred to the serious problems facing the medical profession, suggested an improved practice of medicine as one of the remedies, and then lauded the State Medical Association of Texas for its many contributions to human welfare. During most

370

of his address, he was speaking as a philosopher. Obviously a close follower of Sir William Osler, he spoke of candor, high ideals, truth, justice, and fair play. "The physician must have character and understanding, for these, rather than money, fame and power, are the qualities that determine happiness in the practice of medicine. . . . A trained intellect gives the joy of understanding, and understanding builds character. . . . [A doctor] must find a way to make cleanliness, courage, foresight and honor seem desirable to those about him." Finally, said Dr. Hannah, "Every man who aspires to the high calling of medicine should so live that of him can be said: He was learned without vanity, grave without moroseness, pleasant without levity, regular without formality, generous without prodigality, and religious without hypocrisy." [2]

In the balloting for the office of president-elect, Dr. L. H. Reeves, of Fort Worth, nosed out Dr. Preston Hunt, of Texarkana, by a single vote. In quick succession, three members were nominated and elected vice-presidents: Drs. Louis B. Holland, of Wichita Falls; J. W. Ward, of Greenville; and Fred B. Shields, of Victoria. San Antonio was chosen as the meeting place for 1939.

A note of interest in the official family of the Association was the retirement of Brigadier General Holman Taylor from the National Guard. Over a period of forty-seven years, Dr. Taylor had been in military service, very little of which was in the Medical Department.

The San Antonio session of 1939, according to Dr. Holman Taylor, was an outstanding success. The number of registrations was 1,250, this being 86 short of the highest attendance, in Dallas in 1935, and being well above 25 per cent of the membership of 4,200. As in the past, poor attendance at the general meetings was causing great concern. The same may be said about the empty seats at the memorial exercises; some might have stayed away on the theory that there were better ways of honoring the dead than by boring the living. But such an explanation was not adequate; the real explanation was that times had changed rapidly, and attitudes of sentiment had changed with them. As a contrast, one feature which had been instituted a few years earlier was growing in interest, the clini-

---

[2] The portion of this quotation following the colon was taken verbatim from William MacMichael, *The Gold-Headed Cane* ([New York, 1926], 102), without proper acknowledgment.

cal luncheon sessions. These two-hour noon meetings were divided by specialties and had one or more guest speakers assigned to each of them.

The problems of the general meetings were difficult to explain and difficult to solve. Certainly the best of programs were being provided by speakers of wide reputation. In 1939, for instance, the following visitors were present at San Antonio: Dr. John Zahorsky, of St. Louis; Drs. Hubley R. Owen and Eugene P. Pendergrass, of Philadelphia; Dr. Chester S. Keefer, of Boston; Dr. Russell L. Haden, of Cleveland; Dr. J. H. Stander, of New York; Colonel Charles F. Craig, of San Antonio; and Dr. Hugh Young, of Baltimore. For Dr. Young this was a homecoming. He had been born in San Antonio sixty-nine years before and had practiced medicine there at the age of twenty-four. He was in the heyday of his worldwide eminence as a urologist. At this meeting he was able to report 1,049 consecutive perineal prostatectomies with a mortality rate of only 3.4 per cent. And yet, when he appeared before the Association at its final general meeting, a pitifully small group was on hand to greet him.

The expenses of the invited guests at the previous session amounted to $1,156.30. All told, the Galveston session had cost $6,350.04, and the technical exhibits had brought in only $2,345.00. It was a credit to the management of the Board of Trustees, with constantly increasing demands on the treasury, that the net decrease in investments was only $2,000.00.

The several committees which touched on the question of medical economics dealt with it in general terms. The New Deal Committee to Co-ordinate Health and Welfare Activities had come out with several health features, such as aid for crippled children, rural health, and improved public health, all of which were desirable; but there were other features which the doctors feared would lead to complete socialization. Dr. E. H. Cary, as chairman of the Legislative Committee of the American Medical Association, was charged with checkmating such designs. He did an excellent job in this capacity. Among other things, he and his committee interviewed President Roosevelt. "Mr. President," asked Dr. Cary, "do we understand that you contemplate any kind of legislation that would change the practice of medicine as we understand it now?" "No, no," replied the President. By contrast, the committee got this opinion from Vice-President John ("Cactus Jack") Garner: "I can take the doctors and the bankers of this country and whip any legislation that comes before Congress."

In response to the publicization of the indictment of the American Medical Association and two affiliated societies, the national association had just completed a survey of medical conditions over the nation in an effort to help convince the public that the practice of medicine in the United States was the best in the world. The State Medical Association of Texas co-operated in this survey, and Dr. W. F. Starley and his Council on Medical Economics "established beyond doubt or equivocation that the need and supply of medical care in Texas are in hand and well balanced, yielding to our people a personal service more generous than any other at their command."

The plaint of the family doctor, of which there was ample justification and for which there was no suitable remedy, came before the House of Delegates this year as it had before. The day of his passing was obviously near at hand, but there were those who would delay that unhappy eventuality. Dr. J. Gordon Bryson, of Bastrop, a man of apparent iconoclastic trends, made a speech of 3,000 words, in which he described, in diary form, the crowded hours of a doctor's day. There was no doubting that the family doctor was obscure, poorly paid, and much loved. But that was not enough. His surgery was being taken over by the city surgeons, and his hospital was being supervised out of existence. Dr. Bryson concluded by saying: "I believe I have conveyed to you the idea that the country doctor is an overworked, misunderstood, overtaxed, and underpaid cog in the wheel of medicine, and the object of this foray into the sacred sanctuary by one of the unredeemed is not in the form of an application, for we have lived long and realized full well that the major part of our professional life lies in the background, and over which we hold no grief."

Others were passing besides the family doctor. This half-decade saw the death of five past presidents: Dr. John S. Turner in 1936, Dr. John W. Burns in 1939, Dr. S. C. Red in 1940, Dr. C. R. Hannah in 1940, and Dr. A. C. Scott in 1940. The combined capacities of these five were beyond measurement. At a time when the Association was so worried about enemies abroad, it could ill afford to lose their influence and their guidance.

Dr. E. W. Bertner, caught up as he was officially and personally in the storm that was gathering around the subject of state medicine, chose for his presidential remarks the topic "The Present Status of Texas Medicine." He depicted the national medical scene and the devices he perceived being concocted in Washington. He looked across the sea and recalled that "Bismarck rode into German political power on the expediency of State Medicine, which promised the will-o-the-wisp delusion of 'free medical care.'" He attacked the Wagner Bill and decried the implications of the suit being prosecuted against the American Medical Association. He inveighed against "the blackjack method of threat and coercion" then being used against the medical profession. In this situation he saw a threat to the liberty of all. Thurman Arnold, assistant United States attorney general, was reported as saying that "if 150 additional attorneys were placed at his disposal, he could reach every business and industry through Federal Grand Jury indictments." But Dr. Bertner's confidence in the cause and the survival of the medical profession was strong and unshaken. "There is an ineffable value," he said, in the doctor's "human touch that transcends all legislation which seeks to dip its partial fingers into the sterile waters of the healing art and arbitrate over his mission of mercy. The priceless human bond that exists between him and his patient can never exist between a medical politician and a patient with a government number and a red-taped record with no significance."

The new officers elected for the coming year were Preston Hunt, of Texarkana, president-elect; and W. A. Lee, of Denison; H. E. Griffin, of Graham; and A. M. Long, of Valley Mills, vice-presidents. Dallas was to be host to the association in 1940.

In the midst of taking pot shots at each other, the New Deal and the doctors came together long enough for the Post Office Department to issue two special stamps in commemoration of the life and work of Dr. Crawford W. Long and Dr. Walter Reed.

XXI

War Again, 1940–44

THE UNITED STATES declared war on Japan on December 8, 1941, and on Germany three days later. Medical preparedness started early and was carried out with efficiency. At its meeting in June, 1940, the American Medical Association offered its facilities to the government in the anticipated emergency. Questionnaires, establishing the fitness and availability of the recipients, were sent out to its 115,381 members, and in ten days nearly half had been filled out and returned. As early as August, 1940, Dr. Holman Taylor was urging co-operation. Primarily a doctor, he had long been a line officer in the Texas National Guard and knew the importance of preparedness. Texas doctors were strongly advised to get into the Medical Reserve Corps. The pay of a captain and a first lieutenant were to be $3,450 and $2,696. When the emergency came, the doctors of Texas answered the call. This circumstance had become a tradition. When the Texan Army had laid siege to San Antonio in 1835, every doctor of the area was on hand. And so it had been in 1836, 1846, 1861, 1898, and 1917.

The Dallas session of 1940, according to Dr. Holman Taylor, "was big in detail and in perspective. It was just such a meeting as it takes to make a true temple of the art and science of medicine." And his appraisal was not overdone. Attendance climbed to the all-time high of 1,562, three-eighths of the total membership of 4,484. President L. H. Reeves was happy to announce that the doctors of every county in the state were embodied in local societies. The 254 counties were represented by 129 county medical societies. The papers presented by the members were exceptional, and the several guests were distinguished. Dr. Olin West, secretary and general manager of the American Medical Association, spoke on "The American Medical Association and the Public"; Dr. Frank J. Heck, of Rochester, on "Iron Requirements in Childhood and Adult Life" and "Diagnosis and Treatment of the Leukemias"; Dr. Roy R. Kracke, of Atlanta, on "The Effect of Sulfanilamide and Related Compounds on the Blood" and "Infectious Mononucleosis"; and Dr. Alan Brown, of Toronto, on "A Consideration of Some Common Pediatric Conditions" and "Nutrition in Infancy and Childhood." Dr. Joseph C. Beck, of Chicago, assayed "Sulfanilamide as an Aid to the Treatment of Eye, Ear, Nose and Throat Conditions" and "Hearing Aids for the Deafened—(a) Physical, (b) Medical, (c) Surgical"; Dr. Claude S. Beck, of Cleveland, discussed "Extrinsic Lesions of the Heart" and "Resuscitation of the Heart and Experiences in Defibrillation of the Human Ventricles"; Dr. W. C. Williams, of Nashville, "Public Health and the Practice of Medicine"; Dr. A. C. Christie, of Washington, D.C., "Diagnosis and Treatment of Bronchiectasis" and "Diagnosis and Management of Cancer of the Breast"; Dr. H. M. Tigert, of Nashville, "Endometriosis" and "Post-Menopausal Bleeding"; and Dr. Frank Lahey, of Boston, "Management of Surgical Lesions of the Gallbladder and Bile Ducts" and "Advances in the Management of Thyroid Disease."

Dr. John T. Moore reviewed the progress of the association during his twenty-nine years as chairman of the Board of Trustees. Membership had increased from 2,992 to 4,348. In 1911, surplus and assets were $9,787.72; in 1940, they were $109,755.59. Income had risen from $7,549.74 to $58,857.91. Ever watchful of the funds of the Association, Dr. Moore regretted that the hotels were now charging a dollar for the luncheons instead of seventy-five cents.

Medical economics received its usual share of attention. One sidelight, evincing general interest in the subject, appeared in the report from the library that ninety-eight packages dealing with socialized medicine had gone out, many of which were destined for use by high-school debaters. The Executive Council and the Council on Medical Economics took the matter to heart. The latter group, of which Dr. Claude C. Cody, of Houston, had become chairman, gave a detailed study of health insurance. They felt that the subject required further investigation, although they were deeply enough convinced to recommend that the House of Delegates approve voluntary health insurance in principle. In the meantime, the problem was solving itself in that the voluntary plan was becoming popular and more and more individuals and groups were buying health insurance.

The building of a creditable library was a constant concern of the Board of Trustees. This year, President Reeves appointed a Library Endowment Committee, of which Dr. Sam E. Thompson was chairman. Three endowments of $1,000 each were announced. These came from Dr. and Mrs. Thompson, Dr. E. W. Bertner, and the Texas Pediatric Society. A picture of the three checks in payment adorned the first editorial page of the July, 1940, *Journal*.

Dr. Reeves gave his presidential address on "The Philosophy of Medicine." In presenting his subject from the standpoints of medical history, religion and medicine, humanitarianism in medicine, idealism in medicine, and the ethics of medicine, he traced the moral and ethical development of the doctor from early times. Technical progress and professional idealism had developed side by side. Always there had existed that sacred relationship between patient and doctor, based on mutual faith, hope and confidence, and that relationship, Dr. Reeves warned, must continue if the practice of medicine at its best is to continue. Selfless service is still the ideal of the true physician. "Let us forget personal profit and glory for the moment," he pleaded, "losing our individuality not for the State or some lay organization, but for the general good of the profession. By so doing, we may not profit financially; we may not gain fame or win patients, but we will achieve the reward of contentment, which in itself is success, maintain the position of the doctor in its wonted place in human society, and by so doing, *make practical the ideals of our profession.*"

Dr. N. D. Buie, of Marlin, became president-elect; and Drs. G. A. Schenewerk, of Dallas; James J. Gorman, of El Paso; and S. J. R. Murchison, of Fort Worth, were elected vice-presidents. The next meeting was allotted to Fort Worth.

The Federal Trade Commission entered the Texas medical scene this year and ordered the Crazy Water Company of Mineral Wells to "cease and desist from misrepresentations" concerning its products. Great satisfaction came to the medical profession when the commission held that "the products possessed no therapeutic value in excess of those of cathartic or laxative, and serve no other purpose than to assist in the temporary evacuation of the intestinal tract and to tend to temporarily neutralize excess acidity."

Medical preparedness continued to be the dominant theme of the Association as the seventy-fifth annual session convened in Fort Worth in 1941. War was still six months away, but the Association had been active during the year just as though war were already a reality. The Committee on Military Affairs, in existence but rather inactive for several years, now assumed a position of great importance under the chairmanship of Dr. Holman Taylor. This committee assumed full jurisdiction over all phases of medical military affairs in Texas. Co-operating with the Committee on Medical Preparedness of the American Medical Association, it expedited the collection of personnel data requested by the national organization. Thus there were accumulated the names of all physicians in Texas, their addresses, choice of service and adaptability to the armed forces, the expanding industries, the civilian population, and the public health activities. The state and national military affairs committees worked in close contact with the Procurement and Assignment Service for Physicians, Dentists, and Veterinarians. The name and creation of this agency was suggested to President Roosevelt by the Committee on Medical Preparedness. Colonel Sam Seeley, a Texan, was made national chairman of the agency.

Dr. John W. E. H. Beck, of De Kalb, with the rank of colonel, was appointed state medical officer for Selective Service. He appeared before the Association and asked assistance of all physicians in the examination of draftees in their respective neighborhoods. These examinations were, according to law, to be made without cost. In addition to this contribution, there were doctors on the Selective Service appeal boards and on medical advisory boards.

With some of the measures emanating from Washington the state association attempted to co-operate. In some respects, it was more of a sparring match than co-operation. The National Youth Administration had been set up to create work for young men and older boys during the depression. About 15,000 men were put in camps over the state and were working on about 400 local projects. The Association entered into an agreement to do the medical practice for these groups at reduced fees. The same arrangement was made with the Farm Security Administration, set up partially for

378

the purpose of determining the relationship between poverty and disease. The medical program was started in forty counties, four of which discontinued it during the year.

One phase of distribution of medical service which occupied the attention of the Association was the construction of hospitals. According to the New Deal, every community should have a hospital, and this was provided for in the Hill-Burton Bill. Incidentally, President Roosevelt credited himself with certain expert knowledge of hospital construction. He estimated, somewhat inaccurately, that permanent fireproof construction could be had for $1,500 a bed and even drew up plans for such hospitals.

The imminence of war, as well as the slowness of recovery from the depression, was affecting the membership of the Association, which stood at 3,879 for 1941, a drop of 603 for the year. This meant a loss in Association income of about $5,000. Already there were 300 Texas doctors in the armed forces. The suggestion had been made that the dues of these members be refunded. At the request of the Board of Trustees, however, this proposal was rejected.

Guest speakers this year continued to be of the usual high type: Drs. Ralph Majors, of Kansas City; F. W. Schultz, of Chicago; E. D. Plass, of Iowa City; A. B. Reese, of New York; Roscoe R. Graham, of Toronto; George Holmes, of Boston; J. B. McNaught and William J. Kerr, of San Francisco; L. S. Fallis, of Detroit; and W. S. Leathers, of Nashville.

President Preston Hunt, speaking on "The Usefulness of Medicine," expressed disappointment that doctors had made such slow progress in convincing the public of the real purposes and ideals of the medical profession. He dealt with the problems which were of immediate concern: socialized medicine, distribution of medical service, and medical preparedness. These problems were being handled satisfactorily by the medical profession and would continue to be, he felt, provided governmental interference and hindrances were not interposed. "The medical profession of this country," he said, "very much desires to be useful to the public, and it solicits the opportunity of rendering the service which it has traditionally sought to render."

Dr. Judson L. Taylor, of Houston, became president-elect and Drs. C. O. Terrell, of Fort Worth; Mitchell Gibson, of Lufkin; and R. B. Touchstone, of Lytle, vice-presidents. Corpus Christi was decided on as the location for the 1942 session. But the session, as it turned out, was not held there. The ability of Corpus Christi to accommodate the Association hinged on the completion of the Robert Driscoll Hotel. It was completed, but the hotel management refused co-operation with the Association and the other hotels of the city. Thus it became necessary for Houston to invite the Association.

In the face of incessant conflict between the medical profession and the New Deal, it was time that someone presented clearly the platform and the credo of organized medicine. Dr. Nathan B. Van Etten, president of the American Medical Association, did just that in his annual address to that body:

The American Medical Association stands for orderly and continuous progress toward better health for every American citizen. It stands for the elimination of every influence which may be destructive of the public health. It stands for the elimination of every communicable disease. It stands for the elimination of quackery. It stands for better general understanding of personal health problems. It stands for the promotion of research into fundamental causes of diseases and curative therapy. It stands for better education of all physicians, not only the undergraduate but the general practitioner who has been long in service. Its platform stands for the co-ordination of all government health functions in order to promote efficiency and eliminate duplication of effort and wasteful extravagance of the people's money. It stands for the treatment of the sick in their homes by local physicians and welfare agencies—where the real individual troubles are known—and it desires as little interference by the central government as may be consistent with constructive relief of personal suffering. Its program is entirely forward looking and it seeks to carry it on in conformity with the best traditions of an advanced democracy.[1]

War had been declared five months before the 1942 session of the state association convened in Houston. Naturally, preparation for war was the keynote of the session. And it was soon clear that the plans which the medical profession of the state and nation had set up were workable. The entire resources of the State Medical Association of Texas were made available to the national government. The Committee on Procurement and Assignment of Physicians, supplanting the Committee on Military Affairs, established itself in the Association offices in Fort Worth and set energetically to the task of properly distributing and utilizing the services of the doctors

[1] "Better Health for America," *Journal of the A.M.A.*, CIX (1941), 2250.

of Texas. Thus, this important activity became an integral part of the work of the Association, and the extra expense entailed thereby, $2,707.24, was paid by the Association. This committee worked in close co-operation with Selective Service authorities. The Council on Medical Economics kept in touch with the rationing authorities and obtained for physicians a liberal interpretation of the regulations pertaining to the rationing of automobiles, tires, and gasoline. As tangible proof of the co-operation of the Association, 1,250 of its members were in uniform within a few months, and it was estimated that this figure would increase so as to include at least 50 per cent of the membership.

On hand as guest speakers in 1942 were Colonel Leonard G. Rowntree, of Washington; Dr. Tom D. Spies, of Cincinnati; Dr. E. G. Hamblen, of Durham; Dr. Fred J. Hodges, of Ann Arbor; Dr. E. T. Bell, of Minneapolis; Dr. O. J. Dixon, of Kansas City; Dr. Vilray P. Blair, of St. Louis; Drs. John H. Musser and Chester A. Stewart, of New Orleans; and Dr. Louis A. Buie, of Rochester. Colonel Rowntree spoke on "Medical Aspects of Selective Service" and "Rehabilitation of Registrants." Other subjects reflecting the war were "The Rationale of the Use of Concentrated Plasma Protein Solutions in the Treatment of Hematogenic Shock," by Drs. E. E. Muirhead, J. M. Hill, and C. T. Ashworth, of Dallas; "Otolaryngological Problems in Aviation Medicine," by Captain C. M. Kos, of Randolph Field; and "Eye Problems in Combat Aviation," by Lieutenant Colonel V. A. Byrnes, of Randolph Field.

The Houston session was dominantly influenced by the state of war that existed. There was much discussion on the procurement and assignment of Texas doctors. As chairman of the committee dealing with this activity, Dr. Holman Taylor presented the matter in great detail in his reports and in his editorials. As a result, the medical profession of Texas did more than its part in providing doctors for the armed forces. Baylor University and the Medical Branch of the University of Texas stepped up their teaching programs so as to graduate their medical students in three years. This acceleration was made possible by doing away with the usual summer vacation. Thus, with brief recesses, classes were in session more or less continuously.

The House of Delegates passed a resolution asking the Board of Trustees to refund dues paid by members in uniform and to omit all subsequent dues so long as they were in military service. The board granted this request in 1943, and during that year the revenue of the Association diminished by $6,579.

At the 1942 session the subject of state medicine was not for the moment of first importance; war clouds obscured all else. But the Executive Council recognized that this threat was only dormant. "Beyond any doubt," the council warned, "those who advocate the socialization of medicine are lying in wait, watching for favorable opportunity to advance their cause through exigencies of the war emergency."

The Committee on Library Endowment, with Dr. L. H. Reeves as chairman, reported two additional subscriptions of $1,000 each, by Dr. Preston Hunt, of Texarkana, and by Dr. and Mrs. N. D. Buie, of Marlin. This increased the Texas Memorial Medical Library Fund to $5,000.

The Committee on Liaison with the Lone Star State Medical, Dental, and Pharmaceutical Association had been in existence for several years. Its assignment was not easy. From time to time more or less routine reports had been made, but this year the committee brought in constructive suggestions. It may be that the urgency of war was needed to point up the importance of our colored medical brethren. Improvement of the Kerrville State Sanitarium for Tuberculous Negroes and active support of the Postgraduate Assembly for Negro Physicians at Prairie View Normal School were advocated. It was urged that Negro doctors be fitted into civilian defense and also into the armed forces wherever proper qualifications were in evidence. "It is our opinion," the committee concluded, "that the members of our organization throughout the State are lending a helpful hand to Negro physicians whenever and wherever such aid is indicated. As has been observed heretofore, the Negro physician is with us, and it is a professional obligation that he be helped. We cannot at this particular time help him as we help our own, by taking him into our medical societies, but we can do the next best thing and support his institutions, and in many instances give him the advantage of participating in our own activities."

At the request of the Board of Regents, the Association took a reluctant hand in the controversy that was raging between Dean John W. Spies and the faculty of the Medical Branch of the University of Texas. On July 16, 1941, the Executive Council met in called session and concluded that "the national defense, the public health, and the welfare of the public" would be advanced by the

382

retention of Dr. Spies. As time and developments unfolded, however, it was obvious that this conclusion did not represent the will of the membership of the Association. On March 1, 1942, a second meeting was called at which the council reversed its action and decided to refrain from participation in the controversy. This was a wise decision, because feelings were aroused all over the state in both medical and lay circles. This disagreeable controversy was far reaching in its effects. It played a part in the probation placed on the Medical Branch by the Council on Medical Education and Hospitals of the American Medical Association, and it disrupted the work of the school. A group of students hanged in effigy Dean Spies, President Homer P. Rainey, and Dr. K. H. Aynesworth, acting chairman of the Board of Regents. The controversy caused factional disagreements in the medical profession. And it was not to be settled until Dean Spies had been succeeded by Chauncey D. Leake and Rainey had been replaced as president of the university.

Dr. N. D. Buie began his presidential address by relating his experiences as a member of the Electoral College at the second inauguration of Franklin D. Roosevelt. He then proceeded to narrate the things which he had been able to bring about through political influence in the Democratic party. These included "a satisfactory plank on health" in the party platform, deferment of medical students, continuous sessions of the medical schools of Texas, and increase in expenditures at the University of Texas and Baylor. He decried the passing of men with large fortunes. Because of tax burdens imposed in Washington by the political party he had helped to power, "the accumulation of large fortunes will not be possible in the future," he said, with the natural result that all fields of education would suffer. He felt that serious thought should be given to federal assistance to public schools. "Our part in medicine," he said, "is to lead and direct proper teaching, no matter who or what agency furnishes financial support."

The papers presented at this session and published in the *Journal* came in for praise from "a high official" of the American Medical Association: ". . . so many excellent papers, especially interesting observations—Muirhead, Hill, and Ashworth, Minter, and the heart evaluations of Mitchell, Roberts. Debunking the Rale—Thompson and Herman, as well as other timely subjects—military and otherwise. I never neglect the Texas State Journal."

Dr. Charles S. Venable, of San Antonio, became the new president-elect. Chosen as vice-presidents were Drs. R. B. Homan, Jr., El Paso; Howard Wells, Waco; and H. H. Cartwright, Breckenridge. San Antonio was selected as the site of the 1943 session. It soon became apparent, however, that San Antonio could not take care of the Association because a large part of the hotel space was occupied by permanent military personnel. In the emergency, Fort Worth offered to act as host, the Executive Council accepted, and the change was announced in the August *Journal*. But the session was not held in Fort Worth. It was not held at all. The November issue of the *Journal* notified its readers that except for a small meeting of the official family of the Association, on the regular date, the 1943 session would be abandoned. The American Medical Association had made a similar decision the previous month. Reasons were shortage of doctors, inadequate hotel accommodations, and travel difficulties.

The House of Delegates assembled, as scheduled, at Fort Worth on May 5, 1943. It was a meeting of much discussion and many decisions. The military theme was of necessity dominant. Colonel Ozro T. Woods, of Dallas, reported on the plans and problems of civilian defense. These anticipated the possible bombing of cities or important industries and installations. The institution of first-aid stations and blood banks was the main tangible result.

Dr. Holman Taylor, reporting for the Committee on Procurement and Assignment, gave a long and detailed survey. The problems were many. Maintenance of a proper ratio between doctors in civilian practice and doctors in the army was not easy. On a voluntary basis, 1,248 doctors were in service on January 1, 1943; this number was 57 per cent above the state quota.[2] It was the function of this committee to shift doctors to critical areas. And besides, there was considerable voluntary moving of physicians, some from out of the state. These newcomers, in some instances, took over the offices and practices of men in uniform and were sources of discord in the postwar era.

Routine reports showed a membership of 3,445, which represented a loss of 885 during the year. The total assets of the Associa-

[2] It is noteworthy that this same excess held for all the southern and southwestern states. It did not extend to some of the eastern states.

tion amounted to $110,230.00, a loss of $2,114.60. Secretary Taylor reported the death of five honorary members, including former President R. W. Knox. Dr. W. R. Thompson, of Fort Worth, was elected a member emeritus, a fitting reward for his services as secretary of the Board of Trustees since its inception in 1904, he being the only surviving member of the original board.

Because of the stress of war, there was a general feeling in the Association that no controversial legislation should be considered, and this was the policy of the Legislative Committee. While the guards were thus down, a bill legalizing chiropractors—according to Dr. Holman Taylor, "one of the most iniquitous measures ever introduced in our Legislature"—was passed. The veto of Governor Coke Stevenson terminated this threat.

There was a general feeling, too, that politics should be adjourned for the duration, that all "untried far-reaching schemes of so-called special reforms" should be abandoned "to the end that all resources and all efforts be concentrated on the grim and dangerous task of winning a war." But such, the doctors perceived, was not the idea of the New Deal in or out of Washington. Instead, they felt, the National Youth Administration, the Farm Security Administration, and the Sheppard-Towner Maternal Welfare Act had all extended medical socialization. And now this year the Children's Bureau of the United States Department of Labor had a new plan for obstetrical and hospital care of wives of enlisted men and for the pediatric care of young children of enlisted men. The much reduced fees—prenatal care and delivery ranged from $25 to $35—were to be paid by the United States government through the State Department of Health. The medical profession of Texas accepted the plan with certain reservations; it could not afford to do otherwise.

The Executive Council, the Council on Medical Economics, and the Legislative Committee all recognized these developments and pointed out the hazards involved. Dr. John H. Burleson, chairman of the Legislative Committee, put the situation very bluntly: "We are looking regimentation straight in the face. . . . The New Deal always comes back to regimentation, Federal control. They have no interest in hospitals and doctors working out a satisfactory plan, as they already have an objective plan of Federal 'control.' " He saw great danger in this fact: $1,658,000 in federal funds were spent annually in Texas through the state health department, while the state of Texas appropriated only $341,000.[3] The state health officer, he said, seemed content with this disproportion and showed little inclination to co-operate with the Legislative Committee. This committee was convinced that, if these trends should continue, there would be "no more incentive for sacrifice and hard work; labor union medicine is the easy way. Socialized medicine has arrived in Texas; at least this is the conclusion arrived at by your Legislative Committee after a careful survey of our State Health Department."

President Judson L. Taylor made a short address to the House of Delegates in which he stayed away from the two subjects that were uppermost: war and socialized medicine. His topic was "Scientific Medicine is Fundamental." He traced the "slow, hard, but stimulating journey" of medicine and found it strewn with high ideals, hard work, worthy ambitions, and many triumphs. He was sure that "civilization today with all of its wonders and comforts could never have been reached by man without the advancements in public health and the improvements in the treatment of the sick made by highly trained scientists and properly qualified Doctors of Medicine."

New officers were elected as usual: H. F. Connally, of Waco, president-elect; and B. C. Ball, Fort Worth; T. C. Glass, Marlin; and S. D. Coleman, Navasota, vice-presidents.

This 1943 meeting of the House of Delegates closed in an atmosphere of disquietude. To many it seemed that the practice of medicine was seriously imperiled, and that enemies, deeply intrenched in the national government, were increasingly urgent and abusive with their propaganda. Eleanor Roosevelt, respected by some of the medical profession, was quoted as saying in her column "My Day" that "there are those in the medical profession who are obstructionists and who will have to be dealt with in order to insure proper medical care is given the American people." And, of greater significance, the Wagner-Murray-Dingell Bill had been introduced in Congress. This bill, most doctors believed, would create a glorified national social insurance system and was designed to scrap the private practice of medicine and to substitute for it a political and bureaucratic system.

Thoroughly aroused, President C. S. Venable chose to meet this

[3] He might have added that at the time a new home for the State Department of Health was being built in Austin, and nearly two-thirds of the cost was coming out of Washington.

threat head-on. He assembled the Executive Council at Fort Worth on July 13 and, in a prepared address, painted the picture as he saw it. The picture held little promise. But despite the inhibitions of war and despite the ranks thinned by the call of one-third of the membership to military service, the Executive Council took a bold stand. The Association had previously made some commitments, such as the arrangement with the Farm Security Administration; these were recognized as mistakes of hasty judgment and misplaced confidence. From now on, organized medicine would be on guard against the New Deal bearing gifts.

The discussion by the Executive Council centered around a resolution by Dr. Sam Thompson. This stated clearly that contracts and agreements with federal agencies would lead to ultimate regimentation of the medical profession. Then the resolving clause advised and directed all officers and divisions of the Association "not to sign or agree to any plan, agreement, or contract sought for the purpose of providing hospital and medical care for any designated group or groups." Dr. C. C. Cody spoke for the Council on Medical Economics when he said, "Americanized medicine is superior to socialized medicine; . . . Americanized medicine is indigenous to our soil and developed in our country while socialized medicine is a German product planned for the regimentation of Labor; . . . socialized medicine is costly, inefficient and primarily political." The resolution, which did not prevent the individual physician from entering into such contracts, was thoroughly discussed and adopted.

Following this meeting, President Venable took two important steps: he formed a Speakers' Bureau and appointed a Committee on Public Relations, with Dr. M. M. Minter, of San Antonio, as chairman. Both of these were designed to bring to the public, in a forceful and sometimes graphic way, just what socialization of medicine would mean to them as patients. Within a few months, more than two hundred speakers were available, and some were traveling long distances to speak before civic organizations, parent-teacher associations, and other groups.

Dr. Minter's committee, composed of Drs. Walter G. Stuck, of San Antonio; Walter A. Coole, of Houston; and O. E. Egbert, of El Paso, accepted its obligations seriously. It collected and prepared material to be used by the Speakers' Bureau. Articles suitable for newspaper editorials and news items were furnished. The radio was often used as a medium of great value. The work of this committee was outstanding and the results were soon evident. Naturally, the expense was great: $9,201.43 the first year. Any necessary expense had been sanctioned by the Board of Trustees, and through the *Journal* an additional $3,677.95 was raised by private subscription.

So successful had been the counterattack of organized medicine in Texas and elsewhere that by the time the Executive Council met again on December 13, 1943, there was a feeling of deep satisfaction. This second meeting of the Executive Council was held in San Antonio and was well attended. The chief accomplishments were to enlarge and accent the machinery that had already been set in motion. A heartening note came from Dr. E. W. Bertner when he announced that $40,000 had been raised in Houston for the Committee on Constitutional Government. This committee saw in the Wagner-Murray-Dingell Bill a threat to all forms of private enterprise. This committee and the National Physicians Committee saw eye to eye. Valuable allies were flocking to the aid of the medical profession: insurance companies, industry, and professional men. This was not all altruism; these allies could all project themselves into the position of the medical profession. It was all very clear now, and all very complicated. There was, the committee pointed out, a paradox involved: federal agencies were admittedly out to destroy the medical profession and at the same time, so as to have more money to hasten the process, were urging the doctors to buy government bonds.

The medical schools of Texas were caught up in the war. And there were some changes. The probation which had been placed on the Medical Branch of the University of Texas by the American Medical Association and the American Association of Medical Colleges was lifted. Baylor moved from Dallas to Houston, and at Dallas ground-breaking ceremonies were held for the Southwestern Medical College. These schools entered into the military medical-training program under Army and Navy auspices. At each school, the students were enlisted in a medical unit and received regular service pay of $50 a month.

The 1944 session of the state association was a compromise between the normal session and the meeting of 1943, when only the House of Delegates assembled. The plan called for multiple meetings, so arranged that hotel accommodations would be utilized for only a short time. The Section on Public Health met in Austin on April 19 and 20. The sections on medicine; eye, ear, nose, and throat; and pediatrics convened in Fort Worth on April 20 and 21. San Antonio was the meeting place, May 3 and 4, for the sections on surgery, obstetrics and gynecology, radiology and physiotherapy, and clinical pathology. The House of Delegates met in Dallas on May 10 and 11. The attendance in the four cities totaled 860, there being, of course, some duplication.

The deliberations of the House of Delegates were for the most part a repetition of what had been considered in the meetings of the Executive Council in the interim: medical economics, socialization of medicine, procurement of medical personnel, and medical legislation. The Committee on Public Relations, now much enlarged, had assumed increasing importance. Dr. M. M. Minter gave a comprehensive report of what had been accomplished and made recommendations for extension of the work. The services of Jeff Reese, who had served as public-relations counselor with the Association for a quarter-century, were utilized in this project. The committee, however, thought that the advice of a public-relations agency should be sought. The Association, it argued, had a selling job to do, and it needed further guidance. The firm of Aniol and Auld, of San Antonio, was therefore employed. An appropriate slogan for the campaign of publicity was adopted: "It is true that we do have an economic problem in the practice of medicine, but it is unwise for us to exchange an economic for a political problem." The Board of Trustees had underwritten the expenses of this committee up to $6,000 a year, which did not seem adequate to the committee now that it had taken the long look at the situation. A carefully considered budget of $28,250 was submitted. With a view to offsetting such a demand and to make up a loss of $7,016 from military members, the House of Delegates amended the bylaws, increasing dues from $9 to $20.

The question of health insurance received rather inadequate attention by the House of Delegates. It was discussed, and it was agreed by all that compulsory health insurance was synonymous with socialized medicine. A resolution approving the prepayment plan for medical care was adopted, but approval was not very emphatic or heartfelt. Meantime, the public was accepting the plan with enthusiasm, and literally thousands were buying it.

Nothing that was happening on the local battlefront, of course, could crowd the war in Europe and Asia into the background. Enlistments in the medical services continued apace, and members in uniform were appearing more and more on the obituary pages of the *Journal*. Although not much was said of the work of the medical soldier, one reporter gave him full credit: "There is little glory in the Medical Corps. It is just hard, dirty work and mighty dangerous. The Red Cross seems to mean little to the enemy. He has bombed hospital tents from Anzio to Aachen. These medics are tough, but among the torn and dying men learn to be tender, too. They shun glory, but they have their pride. They are proud to have saved 97 out of every hundred wounded. They are proud that their miracle drugs and blood banks send from 50 to 80 back to fight again. They are proud because nobody in our whole vast Army, not even the foremost combat crew or the deadliest flying wing, has done a finer job than the Medical Corps." [4]

President Venable had the opportunity and *task* of delivering his annual address in the four cities where branch meetings were held. Certainly, it was a well-deserved compliment, because he had worked diligently and effectually at the job of informing the doctor and the public of the gravity of the threat of socialized medicine. Aptly, he chose as his subject "Socialized Medicine Shall not Pass." He took time to refer to Aesculapius and what his followers had accomplished in the many intervening years. He spoke of the German school of medicine and the heights to which it rose, only to be debased by the socializing influence of Bismarck in 1888. American medicine had assumed leadership in the world and if let alone would continue to lead. He quoted Samuel Gompers, who had been president of the American Federation of Labor and who had died in San Antonio in 1924, as saying that "compulsory social insurance is in its essence undemocratic and it cannot remove or prevent poverty." There was one obvious answer, Venable declared, to the vocal, government-paid propagandists of socialism: a vigorous support of the prepayment plan of voluntary health insurance. The various agencies should continue to work on the problem and should continue to checkmate every New Deal move. But what the public wanted and needed was a voluntary plan which would permit free choice of doctor and hospital, assure good medical and hospital care, allay fear of illness in the family, and afford a feeling of pride to the possessor, all at a price he could afford to pay. Thus the patient and

[4] *New York Times*, January 5, 1945.

the doctor would jointly compass "the ultimate destruction of such faithless subversiveness that would destroy the America of our birth."

The November issue of the *Journal* carried the news that the Executive Council had met on October 8 and decided that the Association would meet in regular session in Galveston, May 7 to 10, 1945. Three months later, the *Journal* announced that the session might have to be abandoned because the federal government had ruled that no meeting with more than fifty in attendance could be held unless it was in line with the war effort; and in the mind of these authorities, the work of a state medical association was not essential to winning the war. By March, the Office of Defense Transportation had definitely ruled that the session could not be held. By this time, all arrangements had been made, and the program appeared in the April issue of the *Journal*. The Executive Council then applied for a permit for a meeting of the House of Delegates. Whether the denial of this application constituted conservation of travel facilities or simple harassment of organized medicine is open to question.

XXII

National Postwar Confusion and Indecision, 1945–49

WORLD WAR II came to a close on September 2, 1945, with General Douglas MacArthur accepting the surrender of Japan, a most welcome event for the whole world. Five months before, President Franklin Roosevelt had died suddenly, to be replaced by a new president, Harry S. Truman, who may have seemed timid and even bewildered at first but who soon gathered aggressiveness and enthusiasm.

President Truman's ideas concerning medicine brought him into early collision with the profession. Roosevelt was a forgotten adversary as many doctors fought for what they considered their professional freedom against President Truman and his supporters, notably Senator Claude Pepper of Florida, Surgeon-General Thomas Parran, and Oscar Ewing, federal security administrator.

But regardless of politics, the war was over, and the soldier-doctors of Texas began moving back into civilian practice. It would take more than a year for most of the two thousand in uniform to return, and as they came back, many would run into difficulties of adjustment. Practices had to be rebuilt, office space had to be found in towns already bulging with professional occupants, and new competition had to be met. But time and energy would solve most of the problems, and soon the doctors found themselves fitted once more into the life of their particular communities.

Since neither the Association nor the House of Delegates had met in 1945, the Association's attorney ruled that all officers elected at the past session would hold over until new sessions could be held. Shortly after the war ended, travel restrictions were lifted, and President Connally called a meeting of the House of Delegates at Waco on November 13, 1945. This was the second called session in the history of the Association, the first having been in 1903, when President F. E. Daniel called the house together to consider the state legislative situation.

Prior to the meeting, there must have been considerable discussion and consequent disagreement as to who would serve as president, even though the Association's attorney had expressed the opinion that Dr. Connally should continue for the year. Dr. L. B. Jackson, of San Antonio, reviewed the whole situation and moved that Dr. Connally continue to serve until the next annual session. President-Elect Cody, however, objected. He felt that the meeting in November was a postponed annual meeting, and he was insistent that his term as president should end in May, 1946, whether the unexpired term was six months or six hours. He amended Dr. Jackson's motion to the effect that the House of Delegates take up the question of the postponed session. Dr. Connally ruled the amendment out of order. Then John T. Moore made a motion that the chair be not sustained. After full discussion, the chair was sustained, and the original motion was passed. As a protection to Dr. Cody, it was voted to reaffirm him as president-elect. This was the principal business of the called session. Several honorary members were elected, and two minor amendments to the constitution were adopted.

The *Journal* gave every possible assistance to the homecoming medical officers. Beginning with the November issue, it published lists of returned members, giving home address, branch of service, and date of release. Attention was called to a ruling by the Judge Advocate of the Army that medical officers could be sued for malpractice. The armed services were prepared to furnish legal counsel, but there was no provision for paying indemnities. All men still in service were urged to protect themselves against possible malpractice suits.

There was editorial comment as to the needs of the medical officers. The question of office space was paramount. Giving up some space or sharing space was recommended to those who had stayed at home. A form was devised for insertion in local newspapers by local societies; it would call attention to the return of a doctor and would urge his former patients to return to him. One embarrassing suggestion was to extend credit at local banks to those in need of funds. All this was altruistic enough, but the results were not practical. It was, after all, up to each returning doctor to solve his own problems as best he could.

President Truman lost little time in putting himself forward as champion of the cause of socialized medicine. He urged the passage of a five-point program. Two points had to do with adequate hospital construction and compensation for loss of wages due to illness; with these two, the medical profession was in accord. One point of the program approved compulsory health insurance as provided in the Wagner-Murray-Dingell Bill, a new version of which was introduced into Congress. This bill would create panels of patients for participating doctors, would limit the number of patients to be treated by each doctor, and would designate the qualifications of specialists—all under the authority of one man, the surgeon-general of the United States Public Health Service. A fourth point was embodied in the Pepper Bill, which attempted to extend to all segments of the population, regardless of the economic need, the benefits of the Sheppard-Towner Bill. But the least-liked of all the proposals would give the federal government control of medical education and medical research, particularly in the fields of cancer and mental disease.

Surgeon-General Parran of the United States Public Health Service caused consternation in medical circles when on December 10, 1945, he sent a letter to all officers in his department, in which he gave full support to the President's program. He hailed it as the "goal of all public health workers." It had been taken for granted that Dr. Parran was an opponent of socialized medicine. Indeed, the doctors believed that his published statements confirmed this. However, certain trends could be observed in organizations such as the American Public Health Association, where his influence was great, that might have alerted the profession. At any rate, he had taken a stand, and it was against organized medicine.

The medical profession of Texas and the United States prepared to meet this new threat. Few there were who said, "This is inevitable, and we might as well get on the band wagon. We cannot stop it." The *Journal* took the lead. Every issue pointed out grave dangers besetting the doctors of Texas. No attempt was made to belittle the opposition. The political complexion of Congress had changed,

394

favorably; an unofficial poll showed a majority against socialized medicine. Seventeen of the twenty-three members of Congress from Texas were unequivocally opposed to the President's program, and replies had not been received from the remainder.

The Speakers' Bureau was revived, and the Committee on Public Relations began to assemble new material. Two prominent laymen, Walter W. McAllister, of San Antonio, and R. L. Thomas, of Dallas, gave radio speeches over the Texas State Network. These addresses were later published in the *Journal*. Very outspoken was Mr. McAllister in his address on "Socialized Medicine and Its Pay Roll Taxation": "By adroit usage of words, the bureaucrats in Washington have pasted a soothing label on a bottle of nitroglycerine—but that doesn't make it any less explosive. . . . I should think no one could fool himself after the past twelve years' experience with government alphabetical bureaucracies. . . . The doctors of our nation oppose the Wagner-Murray-Dingell bill not for selfish reasons, but simply because they know if this measure becomes law, the public health of Americans will suffer. . . . People say there is no alternative. Of course, there is an alternative—it lies in group and individual health insurance and in untrammeled medical practice."

Mr. Thomas, in speaking on "Should Our Doctors Be Regimented?" was equally emphatic. "I want you to know that I am not speaking in defense of the medical profession, for this great humanitarian profession needs no defense." He found no justification for what he called this "experiment in social revolution at a time when surely retrenchment in government spending is in order, and at a time when there is real danger in rocking the boat. . . . Your dollar, after going to Washington, would come back to you as about 50 cents to pay for medical care. It would seem more business-like, therefore, to keep your dollar in your pocket and buy health insurance from some commercial company or nonprofit group and pay your doctor when you need him."

The eightieth session of the Association was held in Galveston, May 6–9, 1946. This was the first full meeting since 1942. The membership registration was 1,024. Including auxiliary members and visitors, the total attendance was 1,799. Total membership was 4,339; in 1942, it had been 3,861. Total assets amounted to $174,-789.53, as against $112,344.60 in 1942. Income for the coming year was expected to be $114,930.00. Of this amount, $92,100.00 was to be spent on the estimated budget. Investments totaled $70,546.26. These increased amounts resulted from the raising of the dues in 1944. The library fund had increased to $12,385.76. Part of this increase was due to two donations of $1,000.00 each obtained by the Woman's Auxiliary and to the Stirling E. Russ Memorial Fund created by Dr. and Mrs. W. B. Russ.

The results of the work of Dr. M. M. Minter's Committee on Public Relations continued to be impressive. As an illustration of the committee's industry, 400,000 pamphlets opposing socialization of medicine were circulated. Three thousand appropriate reprints or manuscripts were sent out to medical and lay speakers. Nine broadcasting stations in the state were regularly using subjects such as "Medicine Serves America," "More Life for You," "Dodging Contagious Diseases," and "Guardians of Your Health." Through all these media, the readers or listeners were urged to buy voluntary health insurance and to pay their poll taxes. As a result of this dignified but accurate appraisal, many organizations adopted resolutions condemning socialized medicine. Dr. Minter attended one meeting in Chicago and one in St. Louis, where the problems of government interference with the practice of medicine were considered at the national level. The expenditure of $22,997.25 by the committee during this year was accepted by all as an excellent investment.

With the war over, the Council on Medical Economics, with Dr. H. E. Griffin as chairman, devoted most of its report to health insurance. In passing, it observed that "governmental control during war is tolerated by all, freely and voluntarily, but when war is over citizens of all walks of life should be relieved of as much governmental control as is compatible with public security. The business of the medical profession is no exception to this rule."

This council considered the subject of health insurance from several angles. It set down certain rules of control; and if these were adhered to, it mattered not whether the insurance was handled by co-operative groups, nonprofit organizations, or insurance companies, except that the voluntary prepayment feature was to be stressed always. Since the American Medical Association, after a slow start, had come out with its ten-point national health program and since Point 6 advocated "the establishment of voluntary nonprofit prepayment plans for the costs of hospitalization (such as the Blue Cross plans) and voluntary nonprofit prepayment plans for medical care (such as those developed by many state and county medical societies)," this problem of protection from disease and injury was being satisfactorily solved. For instance, the Blue Cross plan had an enrollment of 148,000 in Texas and 21,000,000 in the United States.

The Legislative Committee had put in a full year and could see much activity ahead. The Sanitary Code Bill was helped through the Legislature without much difficulty. What had come to be known as the "osteopath hospital measure" had first been brought up in the Legislature in 1935. Each time it had been defeated, and the same fate overtook it this year. This measure would have compelled all tax-exempt hospitals to accept on their staffs any physician licensed to practice in the state. In discussing this measure, a reference committee headed by Dr. S. H. Watson, of Waxahachie, dismissed the idea thus: "The gap separating our body from the osteopathic physicians is too well known and fundamental." In the way of future legislation, the Legislative Committee was interested chiefly in two measures: the Basic Science Bill and the revision of the Medical Practice Act. At a called meeting of the Executive Council at Fort Worth, September 29, 1946, these two pieces of legislation were fully discussed, and, after suggested changes were made, adopted.

The several councils and committees dealing with war and the results of war have been emphasized to the detriment of other divisions of the Association. These others—the Board of Councilors, the Council on Scientific Work, the Committee on Cancer, the Committee on Tuberculosis, and the Committee on Library Endowment, to mention only a few—had carried on the usual work of the Association, had embodied their efforts in good reports, and had been content to let their work remain in the background, receiving no commendation and expecting none. In retrospect, the work of these wheel-horse committees stands out for what it is.

The membership of the Association, after a respite of four years, must have been glad to sit down and listen to such speakers as Dr. James L. Wilson, of Ann Arbor; Drs. Nicholson J. Eastman and Jack S. Guyton, of Baltimore; J. C. Ketchum and Dr. M. H. Barker, of Chicago; Dr. O. Theron Clagett, of Rochester; and Dr. Wiley D. Forbus, of Durham.

As a member of the Texas State Board of Medical Examiners for fifteen years, Dr. H. F. Connally had had ample opportunity to learn of the shortcomings of medical education. Hence he was in a position to speak as president of the Association on "The Responsibility of the State Medical Association with Regard to Postgraduate Medical Education in Texas." He praised the constructive work of the Federated State Medical Boards of America, the Committee on Medical Education and Hospitals of the American Medical Association, and the several specialty boards. He deplored the condition of postgraduate teaching in Texas. "Nowhere in Texas," he charged, "is there a place where our young doctors can go for postgraduate training and qualify themselves to pass the American boards of any of the major specialties." This charge was unduly hard on the medical schools of Texas and not altogether accurate. He applauded the prospects of the Texas Medical Center in Houston and the medical educational movement in Dallas spearheaded by Dr. E. H. Cary. But he felt that the medical students at Galveston were being penalized. He advocated a plan whereby junior and senior medical students at the Medical Branch of the University of Texas might be transferred to Houston, where more abundant clinical material was available.

The new officers were B. E. Pickett, Sr., of Carrizo Springs, president-elect; and S. D. Whitten; C. P. Yeager, of Corpus Christi; and J. M. Campbell, of Goldthwaite, vice-presidents.

Before the next session would convene, in Dallas, three men of importance would have died. One was Dr. H. W. Cummings, of Hearne, one of the dependable, hard-working members, and president of the Association in 1908. Another loss was more immediately critical and less expected. Dr. Reuben B. Anderson, Jr., assistant secretary of the Association and assistant editor of the *Journal* for twenty years, died at the age of fifty-one. While his principal service was with the *Journal*, as Dr. Holman Taylor's right-hand man he was thoroughly familiar with every activity of the Association. A few months later, Dr. Harold M. Williams, of Fort Worth, was chosen to fill the place vacated by Anderson's death. The third loss was the death of Dr. K. H. Beall, treasurer of the Association for twenty-three years. This long service was second only to the record of twenty-eight years set by Dr. J. Larendon early in the history of the Association.

Just before the 1947 session of the state association, Texas medicine was honored by the American Medical Association, which was one hundred years old that year. One phase of the centennial celebration was a series of historical presentations over the National Broadcasting Company network under the title "Doctors—Then and Now." On April 26, a half-hour program was devoted to the life of Dr. Anson Jones, a hero of the Battle of San Jacinto, a practicing physician, and the last president of the Republic of Texas.

If a graphic chart were made of the attendance figures of the sessions of the Texas Medical Association for the past four decades, the curve would be irregularly but gradually upward with a definite peak every five or six years. Those peaks would coincide with the choice of Dallas as the place of meeting. No exception was the 1947 meeting, for which 1,364 members were on hand. If the chart were projected another year, however, it would show Houston recording an attendance of 1,685 in 1948, thus exceeding the high mark of 1,562 set at Dallas in 1940. No subsequent session has surpassed 1,685.

Postwar growth of the Association was quite rapid. The secretary reported to the Dallas session of 1947 a membership of 5,078. During the next three years, the figures were 5,382, 5,559, and 5,917. This increase was due in part to the increase in the number of doctors coming to Texas. This was not, however, the full explanation. There was evidence that a larger proportion of physicians were recognizing the importance of organized medicine. They were believing with Aesop that "united we stand, divided we fall." One interesting piece of evidence of the trend toward organized medicine is found in the obituary figures: in 1927, members of the Association had comprised 34 per cent of the deaths of physicians reported by the secretary; in 1947, they accounted for 60 per cent.

The discussions and reports at this meeting were similar to those of the preceding year. The subject of socialized medicine received its usual attention. One new but not surprising phase of the subject was presented by Arthur L. Conrad, associate administrator of the National Physicians Committee. A new Wagner-Murray-Dingell bill had been introduced in Congress and was being considered by the Senate Committee on Education and Labor. Eighteen doctors, representing an organization claiming 3,000 members, were permitted to appear before the committee and speak for the bill. Six were federal employees, and 4 were professors in medical schools. In contrast, only 14 physicians were allowed to testify for the 125,000 members of organized medicine. Other proponents of the bill were

James B. Carey, an official of the C.I.O., and Leo J. Linder, from the left-wing National Lawyers' Guild.

The Legislative Committee, soon to become a council and soon to be headed by Dr. J. B. Copeland, of San Antonio, surveyed the legislative horizon and girded its loins to do battle for the Basic Science Bill. As the name implies, the measure sought to establish for all practitioners, regardless of their schools of medicine, minimum standards in the basic sciences: anatomy, physiology, chemistry, bacteriology, pathology, and hygiene and public health. Judge Ralph W. Yarborough, of Austin, later to be aided by J. W. Townsend, of Austin, was employed to write the bill and to give legal direction to the legislative efforts of the Association. This bill was consistently opposed by the osteopaths, chiropractors, and naturopaths. Little progress had been made. Lieutenant-Governor Allan Shivers advised a compromise with the dissenting groups, but nothing came of this effort during the 1947 session of the Legislature. After concerted and continued work by the Council on Legislation and other groups, however, the bill was passed in April, 1949.

The Committee on Public Relations, under the sturdy leadership of Dr. M. M. Minter, continued to grow in importance. Jeff L. Reese, who after twenty-four years of service as legislative counselor retired in 1947, had been of constant assistance to this committee and to many others. Joe A. Clark was selected to take his place as executive secretary of this committee.

The Council on Medical Economics made a detailed report on its extended negotiations with the Veterans Administration. An attempt had been made to work out a plan for the care of sick veterans in their homes. No agreement was reached by the council or the House of Delegates. The problem could have been solved by recalling that in 1943 the Association had decided that it would make no contract with any department of the federal government. President Pickett, however, thought the matter of sufficient importance to call a special meeting of the House of Delegates at Fort Worth in January, 1948. Here, after long and tedious consideration of the question, it was again affirmed that the Association would not enter into any contract with a federal agency.

In 1946, the Board of Trustees had announced that the fiscal year and membership year had been changed to coincide with the calendar year. The publication year of the *Journal* was changed similarly in 1948. This meant that Volume 44 extended from May to Decem-

400

ber, 1948, so that the next volume could cover the calendar year.

At this Dallas meeting, five former presidents were honored by election to emeritus status: Drs. Sam E. Thompson, A. A. Ross, W. B. Russ, John H. Burleson, and E. H. Cary. One amendment to the bylaws set up a Section on General Practice, thus bringing the scientific sections to nine. A second amendment was intended as a further effort to curb the competitive and oftentimes extravagant entertainment by the host cities. The Dallas County Medical Society this year had put on an elaborate affair at the Plantation on Wednesday night at a reported cost of nine to ten thousand dollars. The amendment provided that no entertainment could be given which would conflict or interfere with any meeting of the House of Delegates, scientific sessions, or general meetings, or detract from the president's ball and reception. "Thus," Editor Taylor concluded, "the urge to keep up with the Joneses has rather definitely been suppressed."

Dr. C. C. Cody, in his presidential address, spoke on "Our Changing Methods." Reviewing the rapid strides which had been made in the fields of physics and biology, he pointed out their reflection in the practice of medicine and particularly in the distribution of medical care, although increasing industrialization and rapid transportation, too, had played a prominent part. All this had resulted in a marked increase in the life span. The result was the development of retirement plans, pensions, old-age benefits, and the ensuing political opportunities to a socially inclined government. He drew a parallel between Americanized medicine and socialized medicine, and found much wanting in the latter: it was impossible, he thought, to compare a superior article with an inferior one. He reminded his auditors that prepaid hospitalization had its origin at the Baylor Hospital, in Dallas, and that it was later expanded into the Blue Cross Plan. This was the beginning of the plan which was to be the solution of the problem of medical and hospital expenses. There were several modifications of the plan. It was the purpose of the State Medical Association to encourage "a prepayment plan with an ethical and equitable policy issued by any nonprofit or casualty insurance corporation whose financial resources are sufficient to guarantee its contracts." There had come to the doctors of Texas, President Cody said in conclusion, "the priceless heritage of Americanized Medicine at its best and finest. Let us keep it so."

The following guest speakers took part in the Dallas session:

Drs. Thomas B. Magath and Harry M. Weber, of Rochester; Waldo
E. Nelson, of Philadelphia; Joseph M. Donald, of Birmingham;
Walter L. Palmer and Harold O. Jones, of Chicago; Herbert D.
Adams, of Boston; R. H. Kampmeier, of Nashville; and John J.
Shea, of Memphis; and Rear Admiral William L. Mann, of George-
town, Texas. Dr. Tate Miller, Dallas, was chosen president-elect;
and Drs. Frank A. Selecman, Dallas; X. R. Hyde, Fort Worth; and
E. W. Jones, Wellington, were elected vice-presidents. Houston was
chosen as the place of the 1948 meeting.

In the interim between sessions, a forward step was taken in the
library of the Association, which with little success had been begun
in 1910 and revived in 1919. In 1927, Dr. R. B. Anderson had become interested in collecting medical books and journals. He set
about the task with ability and enthusiasm. With the assistance,
from 1929 to 1947, of Lurine Hightower, he reorganized the library
and instituted the package library service. The result in 1947 was
a good, workable library with more than 200 current journals, 5,000
books, 100,000 classified reprints, and 135 medical motion-picture
films. Estelle Parnell, an assistant since 1944, became librarian in
1948 and served until 1950. In recent years the library has enjoyed
a steady growth, so that in 1953 it could boast 395 current journals,
10,404 bound volumes, 4,605 unbound volumes, 200,000 reprints,
and 200 motion-picture films. By 1953, too, the staff had been enlarged to include its first trained medical librarian, Pauline Duffield; the assistant librarian, Katheryn Wendler; and library assistants Alliece Pigott, Mary Talley, and Alice Walker.

In December, 1947, the Association suffered a great loss in the
death of Dr. Holman Taylor. No man has done any more for organized medicine in Texas than he. A member of the Association
for forty-five years, secretary of the Association and editor of the
Journal for thirty-seven years, chairman of many committees, an
important cog in the machinery of the American Medical Association, possessor of an unequaled personality, he was close to indispensable. On the night of December 4, a large group of his friends
assembled in Fort Worth at a banquet in his honor. They had come
to tell him and to show him how thoroughly successful his career
had been and to remind him of how much he had accomplished.
Dr. John T. Moore was there, Dr. W. B. Russ, Dr. E. H. Cary, and
many others. The banquet was an enjoyable affair, with many speakers. Dr. Russ gave the principal address, in a spirit of blended levity

and dignity and esteem. Dr. Taylor was obviously pleased. He responded to the many expressions of commendation and friendship. This occasion, he said, was the happiest of his life. The banquet ended, and most of the guests left. In the elation of the hour, Dr. Taylor remained to talk with a few friends. Suddenly he was seized with a heart attack and died, peacefully, a few minutes later. Thus dramatically and appropriately came the end of this good and faithful servant of the Texas Medical Association.

Continued narration of the work of those committees busily active in opposing the New Deal and of those fostering desired medical legislation could become repetitious and tiresome. There was no letup in the activities of these committees, but in this account of the 1948 session of the Association, their earnest activities in these much discussed fields will be passed over in favor of three questions which became especially important at this time: the removal of the Association headquarters from Fort Worth to Austin, the building of a home for the Association, and the complete revision of the constitution and bylaws.

At the very beginning in 1853, the constitution and bylaws stated that the annual meetings of the Association would be held in Austin. The revision in 1869 designated Houston as the meeting place. One could infer from this that these cities were the headquarters of the Association at these respective times. The 1889 charter stated that "the principal office of this Association shall be in Austin, Travis County, Texas, or wherever the Secretary of the said Association may reside." The 1901 charter contained the provision that the Association should "have its principal office and place of business in the City of Austin, Texas," but no reference was made to the residence of the secretary.

Despite this background, it will be recalled that in 1935 the Association bought a home at 1404 West El Paso Street, Fort Worth. This purchase brought great prestige to the Association and was a source of pride to the membership. Here, for a period of thirteen years, the building was adequate for the needs of the staff, and the work of the Association prospered. But the time came when this building, much in need of repairs, was outgrown. The question of a new building or a new location came up. The Council on Medical Economics, with Dr. H. E. Griffin as chairman, perhaps stepped out of role to speak of the building's being inadequate, "void of professional dignity," and "filled with inconveniences." Dr. George A. Schenewerk, of Dallas, reporting for the Committee on Public Relations, urged the construction of a building adequate for all the needs of the Association or, as an alternative, thorough renovation of the old building "in a manner befitting the dignity of the medical profession of Texas." The Committee on Financial Needs of the Association enlarged on the condition of the old building and concluded that a new building was needed.

On the afternoon of April 26, 1948, Dr. William M. Gambrell, of Austin, introduced a resolution in the House of Delegates providing for removal of the central offices of the Association to Austin. Two days later, the Reference Committee on Resolutions and Memorials, to which Gambrell's resolution had been referred, brought the resolution back to the House of Delegates for consideration. Dr. Gambrell moved that the resolution, which was based solely on the cited provision of the 1901 charter, be adopted. The motion was seconded by Dr. A. W. C. Bergfeld, of New Braunfels. Dr. Truman C. Terrell, of Fort Worth, chairman of the Board of Trustees, was the chief opponent of the measure. At considerable length, he cited the advantages of Fort Worth over Austin: greater accessibility by rail, highway, and air; proximity to the medical population of Texas; better postal facilities; and better hotel accommodations. It would be expensive and disruptive to move, he argued; and it would not be politically wholesome to have the home of the Association located in the shadow of the state capitol. As for the charter, it could be amended.

Dr. Gambrell, at still greater length, answered the arguments of Dr. Terrell and added some of his own. As an offset to the expense of moving, the Travis County Medical Society was offering a suitable building site, and the city of Austin had agreed to give the Association $100 per month for a limited time and to furnish janitor service, lights, and water. When the ballots were cast, 106 members voted in Austin's favor, 40 against. But the move was not effected so easily as the narration of the proceedings would indicate. The doctors of Austin had to work hard and long on the project. The entire membership of the Association had been circularized, and many personal contacts had been made. Most minds were made up before the 1948 meeting; it is doubtful whether many opinions were changed after the Houston session convened.

The resolution authorizing the change in location provided that the central office and library should be moved from Fort Worth to Austin prior to the next session of the Legislature. The Board of Trustees decided that the move should be made by September 1. This plan was carried out, and the transition was made with a minimum of disturbance to the varied activities of the Association. The old John Bremond home, at 700 Guadalupe Street, furnished temporary quarters at a rental of $425 a month. The building, leased for three years, was not fireproof and contained only a little more floor space than the building in Fort Worth. But the staff showed itself to be versatile and adaptive. They fitted themselves and their work into these cramped quarters, hoping and believing that a new building was not far away.

The question of a new and adequate home for the Association was closely tied up with the decision to move to Austin. Dr. George Turner, of El Paso, introduced a resolution at Houston which would authorize the Board of Trustees "to develop plans and specifications for the erection of a suitable home office building and library." A special committee was proposed whose duty it would be to study the advisability of paying tribute, in this new building, to those who had made worthy contributions to the cause of the Association. The names of Drs. Holman Taylor and R. B. Anderson were mentioned. This resolution was accepted without discussion. Before the next session, the Travis County Medical Society gave the Association a very desirable building site at the corner of Lamar Boulevard and Nineteenth Street.

Through the years, as times, attitudes, and problems changed, certain changes had been made in the constitution and bylaws of the Association. In 1948, after much constructive work by a committee composed of Drs. C. C. Cody, Jr., Holman Taylor, F. J. L. Blasingame, T. C. Terrell, E. A. Rowley, and M. M. Minter, a thorough revision was accomplished. This revision was necessitated mainly by the fact that the Association now had a membership of more than 5,000, whereas the old constitution and bylaws had been designed for a membership of 1,500. In the discussion, which was full and earnest, there were frequent references to a desire to streamline the Association so as to expedite the work of the House of Delegates and the various subdivisions of the organization.

The major change with respect to the officers was to replace the three vice-presidents with one vice-president and to add a speaker of the house, who would serve as its presiding officer. The committee was careful to explain that the latter change was not intended to reflect on the prestige and authority of the president, but rather to relieve him of some of his burdensome duties so that he would have more time to serve as official host at the annual session.

The membership of the Executive Council was enlarged but, more important, its duties were expanded so that it acted as the agent of the House of Delegates between sessions. Likewise, the council was to act in an advisory capacity to all officers and committees. Its meetings were to be held in January and August. Another function of the council was to carry on the work of the Association in time of war or civil disorder when perhaps the House of Delegates could not meet, as in World War II. Under these conditions, it was to be known as the War Council. One binding obligation was placed on the Executive Council: "If for any reason a member of the Association holding any office may not perform the duties of such office, the Executive Council shall request the President to call for the resignation of said member. Within ten days after the death, disability, or removal of both the President and Vice-President, the Executive Council shall assemble on call of the President-Elect for the purpose of electing a President for the unexpired term."

The bylaws were revised, also, by raising the dues from $20.00 to $35.00. This increase was to cover the ever increasing cost of operating the central office. Further justification for the raise was found in the fact that it cost $10,590.70 to move the Association headquarters to Austin.

The usual high standard of guest speakers was maintained at this Houston meeting. The guests were Drs. Frank Lahey, of Boston; John A. Kolmer, of Philadelphia; Waltman Walters and W. L. Benedict, of Rochester; Wingate M. Johnson, of Winston-Salem; Leo G. Rigler, of Minneapolis; L. S. Goin, of Los Angeles; Willard O. Thompson, of Chicago; and Ralph Luikart, of Omaha.

In opening his presidential address, "Blueprint for Action," Dr. B. E. Pickett asked this question: "Has socialization of the medical profession become a political issue?" The answer was self-evident. A congressional committee had revealed that as many as 45,000 government employees were active in the socialization campaign and that $75,000,000.00 of the taxpayers' money was being spent each year to promote these activities. The pressure from above was great, and the battle was on. Unless the medical profession bestirred itself, state medicine was inevitable; and that for the doctor meant, Dr. Pickett thought, "abject slavery, the necessity of catering to the ward committeeman or the precinct captain rather than to the needs of the human beings who are his patients." This dire calamity could be averted by the concerted effort of all branches of organized medicine, proper utilization of every opportunity to inform the public, exposure of New Deal tactics, and close co-operation with those business groups whose welfare was likewise jeopardized.

The five-city cycle was complete again, and it became the turn of San Antonio to entertain the Association. New officers were Dr. G. V. Brindley, Temple, president-elect; Dr. R. E. Windham, San Angelo, vice-president; and Dr. R. B. Homan, Jr., El Paso, speaker of the House of Delegates.

Presiding as the first speaker of the House of Delegates, Dr. R. B. Homan added dignity and dispatch to the proceedings of the San Antonio session. Dr. Harold M. Williams, reporting on the first full year of his tenure as secretary, stated that twelve out of the fourteen employees of the Association at Fort Worth had moved to Austin. In the meantime, the number had been increased to twenty-one, due chiefly to the increased activities of the Committee on Public Relations. Dwight Plackard and the firm of W. E. Syers Company, of Austin, had been retained as public-relations counselors.

Secretary Williams made a point of stressing one facility of the central office of the Association: the relocation service. As doctors came back after the war, it became necessary or desirable in some instances that new locations for them be found. The Association served well in making these adjustments. Later, assistance was given to out-of-state physicians desiring to come to Texas, and to local communities seeking resident physicians. In 1949 forty-seven communities were assisted in obtaining physicians, and eighty-four more requested assistance. As was to be expected, the greatest need lay in rural areas and small towns. Wacille Johnson has been of much help to the chairman of the Council on Medical Economics in this work.

The Board of Trustees authorized, at the 1948 meeting, a striking change in the format of the *Journal*. Little change had been made since the first issue, in 1905. The present change followed prolonged study by the staff, with assistance from the American Medical Association. The suggested improvements were accepted by the board and were embodied in the first issue of Volume 45, which came out in January, 1949. A blue-bordered design on the cover, new type face, improved arrangement of reading sections, and other changes gave the *Journal* a fresh, attractive appearance. The transformation was so marked that within a few months the *Journal* received an award for general improvement from the Society of Associated Industrial Editors. This comment came with the award: "Along comes the Texas State Journal of Medicine—a new look, and better; the sort of thing we laymen thought the Doctors were agin'. . . . MD's in Texas are *alive,* says your new format. Medicine is looking forward, not backward in Texas, the color and modern type on the cover tells the world. So there's more than just the mechanics of magazine production involved. There's proof that Texas doctors have the stuff it takes to fight the onward march of Socialism—not by merely trying to preserve the status quo, but by girding themselves with modern armor. Congratulations on bringing your magazine up to 1949 standards."

To emphasize the extent of the zeal of the Committee on Public Relations, now under the chairmanship of Dr. George A. Schenewerk, of Dallas, a word should be said about two of its publications. The first, *The Physician Meets the Public,* appeared early in 1948; it was a manual of medical public relations. The first printing of one thousand copies was quickly exhausted, and a second issue became necessary. Favorable comment appeared in the *Journal of the American Medical Association, Editor & Publisher,* and *Public Relations News.* Requests for copies came from individuals and business concerns all over the United States, from Canada, and from several foreign countries.

The second publication was the *Handbook and Directory of the State Medical Association of Texas,* which came out in 1948 and was enlarged in 1949. Seventy-five hundred copies were printed, and each member of the Association received a copy. The remainder were offered for sale at ten dollars. The scope and utility of this book can be judged from its table of contents: (1) alphabetical listing by name of all members of the Association, indicating specialty; (2) alphabetical listing by location of practice of all members; (3) state association officers and committees; (4) county society officers; (5) names and location of registered hospitals; (6) membership of the Texas Dental Association; (7) membership of the Texas Gradu-

408

ate Nurses Association; and (8) general information about medical economics alphabetically by counties.

The medical profession of Texas was grateful to the Legislature for the passage of two bills during 1949. The Basic Science Bill, its name changed to the Minimum Standards Bill, passed the House by a vote of 93 to 43 and the Senate by a vote of 25 to 1. Thus after a long struggle the people of Texas were assured a higher type of medical practitioner. The passage of this bill was the direct result of persistent efforts of the Texas Medical Association, with able guidance and assistance from Philip Overton. The *Journal* for June carried a picture, taken in Governor Beauford Jester's office, showing the Governor, Lieutenant-Governor Allan Shivers, a large group of senators and representatives, and three doctors who were influential in the bill's passage: Truman C. Terrell, chairman of the Board of Trustees; Merton M. Minter, vice-chairman; and J. B. Copeland, chairman of the Council on Legislation.

The second legislative act concerned an antisocialized medical measure, behind which could be easily detected the hand of the state association. The Senate passed unanimously and the House of Representatives with only one dissenting vote a resolution opposing socialized medicine and compulsory health insurance and requesting the Texas delegation in Washington to resist such legislation. The resolution contained these jabs at the New Deal: "Compulsory health insurance, wherever tried, has caused a decline in national health and deterioration of medical standards and facilities. . . . [Government encroachment] on the profession and on industry, is detrimental to the economic and social rights of the individuals of this great nation. . . . Wherever the government has assumed control of medical services, the result has been tremendous multiplication of costs over original estimates, extreme tax burdens and national deficits, and gradual extension of socialization into other activities of national life."

The growing cost of fighting socialized medicine by the American Medical Association became so burdensome that for 1949 it became necessary to make a voluntary assessment of $25 per member. By the time of the 1949 session of the Texas Medical Association, 2,504 Texas doctors had paid in $62,600. The voluntary factor, however, was not satisfactory, so the $25 assessment became compulsory dues the next year. This national assessment was designed as a replacement for the funds which, for ten years, had been collected by the National Physicians Committee for the Extension of Medical Service. This committee, of which Dr. E. H. Cary was the chairman and moving spirit, had worked earnestly and effectually and did much to curb the progress of social legislation.

New at this San Antonio session was the selection of the General Practitioner of the Year. The award went to Dr. J. R. McGee, of New Boston. New, too, was the Fifty-Year Club, an organization of physicians who had been in practice fifty years or more. Dr. W. M. Brumby, of Houston, was the first president. Of more significance to Texas medicine was the endorsement of Dr. F. J. L. Blasingame, of Wharton, for a place on the Board of Trustees of the American Medical Association. Dr. Blasingame was elected without opposition to this important position one month later, he being the youngest of the nine members.

The House of Delegates requested the Board of Trustees to proceed with plans for a new building and for financing its erection. Dr. Sam Key, of Austin, was named as chairman of a committee to draw up tentative plans for submission to architects. A second committee, with Dr. L. C. Heare, of Port Arthur, as chairman, was appointed to consider methods of financing the structure.

The following guest speakers were present: Drs. Carl A. Moyer, of Dallas; John L. Harter, of Louisville; Willis E. Brown, of Little Rock; Samuel F. Marshall and Charles I. Johnson, of Boston; B. R. Kirklin, of Rochester; Cecil Striker, of Cincinnati; Lauren V. Ackerman, of St. Louis; W. L. Pressly, of Due West, South Carolina; Gaylord W. Anderson, of Minneapolis; A. L. Hoyne, of Chicago; W. P. Holbrook, of Tucson; and W. A. Richardson, of Rutherford, New Jersey. Dr. Richardson, editor of *Medical Economics,* spoke on "Britain's Gamble in Government Medicine." "If such a scheme comes to the United States," he said, "physicians may just as well plan either to take down their shingles and go out of practice or resign themselves to a system in which they will lose their independence, their initiative, and eventually their collective leadership in world medicine."

Dr. Tate Miller, in his presidential address, "Looking to the Future in the Light of the Past," saw "our present national predicament" as a modern counterpart of past years when "benefits were centered in one or a few who gained power by promises or by diversion of the minds of the masses in a way that the masses looked more to the government and less to themselves for their fundamental needs." Better public understanding and better relations with the press were of prime importance. Political activity must not be neglected. The Texas congressmen needed encouragement, even though they were all favorable to the medical profession. But Dr. Miller ventured that "it would probably be futile to hope that President Truman might later see the light, when he apparently is unable to perceive 'light.' "

Hardly half the population of the United States had ever experienced conditions that were even near normal, Dr. Miller said. "All they have known is depression, unemployment, frustration, insecurity, war, strikes, temporary booms, high salaried laborers, contention, stalemate, and turmoil." These young people needed education. "We should cast off our clothing of political inhibitions and wade into the political waters belly-deep." The younger citizenry should be reminded of the "kindness, tolerance, sympathy, understanding, patience, and fineness and sweetness of spirit" of the doctor of old. They should be convinced that a supreme effort is being made "to combine our present-day richness in knowledge and materials with the spirit and the fineness of heart and nobleness of purpose of our medical forebears."

At this meeting, the plan of choosing the meeting place two years in advance was established. Fort Worth was chosen for 1950 and Galveston for 1951. The new president-elect was Dr. William M. Gambrell, of Austin. Dr. Joseph McVeigh, of Fort Worth, became vice-president. Dr. Robert B. Homan, Jr., of El Paso, succeeded himself as speaker of the House of Delegates.

During the summer of 1949, the Association found itself involved in the question of locating a new medical school, provision for which had been made by the Legislature. Two years before, the Legislature had authorized the University of Texas to establish a medical branch at San Antonio. Nothing came of this because the state comptroller made an inaccurate estimate of funds available. Three medical-education bills were introduced in the 1949 Legislature. Two would establish medical branches in Temple and San Antonio. The third provided for the University of Texas to take over the Southwestern Medical College, which was having financial difficulties. The Legislature asked the State Medical Association of Texas to make a survey of the three locations and present a recommendation. These surveys were made by the Council on Medical

Education, with Dr. M. O. Rouse, of Dallas, as chairman. A special session of the House of Delegates was held in Austin on July 13. The Council on Medical Education made its report, and the claims of the three cities were fully presented by local representatives. Dallas was selected as the location to be recommended to the Board of Regents of the University of Texas, the vote being Dallas 79, San Antonio 54, and Temple 6.

A distinct loss came to the Association in 1949 in the death of Judge C. T. Freeman, of Sherman. Judge Freeman had been general attorney for the Association for twenty-seven years. He had piloted the organization through many rough legal shoals. He had helped frame the constitution and bylaws and was consulted often in connection with the Medical Practice Act and many other legislative measures of medical importance. But his most valuable contributions were in the field of medical defense, the ramifications of which he understood thoroughly. Judge Freeman was succeeded as general attorney by Philip R. Overton, of Austin.

XXIII

Centenary of the Texas Medical Association, 1950–53

As the first century of organized medicine in Texas came to a close, political and economic conditions continued to be unpromising. The United States, with the United Nations, was at war with the Communists in Korea. At home, there was no diminution in the contest between organized medicine and the federal government. As will be seen, the Texas Medical Association was drawn directly into the affray.

At the 1950 session, the Board of Trustees reported progress in plans for the new building. The Building Committee offered prizes to the fifth-year students in the Department of Architecture at the University of Texas for the best designs and floor plans. The twenty-six suggestions that were submitted proved to be of value in formulating the final plans. The firm of Staub and Rather, of Houston, was chosen to do the architectural work, and Fred Folmer, Jr., associate librarian at the University of Texas, was retained as a consultant.

The Building Committee was composed of Drs. Sam Key, chairman, David Wade, C. P. Hardwicke, and William M. Gambrell, all of Austin. Drs. F. J. L. Blasingame and M. M. Minter, both members of the Board of Trustees, were appointed to consult with the architects and the Building Committee. The original lot, which was 167 by 180 feet, was considered inadequate for the proposed building; so, at a cost of $17,500, it was enlarged to measure 180 by

413

, feet. By November, 1950, the plans were complete, according to the *Journal* of that month. They called for

a two story and basement structure of approximately 33,000 square feet. The basement will house utility machinery, workshops, dark room, storage space, and book stacks for library expansion as well as an apartment for the building superintendent.

The first floor will contain the main foyer and reception room, reading rooms, research and reference rooms, stack room for library volumes, rare books and committee room, projection room, film storage, workroom, shipping and receiving rooms, supply room, and offices for the librarian and assistants. Also on the first floor will be the lounge, which can be converted into an auditorium seating several hundred, equipped with motion picture projectors of necessary types.

A mezzanine between the first and second floors will accommodate additional book stacks.

The second floor will house the general offices, office of the Executive Secretary, reception room, business and editorial offices of the *Journal*, central files, storage, public relations offices, and work and mail rooms. An outside terrace is included in the second floor plan.

The first and second floors are to be air conditioned throughout, and the lounge will be equipped with a utility kitchen.

Site for the building is at Nineteenth and Lamar Streets in Austin and present plans call for attractive landscaping of the surrounding grounds, which already contain many shade trees.

Three interesting amendments to the constitution and bylaws were offered in 1950. The first would change the name to Texas Medical Association. This amendment was adopted the following year. Thus the name of the Association, after ninety-eight years, had completed the cycle. The constitution of 1853 stated that "this Institution shall be known and distinguished by the name and title of the Texas Medical Association." At the second session of 1853, the name and title appeared as the Medical Association of Texas. At the reorganizational meeting in 1869, it was agreed that "the name and style of this Association shall be the Texas State Medical Association." When a new charter was taken out in 1901, the name appeared as the State Medical Association of Texas. And then in 1951, under the sponsorship of the Board of Trustees, the constitution was made to read: "The name and title of this organization shall be the Texas Medical Association."

Another amendment, proposed in 1950, was accepted in 1951.

414

This set up a state public grievance committee, district public grievance committees, and, where feasible, county committees. The idea was not new. It had been in operation in several states; and some Texas county societies, among them Bexar and Harris, had utilized the good offices of such committees for many years. The main purpose of these committees was to create better relations with the public and thus to checkmate socialization. Patients could now appreciate that here recourse could be found for any complaints they might have. It was anticipated that these committees could help also in the solution of the problems of night and emergency calls. Because it became evident that a conflict in responsibility existed between the state grievance committee and the Board of Councilors, the grievance committee as a separate unit on the state level was eliminated in 1952, but provision for accepting complaints was continued.

The third amendment dealt with a subject which had been controversial with the medical profession for many years. It was a situation fraught with obvious injustices as well as possible complicating pitfalls in the future. It was the admission of Negro physicians to membership in the American Medical Association and the Texas Medical Association. Negro doctors had their own Lone Star State Medical Association, as well as a national organization, but these were not fully successful. The American Medical Association had solved the problem by admitting Negroes many years earlier,[1] and there had been a minimum of criticism. At the 1950 session of the Texas Medical Association, the Committee on Negro Medical Facilities was ready to report. Its members were Drs. Tate Miller, Truman Terrell, and Merton Minter. This report pointed out that the better type of Negro doctor did not come to Texas because it meant giving up membership in the American Medical Association. Its recommendation was to admit Negroes under rather limited conditions: a county society, if it so desired, could vote to accept for membership such Negro doctors as merited this consideration. A reference committee, which passed on the amendment, gave it a favorable report, and the editor of the *Journal* predicted approval at the next session. When it came before the House of Delegates in 1951, however, it was decided to give the matter further study.

Convincing evidence of the Association's continuing interest in the welfare of the Negro doctors of Texas was the program which

[1] The exact date is obscure.

the Committee on Negro Medical Facilities was instrumental in arranging for the Lone Star State Medical Association at its meeting in Austin on June 4–6, 1951. There were nine speakers from the American Medical Association, among them Drs. Richard W. TeLinde, of Johns Hopkins, and Michael E. DeBakey, of Baylor. This was more than a friendly gesture, since the National Medical Association at its meeting at Detroit in August, 1949, had come close to endorsing the socialized medical program of Oscar Ewing and his crew of militant reformers. Dr. C. A. Whittier, of San Antonio, was president of this national association of Negro physicians at the time. After Dr. George F. Lull, general manager of the American Medical Association, had addressed the Detroit meeting on the objectives of the American Medical Association, Dr. Whittier took exception to his views. "The N. M. A.," said Whittier, "should do its own thinking and should be concerned with the masses of the poor and needy people who do not have adequate medical care." [2]

Constant efforts were being made to improve the programs of the Association and to increase attendance at the sessions. At the Fort Worth meeting in 1950, color television showed up for the first time. Smith, Kline & French Laboratories of Philadelphia were the sponsors of this innovation. Operations performed at St. Joseph's Hospital were viewed in the ballroom of the Texas Hotel.

But something more than something new was needed. Attendance at the general meetings and the scientific sections was generally disappointing. The Council on Scientific Work, with Dr. May Owen, of Fort Worth, as chairman, had been wrestling with this problem for some time. One suggestion of the council was readily accepted; it provided for the meetings of the House of Delegates and committees on Sunday; meetings of related organizations and the House of Delegates on Monday; opening exercises, memorial services, a general meeting, and section meetings on Tuesday; and the House of Delegates, section meetings, and a general luncheon meeting on Wednesday. Thus, it was hoped that interest and attendance would be stimulated by a shorter session.

A second recommendation of the Council on Scientific Work was also adopted, but not without considerable debate. It provided for a reduction of guest speakers to "a total of no more than two." The council felt that the presence of ten or more guests overshadowed the local speakers and that there were in Texas many

[2] *Journal of the National Medical Association*, XLI (1949), 233.

men whose high capabilities should be utilized on the program. That relief from some source was sorely needed is suggested by the program of the general meeting on Tuesday, which scheduled seventeen items for a three-hour period. These included six addresses and three scientific papers. The attending member could hardly be criticized if he felt surfeited and sought relief in non-medical circles.

The ever recurring subject of socialized medicine and the determined efforts of the authorities in Washington to bring it about were not neglected at the Fort Worth session. New tactics had been adopted by the federal government, which began in Texas by ordering the Federal Bureau of Investigation to check the records of the Harris County and Jefferson County medical societies. Next the government moved into Association headquarters in Austin and spent several days searching for evidence of antitrust violations. This procedure was repeated in twenty-four instances over the nation, in what appeared to be an attempt to embarrass organized medicine at a time when the Washington campaign was not meeting with success. The Texas Medical Association had nothing to hide; and nothing has been heard from this investigation. It may be that the reason no charges were filed in Texas was that the Oregon State Medical Society had just won a suit in the United States district court. There, the government was soundly castigated by the presiding judge, who asked, "Can it be that a profession may not defend itself by reorganization of its methods, by doing within the profession what has been compelled elsewhere by law? . . . In short [must organized medicine] remain a sitting duck while socialism overwhelms it?"

Dr. John W. Cline, of San Francisco, soon to become president-elect of the American Medical Association, spoke at Fort Worth with courage and conviction on "The Campaign to Socialize Medicine." The socializers, he said, "have bribed the taxpayer by purchasing his immediate future with his own funds while mortgaging him, his children, and his grandchildren. . . . [They have launched] the most vicious, systematic campaign of vilification ever waged against a respectable organization devoted to the welfare of the people. . . . Our adversaries are not gentle or overscrupulous about their methods. . . . Already we have seen the police powers of the federal government unleashed against our associations and societies in a series of politically inspired inquiries designed to bring us cravenly to heel." Businessmen now realize, said Dr. Cline, "that American Medicine is fighting the front-line battle to save private enterprise and individual freedom."

One new weapon in the fight against socialization was the "President's Page," which first appeared in the June, 1950, issue of the *Journal.* This idea was adopted by the *Journal of the American Medical Association* in its issue of September 23, 1950, and has proved its worth. It gave President Gambrell an opportunity to speak out on such subjects as "Our A.M.A." "Freedom to Secure Good Medical Care," and "A Reply to Mr. Ewing."

One serious problem that faced the medical profession of Texas in 1950 was the procurement of adequate medical officers for the armed forces. When the long-titled State Council on National Emergency Medical Service reported at the 1950 session, the attention of the House of Delegates was called to a few minor activities such as examination of recruits for the Texas National Guard. But after General Douglas MacArthur led the forces of the United Nations into Korea in June, the situation changed rapidly and radically. The need for medical personnel became acute, and for the first time in its history the medical profession of Texas fell short of its obligation. This obligation rested chiefly on those young doctors who had been deferred in World War II so as to finish their medical education and on those eligible doctors who did not serve in World War II. A special offer of an additional $100 per month was made, without avail, to volunteer doctors. If we fail, President-Elect Gambrell said a year later on the "President's Page," to "meet our major responsibilities in time of war, we may expect to lose the confidence of the public in us to solve medical problems in normal and peaceful periods." Already many medical reserve officers were being called. The Executive Council met ahead of time on August 24 to deal with the embarrassing situation. But little came of the meeting except to establish a closer relationship with the armed forces and the Council on National Emergency Medical Service of the American Medical Association, and to endorse a bill before Congress, previously endorsed by the American Medical Association, which provided for the drafting of doctors, dentists, and other specialists.

The drafting of doctors in Texas and the United States was something new and not altogether palatable, but here it was. The law was passed on September 9, 1950, and October 16 was set as the

418

date for registration of those doctors under fifty years of age who were trained at government expense, those who had served less than twenty-one months in the military forces, and those who had not served at all. Inasmuch as the law called for induction into the armed forces as privates and not as officers, there were enough volunteers to meet the emergency.

This was the last year the Association invited a large number of guest speakers. These were Drs. Robert J. Crossen, of St. Louis; Orvar Swenson and Paul A. Chandler, of Boston; Thomas J. Dry and Howard K. Gray, of Rochester; Frank W. Konzelmann, of Atlantic City; Howard B. Hunt, of Omaha; Ernest L. Stebbins, of Baltimore; John W. Cline, of San Francisco; and Carl T. Javert, of New York; and a nonmedical man, Cecil Palmer, of London. Mr. Palmer spoke to a large public gathering on conditions in socialist England and later, before the Association, painted a gloomy picture of "Socialized Medicine in Practice."

In his presidential address on "Worthy Objectives," Dr. G. V. Brindley recalled the varied purposes of the Texas Medical Association. After reviewing the radical changes in medical and economic conditions within a decade or two, he presented these purposes in this order: medical legislation, medical education, enlightenment of the public, and current problems. Every doctor should concern himself with medical legislation designed to benefit the public. Especially should he be on guard against socialization of medicine. Equally concerned should he be about medical education. Texas had three excellent medical schools, Dr. Brindley reminded, and those in authority should see to it that they retain their independence, because federal domination would spell their doom. The medical profession, Dr. Brindley warned, had an obligation to take the public into its confidence. Knowledge of disease and methods of treatment had advanced far. The public should be told. The expectation of life had increased remarkably. The public should be told. The American people spent more for alcoholic beverages than for medical care. To take care of the emergencies involved in illness, voluntary health insurance was available. The public should be told that nearly 70,000,000 people were covered by such insurance. Information about all these advances, along with many important current problems, should be shared with the public whose co-operation should be constantly solicited. An informed public would not be an easily misled public.

In the continued effort at full realization of the purposes of the Association, one ally was always at hand. The Woman's Auxiliary to the Texas Medical Association, since its organization in 1918, had proved itself to be of exceptional importance. Through the medium of its benevolent projects, its community programs, and its promotion of better relations among physicians and their families, its work had been outstanding. But the organization's greatest contribution had been in the field of public relations. The press, the radio, and personal contacts with individuals and clubs were utilized successfully by the 70 county auxiliaries and their 3,786 members. Any success which the Association may have achieved in curbing socialized medicine and in molding public opinion must be shared with the auxiliary, the true helpmate of the Association.

Dr. Allen T. Stewart, of Lubbock, became the new president-elect and Dr. Hall Shannon, of Dallas, vice-president. Again Dr. Robert B. Homan, Jr., succeeded himself as speaker of the House of Delegates. The 1951 session had previously been assigned to Galveston, and the invitation of Dallas for 1952 was accepted.

A rather marked departure took place in the central office of the Association during the summer. Dr. Harold M. Williams resigned as secretary of the Association and editor of the *Journal* in May, 1950. Philip R. Overton, always ready for any new assignment, was appointed to fill the place temporarily. And then, by appointment by the Board of Trustees, Grahame M. ("Tod") Bates became executive secretary of the Association and editor of the *Journal*. With the appointment came the recommendation that the bylaws be amended so as to create the position of executive secretary of the Association, a recommendation which was accepted in 1951. This change to lay leadership followed the trend of other medical organizations. The over-all activities of the Texas Medical Association had expanded greatly in recent years, notably in the fields of public relations and economics. The affairs of the central office, likewise, had experienced rapid growth, so that problems of business administration and personnel management were multiplying. In short, the time had come "for the services of a capable business administrator with a background and experience in those fields which a doctor of medicine could scarcely be expected to acquire." After serving for about a year, Bates resigned his position with the Association in July, 1951.

N. C. Forrester became acting executive secretary and later ex-

420

ecutive secretary, and he has carried on the work in a most creditable manner with the aid of a number of willing hands. Jeanie Lannom was secretary to Forrester by 1953, and Jean Clark and Dan Lehman assisted with the public relations program. The organization's correspondence files, grown to sizable proportions, were supervised by Betty Joyce Russell, and Elizabeth Wrightsman handled the telephone switchboard with its three trunk lines and its nineteen intra-office extensions. Don Gholston operated the battery of office machines required to prepare material for mass mailing.

At the time of Forrester's appointment, the assistant editor of the *Journal* was Harriet Cunningham. In that capacity, and more recently as managing editor, her editorial hand has continued to function most capably, assisted by Ruth Trahan, Mary Stuart Warren, and Arleen Draker.

The 1951 session in Galveston put into effect the decided change in the program recommended by the Council on Scientific Work. Absent were the ten or twelve guest speakers. Present were Dr. George G. Finney, of Baltimore, and Martin Dies, former United States congressman from the Second Texas District and chairman of the House Committee on Un-American Activities. The change did not produce the results that were anticipated. The attendance was 1,210, only 34 more than had come to Galveston in 1939; but in 1939 the membership had been 1,456 less. At one of the two meetings addressed by Dr. Finney, about 4 per cent of the registered members were present. Dies, who was much in the news at the time, spoke at the final luncheon to 450 persons, including members of the auxiliary.

There must have been more than a growing conviction among those who cherished the welfare of the Association that many— a great many—members came to the city where the Association was meeting but did not come to the meetings. In other words, they were seeking recreation rather than education. But there were other reasons for lack of interest, not the least of which was the multiplicity of medical meetings. For instance, the August, 1951, issue of the *Journal,* under the caption "Coming Meetings and Clinics," carried a list of ninety-two events. Add to these the county society meetings, the hospital staff meetings, and the meetings of special groups, and it is obvious that a stage approaching satiety had been reached. The answer to the problem was difficult and complicated; indeed, it was questionable whether there was at that time any certain solution. It was not difficult to conclude that the average member of the Texas Medical Association was willing to pay his dues, which of necessity were constantly mounting, but he was disinclined to contribute his time and talents to the Association. He believed in the Association, he knew he was being shielded by its protecting arms, and yet he did not seem to realize that there was a reciprocal obligation on his part.

Paradoxically, the trend of the Association had been toward a plan that would be of greater benefit to the average doctor. The newly created Section on General Practice was aimed at that purpose. At this 1951 session, much was said and done to further the interests of the general practitioner. It was fully appreciated that a large group of alert doctors in rural and small town areas was the best answer to the charges of the New Deal that many areas of the population were being neglected.

Postgraduate medicine was strongly emphasized at this eighty-fifth session as a medium for the improvement of the medical profession. The Council on Medical Education and Hospitals brought in some far-reaching recommendations on the subject. These were passed by the House of Delegates. They gave support to the postgraduate plans of the three medical schools in the state, offered to underwrite these courses to the extent of $2,500 a year in each school, and disapproved the acceptance of personal remuneration by members of the Association from the State Health Department for attendance on these courses. This custom of receiving money from the federal government through the Health Department provoked sharp discussion. To some, it seemed logical; to most, it was an obvious socialistic handout. Chairman Milford O. Rouse of the Council on Medical Education and Hospitals advised the Association to stick to its tradition of "preferred philosophy of financial independence." "Are we going to stultify our consciences," Dr. H. E. Griffin, of Graham, asked, by "continually allowing the federal government to infringe on our rights?" The House of Delegates voted a resounding "No."

The report of the Board of Trustees dealt with routine matters rather briefly and then turned to the new building. Final plans were accepted late in the fall of 1950, and the general contract was awarded to the Yarborough Construction Company of Austin on

422

January 2. Early estimates of costs varied from $500,000 to $632,000. The total contract price was $682,553. Construction, begun on February 15, 1951, was at a reasonably rapid pace.

Well-founded apprehension was expressed by the board over the financial prospects of the Association. A reserve fund of $205,204.00 was available. All this would be required to finance the new building. Besides, the regular expenses had greatly increased as the activities of the Association had expanded. Large sums had been spent on public relations and the doctor draft law; to be exact, these two items amounted to $23,968.15 in 1950. The salaries of staff members, now numbering more than twenty, totaled $55,366.37. The 1950 session of the Association had cost $12,648.31. These facts and figures convinced the board that the financial status of the Association, under existing conditions, was "extremely hazardous." As a way to safety, it was recommended that the annual dues be raised from $35.00 to $50.00. This was done. As a further source of much needed revenue, advertising rates in the *Journal* were increased by 25 per cent, this being the first increase since 1929.

So absorbed was the Board of Trustees in the building and financial problems of the Association that it did not find time to announce that on May 1, one day before the 1951 session convened, a new charter—or rather a fifty-year extension of the 1901 charter—had been granted. The May issue of the *Journal* pictured the signing of the extension in the office of John Ben Shepperd, secretary of state. Shown in the picture, in addition to Shepperd, were Drs. F. J. L. Blasingame, Truman C. Terrell, Merton M. Minter, G. V. Brindley, and William M. Gambrell, and Tod Bates. Accompanying the picture was "The Story of the Three Charters," in which were summarized the facts surrounding the granting of charters in 1853, 1889, and 1901.

The doctor draft law, passed in 1950, was inadequate for the time; as the threat of Communism on a worldwide scale became more acute, there came a resultant need for more medical manpower. The meeting of the Executive Council, held in Austin on August 23, 1950, was devoted principally to this subject. One result was the appointment of Dr. R. A. Trumbull as chairman of a committee to correlate the efforts of the several groups interested in this subject. The work had previously been in the capable hands of Dr. Ozro T. Woods, of Dallas. The agreed-on plan looked forward to the creation of local committees, co-ordinated with the county medical societies, which would "act as an 'informational clearing house' for the society's members and to study and make recommendations on individual cases of physicians being called into the service." The successful accomplishments of the Association in this direction were attested by these words in a letter to President Gambrell from Surgeon-General R. W. Bliss of the United States Army: "Colonel Liston, Surgeon of our Fourth Army Area, has informed me in glowing terms of the magnificent job done in Texas in regard to manning of Recruiting and Induction Main Stations, procurement and assignment, and the making of physicians available for the accomplishment of the thousands upon thousands of physical examinations of inductees rapidly recalled to the military service. He claims that he made his problems known to you and to your executive committee and, from that point on, the doctors of Texas, under your guidance, shouldered the job. Needless to say, it was a most creditable performance."

One reason why the Association could be so commended was that after an initial period during which the organization bore the brunt of clerical expense for the State Advisory Committee to the Selective Service System, public funds were made available for the employment first of one and then of two clerks to work in the Association offices, using its records and the advice of its executive secretary, to carry on the activities of the latest version of the "procurement and assignment" committee. This friendly liaison between the medical profession and military officials continues, with Jeanne Kerwin and Marjorie Weber shouldering the detail work.

In 1950, Drs. C. C. Cody and W. H. Moursund, of Houston, and Joe Gilbert, of Austin, had been elected to emeritus membership. Drs. L. H. Reeves, of Fort Worth, and Felix Miller, of El Paso, became emeritus members at this Galveston session. In 1950, Dr. Jim Camp, of Pecos, had been chosen as General Practitioner of the Year. This year that honor went to Dr. Leo J. Peters, of Schulenburg. There was much to be admired in Dr. Peters' words of acceptance: gratitude to God and man, modesty, and humility.

Two public-health measures, both sponsored by the Texas Medical Association, were passed by the Legislature in 1951. The first, nurtured faithfully by Dr. Arthur C. Scott, Jr., of Temple, authorized the issuance of licenses to "vocational nurses" under certain controlled conditions. This law was intended as a means of remedying the nurse shortage in Texas and, at the same time, improving

424

the qualifications of undergraduate or practical nurses. The second measure was designed to regulate the sale and distribution of barbiturates and kindred preparations. The act made the acquisition of these drugs more difficult and provided stiff penalties for transgressors by fine and imprisonment.

The scientific program under the new plan was excellent. A number of speakers from Baylor, Southwestern, and the University of Texas, interspersed with a larger number from over the state, provided a well-balanced program which reflected medical progress in Texas. Dr. George G. Finney, of Johns Hopkins, spoke to the first general meeting on "Lesions of the Breast" and to the Section on General Practice on "Surgical Treatment of Duodenal Ulcer."

Martin Dies addressed the final general session on "The Communist Threat to America." He traced the history of Communism from the time of Karl Marx, in 1848, to the present.

To Mr. Dies, the socialization of medicine meant the socialization of all industry and all agriculture. Aggressive, offensive action, he warned, was acutely necessary.

You owe a duty to your country to battle this communistic proposal which will completely destroy the progress that the medical profession has made in the past half-century.... You must enter the field of politics. You must become interested in the preservation of your free government. If you don't, you will lose it in the next ten years or sooner.... Your task is to go forth and convince all our people that this is not your fight alone. It is the fight of every decent American who is opposed to the omnipotent state and who believes in the dignity of the individual and in the inviolability of man.... We have a solemn obligation to the next generation, an obligation that we cannot shirk or ignore. We are the custodians and the trustees of their liberty. We must see that they live in a land of freedom and that they enjoy the good life that you and I have enjoyed.

Three important members of the Association died during the year: Drs. Charles F. Craig, of San Antonio, and E. W. Bertner and John T. Moore, of Houston. Colonel Craig had a deservedly worldwide reputation in tropical diseases. Dr. Bertner, a former president of the Association, in his later years was closely connected with the evergrowing medical facilities at Houston. As for John T. Moore, words are inadequate; real replacements for such a man come rarely. In active work and as a member of the Association for fifty-five years and chairman of the Board of Trustees for twenty-nine years, he filled a mighty place in the medical affairs of Texas. At the 1951 memorial services, the name of John T. Moore appeared on the printed program along with 150 others. No special eulogy for him. That was the way he would have wanted it, modest man that he was.

The presidential address of Dr. William Gambrell concerned itself with "Medicine's Modern Problems." The medical profession had faced many problems in its course of progress through the years. None of these, he said, compared in seriousness with the threat of regimentation which a paternalistic government was trying to impose. To meet this threat, organized medicine had some very definite and urgent obligations. Every doctor owed it to his patients and to himself constantly to improve the practice of medicine by regular study and willing acceptance of responsibility. The obligation of leadership, said Dr. Gambrell, fell logically on the shoulders of the doctor. If patients did not receive instruction from their doctors in matters of medicine and public health, they would naturally look elsewhere: "We must remember that a silent majority makes an outspoken minority appear very strong."

And then, Dr. Gambrell continued, the doctor had very obvious obligations to organized medicine, to which he should contribute his abilities and his money. He should vigorously uphold the plan of voluntary health insurance and should help to correct its faults. The Woman's Auxiliary was a most worthy colleague and should receive every encouragement, especially on the county level. But, most of all, doctors had an obligation to take the public into their confidence and, through good public relations and a sensible system of education, to keep them informed as to what an enlightened medical profession had to offer. Dr. Gambrell submitted a program for accomplishing this purpose, for he felt that "if the doctors, the medical teachers, and the researchers are left free and unshackled, the future of medical science, with its blessings and advantages to humanity, will be very bright."

With Dallas already selected for the 1952 session, Houston was chosen for the following year. The new president-elect was Dr. Truman C. Terrell, who was chairman of the Board of Trustees at the time. Dr. Merton M. Minter succeeded to the latter office. Dr. L. C. Powell, of Beaumont, was elected vice-president. Dr. Sam Key, of Austin, succeeded himself as secretary; he had been appointed on an interim basis by the Board of Trustees when Dr.

426

Harold Williams resigned. No change was made in the speakership of the House of Delegates.

The 1951 meeting of the Southern Medical Association was held in Dallas. Three previous meetings had been held in Texas: in Dallas in 1915 and 1925, and in San Antonio in 1934. Dr. Curtice Rosser, of Dallas, was president. Attendance was 2,053.

Bigness and buoyancy characterized the 1952 meeting of the Association in Dallas: membership of 5,859,[3] income of $196,808 for the year, net worth of $496,500, and withal a feeling of pride in the accomplishments of the past several years. However, the registration of only 1,267 fell far below the figure of 1,562 for the 1940 Dallas meeting.

Dr. M. M. Minter's report for the Board of Trustees announced the near-completion of the Association building at Lamar Boulevard and Nineteenth Street in Austin, with dedication being planned for September, 1952. The entire cost, including the lot, building, and fixtures, was approximately $740,000.00. This may seem to be an excessive figure. It represented, however, an obligation of only about $120.00 for each member. Arrangements had been made for a loan of $415,000.00 from the Equitable Life Assurance Society of the United States. Helping in the financing was a gift of $6,417.74 from the Woman's Auxiliary, ever capable and generous partisan of the medical profession.

The Committee on Public Relations continued its work in a serious and efficient manner; in his report to the 1951 session, Chairman Robert W. Kimbro, of Cleburne, clearly revealed that the problems of the committee touched both patient and doctor: "The problem today is not simply one of disciplining members of the profession, but one of improving relations with the public, of clarifying misunderstandings, and of adjusting differences so that individual physicians and the profession itself may continue in the confidence of the American people." In addition, there was a strong desire to emphasize that the business of public relations is bilateral: this committee wanted the public to come to understand and appreciate the mission of the medical profession; at the same time, the doctors had an obligation of leadership to the public, and not in

[3] Membership was classified as follows: regular, 5,325; honorary, 201; intern, 178; military, 145; emeritus, 10.

medical matters alone; full approbation could come by being not only good doctors but also good citizens.

A state grievance committee had been created. Such a committee had found favor in forty-one other states. Through this committee, it was hoped that public confidence in the profession would be maintained in four specified fields: fair fees, availability of doctors for home and night calls, improved office techniques for handling the public, and explanation of actual facts regarding doctor distribution. The campaign to explain the doctor to the public gained great impetus during 1952. Dr. Kimbro and his committee followed through on previously made plans. Comprehensive material on the operation of grievance committees was made available to the county societies: sample advertisements, news stories, editorials, radio scripts, and pamphlets to be used in waiting rooms. Among the last were two reprints put out by the American Medical Association: "The Doctors Clean House," by Alice Lake, from the *American Magazine,* and "Your Doctor for a Friend," from *Reader's Digest.* This material was utilized on a trial basis in Pampa, Austin, Abilene, Fort Worth, Houston, and San Antonio, after which other areas put on local campaigns. One additional gesture of good will was suggested by Dr. John W. Cline, president of the American Medical Association. This was a plaque for office use, addressed "To All My Patients" and declaring: "We shall esteem it a favor if you will discuss frankly with us any source of dissatisfaction arising from our services. It will be eliminated by free discussion between us." The *Journal* of December, 1951, gave editorial support to this idea.

One unusual and effectual approach to the public was had through a series of three articles in the *Texas Parade.* This journal, telling the story of Texas in all of its phases, goes out each month to 21,000 subscribers in the business, educational, and professional world. Dealing with the subjects "Texas Doctors Meet Challenge of Socialism," "Medical Care in Texas," and "When You Need a Doctor," these articles set forth the efforts of organized medicine to retain the private practice of medicine and thus to serve as the first line of defense against socialization of all business and industry.

One feature of the campaign of publicity emphasized the desire of the profession to come to the public with clean hands. Unworthy doctors were few in number, but these could not be shielded. Organized medicine had to have the courage to rid itself of these undesirables. Dr. Louis H. Bauer, of the American Medical Association, expressed this idea very frankly in his presidential address in 1952: "Medical societies must be adamant in disciplining those unethical physicians who prey upon the public. A physician who charges exorbitant fees or who, when summoned in an emergency, refuses to make the call unless assured that the patient can pay, is a disgrace to the profession. Only a few are guilty of such practices, but those few do the profession incalculable harm." [4] Medical education was of prime interest to the Association in 1952. Better doctors for the people of Texas was the repeated and continuing desire. Members of the Association were urged to avail themselves of the excellent postgraduate facilities of the medical schools of the state, but were reminded that acceptance of financial remuneration for attending these courses was in bad taste. These postgraduate courses were given at Baylor and at both medical branches of the University of Texas. In addition, the Texas Postgraduate School of Medicine offered courses at Houston, San Angelo, Corpus Christi, Temple, and San Antonio.

But the main educational emphasis was placed on a series of three hour-long telephone broadcast programs, sponsored by the Special Committee on Postgraduate Work, with Dr. Milford O. Rouse, of Dallas, as chairman. The bases on which this new venture rested were set down by Dr. Rouse:

1. The physician's medical education is continuous.

2. Doctors are sincerely interested in giving a "clinical trial" to the use of modern techniques in medical postgraduate work.

3. The newest medical postgraduate technique, programs broadcast by telephone, brings recent scientific advances to the door of every county medical society.

4. Topnotch programs from a central source will help to solve the perpetual problem of obtaining county medical society programs that will attract attendance.

The first program, on "Pulmonary Embolism," was presented on February 12, 1952, by Drs. Henry M. Winans and Arthur Grollman, of Dallas; Denton Cooley and M. D. Levy, of Houston; and Charles T. Stone, Sr., of Galveston. March 11 was the date of the second panel, on "Recognition and Treatment of Abdominal Emergencies." The speakers were Drs. Michael E. DeBakey, of Houston; Robert M. Moore, of Galveston; W. G. Reddick, of Dallas; Joseph

[4] "Medicine in 1952," *Journal of the A.M.A.,* CXLIX (1952), 624.

Kopecky, of San Antonio; and R. J. White, of Fort Worth. The third program, "Some Psychiatric Principles in the Practice of Medicine," came on April 8. The speakers were Drs. Hamilton Ford and Titus Harris, of Galveston; Alfred Hill, of San Antonio; W. T. Brown, of Houston; J. E. Robertson, of Dallas; and W. B. Adamson, of Abilene.

Relayed by long-distance telephone, these programs were available to any county society or interested group at a modest cost. Prior to the time of each broadcast, abstracts and appropriate lantern slides were sent to each listening group. Informal discussion followed each program.

The reception of this innovation of telephone broadcasts was enthusiastic beyond the hopes of the committee that sponsored the idea; they were so successful that the Association decided to provide a series of four similar programs during the next year. Attendance at meetings of participating societies was far above, probably double, that of other meetings. More important, these broadcasts focused attention on the work of the state association and, as a result, tended to sustain the increased attendance at the county society meetings.

Another step forward, not taken by the Texas Medical Association but applauded by it, was instituted by the Academy of General Practice and the Board of Regents of the University of Texas. This was the preceptor system, whereby senior medical students would spend eleven weeks as assistant and constant companion of designated general practitioners throughout the state. The art of medicine was to be learned at the bedside of the patient and at the feet of the preceptor. There had been a time in Texas when most medical education was conducted in this way. Here was a combination of the old and the new in medicine, one that was calculated to teach the human as well as the scientific side of medicine and one that would emphasize the heart-warming rewards that came to the doctors in rural and small-town areas. The plan was launched on June 30, 1952, under the direction of E. S. McLarty of Galveston and Andrew S. Tomb of Victoria. S. D. Coleman of Navasota became the first preceptor, and his preceptee was Lonnie S. Burnett. Soon thereafter, thirty-five other senior students from Galveston entered eagerly into the promising experiment.

To offset a tendency to leftist thought which was beginning to appear among certain medical students, in 1949 the Student American Medical Association was organized under the sponsorship of the American Medical Association. The membership, representing forty-four medical schools, had grown to 15,000 by 1951, and the association had its own publication, the *Journal of the Student American Medical Association.* Charter membership is held by the three medical schools in Texas. At the Dallas meeting in 1952, the Texas Medical Association invited the membership of the younger association to attend the meetings of its House of Delegates, with the privilege of discussion and debate, and the Board of Trustees agreed to pay the expenses of one student from Texas to attend the annual session of the American Medical Association in Chicago.

The always difficult question of Negro membership in the Texas Medical Association received a partial answer in 1952. This answer was compounded of honesty and frankness, with full realization of the complicating factors involved. The House of Delegates instructed the Texas delegates to the American Medical Association "to sponsor recognition of the Lone Star State Medical Association as an affiliate to the American Medical Association and to join with other Southern states to try and get the American Medical Association to affiliate the other Negro organizations in the South with the American Medical Association." The state association pledged its co-operation in planning meetings for the Lone Star group and invited its members to attend the scientific sessions of the Texas Medical Association whenever "hotels and other places would allow." The county societies were urged to invite colored physicians to attend their meetings; they were encouraged to change places of meeting if necessary to provide proper facilities. The attendance of Negro students at the medical schools of Texas was approved. All this added up to progress but not to a final solution, for the Association decided not to delete the word *white* from the requirements for membership.

Some changes, none radical, were made in the constitution and bylaws. Provision was made for the office of vice-speaker of the House of Delegates. Retired physicians were permitted to become inactive members with dues of $4 a year. It was decided that the Texas delegates to the American Medical Association should be allowed $250 toward paying their expenses.

That the Association had matured was borne out by two facts. At this Dallas meeting, 61 doctors were nominated for honorary membership. And at the memorial services, the names of 98 members and 65 nonmembers were read. Men like Drs. Joe Gilbert, of Austin; Adolph Herff, of San Antonio; J. Allen Kyle, of Houston; and Seth Mabry Morris, of Galveston, had shouldered many burdens for the Association. In memory of these 163 deceased physicians, Dr. George A. Schenewerk spoke very feelingly: "What a wonderful opportunity the doctor has to emulate the work of the Greatest of All Physicians. Every one of our esteemed departed colleagues on many occasions has had the honor of acting as medium for the Divine Healer in saving lives, of bringing into the world a new life or of comforting those departing from this life. On no other group are such honors so lavishly bestowed, but these men we honor did not fail in their position of trust. Thus, we pay a tribute of respect to the revered memory of those to whom many yet living owe their lives; to those who have rendered unnumbered public services and especially the inestimable service of giving above and beyond the call of duty!"

The Association continued its interest in various related problems such as blood banks, alcoholism, tuberculosis hospitals, medical education, and medical legislation. Careful reports on these and many other subjects were submitted, considered, and accepted.

The scientific sessions were excellent and in thorough accord with the expanding activities of the Association. Dr. Robert P. Glover, professor of surgery, Hahnemann Medical College, spoke authoritatively on "The Technique and Results of Commissurotomy for Mitral Stenosis." And well could he so speak, for he was a member of that pioneer Philadelphia team of Bailey, Glover, and O'Neill which has done so much to advance the cause of cardiac surgery.

One popular feature of the scientific program was the clinical luncheons. Held on Tuesday noon, these were participated in by a panel of experts. Many attended the three groups: surgery, obstetrics and gynecology, radiology, and clinical pathology; general practice, internal medicine, public health, and pediatrics; and diseases of the eye, ear, nose and throat.

The second guest speaker at Dallas was Arthur L. Conrad, of Chicago, president of the Heritage Foundation. He spoke ably and aptly on "The Key to Peace." [5] The way to peace, according to Mr. Conrad, is in the direction of an America strong politically, economically, and spiritually. The distilled essence of Americanism

[5] Title taken from *The Key to Peace,* published by The Heritage Foundation.

is this: "At the center of our American heritage is the free individual," and that individual has a solemn obligation to his country and to himself to be a good citizen. In the thickening atmosphere of doubt, indecision, and discord, "there is an urgent need for a crusading zeal for real Americanism." There can be no compromise, said Mr. Conrad; unconditional surrender to Communism, or rapid and complete mobilization of all our resources—material, mental and moral—these are the only alternatives.

The title of President Allen T. Stewart's address was "Full Speed Whither?" Dr. Stewart scanned the American scene and saw much in the way of discouragement: basketball scandals, cheating at West Point, deterioration in private and business morals, and, most of all, breakdown of integrity in government. "Has this canker of dishonesty," he rightly asked, "attacked the medical profession?" Proceeding to a partially affirmative answer to this question, he pointed to doctors—few, but too many—who split fees, padded insurance accounts, performed unnecessary operations, or did anything that would harm the medical profession. To Dr. Stewart, the remedy was simple: clean house professionally and politically. "We must guard jealously the reputation of our profession, cast out those who violate its high purposes, labor to help those who make mistakes, and above all strive to set a good example for those who are younger and who look to us for principles and precepts. The greatest single deterrent to doctors who are tempted is the dread of losing the goodwill and opinion of their fellow practitioners. Last but not least, we must strive to keep the unworthy and unfit from ever starting the study of medicine." And having done this, then the medical profession, with better grace, could use its great influence toward cleansing the local and national political areas.

President-Elect Truman C. Terrell made a short address at Dallas on "The Doctor As a Citizen." He saw signposts of disaster on the road immediately ahead, and an indifferent and apathetic citizenry paid them little heed. And there were clouds on the medical horizon also. In meeting the serious threats that were so obvious on all sides, the doctors of Texas had heavy responsibilities as teachers and as citizens. "We must face the fact," he said, "that it is time to be citizens before we are doctors. There are certain attributes of a citizen which only we can fulfill, if we determine so to do. We must concede the inevitable conclusion that now, more than at any other time in our lifetime, America needs the help of all her citizens."

Early in the 1952 meeting, the General Practitioner of the Year was elected: J. M. Travis, a seventy-five-year-old physician from Jacksonville. Elected by acclamation were the new officers: George Turner, of El Paso, president-elect; Wayne V. Ramsey, of Abilene, vice-president; Robert B. Homan, Jr., of El Paso, speaker of the House of Delegates; Hobart O. Deaton, of Fort Worth, vice-speaker of the House of Delegates; and Robert M. Kimbro, of Cleburne, trustee, to succeed F. J. L. Blasingame, of Wharton. San Antonio accepted its place in rotation for the 1954 session, Houston having been previously chosen for the centenary session in 1953.

Dr. Travis, after due nomination by his colleagues, was chosen December 2, 1952, by the House of Delegates of the American Medical Association as the nation's General Practitioner of the Year. He was the first Texan to receive this recognition.

The dedication of the new library and headquarters building on September 19, 1952, was an event of great importance. By mid-August, the new home of the Association had been occupied, and things were put in order very quickly. Fronting on Lamar Boulevard and facing beautiful tree-studded Pease Park, it has a more lovely setting than any other that could likely have been chosen. Large live-oak trees frame the building to the east and west.

For the dedication, the *Journal* published a special section which carried this description under the heading, "The Latch String Is Out":

The Texas Medical Association building is on a corner lot where Lamar Boulevard, one of the chief north-south arteries of Austin, is met by Nineteenth Street, a convenient east-west thoroughfare. Facing approximately west on Lamar, the limestone edifice with granite trim snuggles against a tree-lined bluff in the rear and overlooks a city park in front. The almost windowless west façade emphasizes the modern architecture which has been modified to lend dignity to the two-story with basement structure. Twin rows of windows across the back permit both floors to have full benefit of the northeastern light.

Formal double doors at the main entrance, an automobile entrance at the rear, and a service entrance offer access to the first floor, which is occupied entirely by the library and an informal lounge-auditorium to seat 300. Two staircases and a service elevator rise to the second floor, where the executive, business, *Journal,* medical services, public relations, State Advisory Committee, and Woman's Auxiliary offices are located. A large basement area is available for storage as well as for housing a

434

photographic dark-room and the furnace, incinerator, and air conditioning equipment.

Plaster walls in soft colors with harmonizing asphalt tile floors, sound-absorbing ceilings, and fluorescent lighting prevail. Wood paneling and leather, together with decorative draw drapes, enhance the beauty of the main reading room of the library and of the auditorium-lounge. A kitchen adjacent to the auditorium will permit refreshments for groups meeting there, and a small kitchen unit in the staff lounge will serve their needs.

Parking facilities on the Association property will take care of 20 automobiles, and an additional 40 cars can be parked within a block of the building.

The obvious features of the new home are structural beauty and utility. Beyond these, however, is the significance of the accomplished fact. Here, at long last, was the realization of the dreams of Texas doctors for fifty years and more. As one walks up the front steps and looks up at the beautiful doors, there is an inviting friendliness about the building which seems to say to the doctors of Texas: "Enter in and be refreshed and renewed in mind and in spirit."

The dedication ceremonies were divided into two parts. At 5:00 P.M., the living former presidents were honored. Each was presented with a medallion struck off in honor of the occasion. Those present were Drs. W. B. Russ, E. H. Cary, J. H. Foster, A. A. Ross, S. E. Thompson, J. H. Burleson, B. E. Pickett, Sr., G. V. Brindley, and Allen T. Stewart. Dr. T. C. Terrell presided at this meeting, and President-Elect George Turner gave a short history of the Association. Senator Lyndon B. Johnson, the principal speaker, expressed his opposition to socialized medicine. He saw the new library as a repository of those resources necessary for the conquest of pain, fear, and disease.

The main ceremony of dedication was held at 8:00 P.M. The following program was presented:

Presiding	Dr. Merton M. Minter, San Antonio, Chairman of the Board of Trustees, Texas Medical Association
Prelude	The Britt Cello Ensemble, The University of Texas College of Fine Arts

Invocation . . . Dr. W. R. White, Waco, President, Baylor University

Dedication of Memorial Library

President's Remarks . . Dr. T. C. Terrell, Fort Worth, President, Texas Medical Association

Appreciatory Remarks

Dedication of Sam Thompson Room

Governor's Remarks . . The Honorable Allan Shivers, Austin, Governor of Texas

Principal Address . . Dr. Louis H. Bauer, Hempstead, New York, President, American Medical Association

Dr. Minter spoke feelingly of the loyalty and devotion of Dr. Sam Thompson. In recognition of a bequest of $50,000 to the Association by Dr. and Mrs. Thompson, the auditorium-lounge of the new building was designated as the Sam Thompson Room and an appropriate plaque was placed on the wall.

Governor Shivers, after paying his respects to the ideals and ambitions of the medical profession, presented Dr. Bauer in his usual direct and felicitous phrases.

Dr. Bauer complimented the Association on the consummation of its hopes for a permanent home. He saw the medical library as the basis of all medical research and medical progress. As for organized medicine, the county society was the mainstay, and to this small unit of organization the membership had a profound obligation; apathy or carelessness could be disastrous. He urged the members to support the Association with their time, their talents, and their money.

When the 1953 session of the Texas Medical Association assembles in Houston, it can be expected that Dr. Robert B. Homan, Jr., will call the House of Delegates to order with his usual dignity and will preside with his usual efficiency and fairness. Dr. Merton Minter, chairman of the Board of Trustees, will pay tribute to those faithful trustees who, year in and year out, have concentrated their efforts on the finances of the Association. Many routine reports will be presented, discussed, and acted on. New problems will arise, and new solutions will be found. Many references will be

436

made to the new building and what it will mean to the Association as the years come and go. Pride of possession will be emphasized. In nostalgic retrospection, much will be said about Drs. Cupples, Smith, Becton, Swearingen, Osborn, Saunders, Paschal, Moore, Rosser, Keiller, McReynolds, Chase, Taylor, and many more of those sturdy medical ancestors who had made all this possible.

At this meeting rounding out the first century of organized medicine in Texas, Dr. Truman C. Terrell will point with peculiar pride to the life and work of the eighty-six presidents who have preceded him. Humbly, he will confess his dependence on all that has gone before. He will review the accomplishments of the past, evaluate the problems of the present, and look hopefully and confidently to the future.

XXIV

In Summary of the Century

As we survey the century that has passed, the Texas Medical Association stands out as a towering beacon. From small and uncertain beginnings, it has come to be one of the sturdiest of state associations.

This accomplishment has not resulted from the efforts of any one individual or of any one group. Rather has it been due to the continuing and cumulative efforts of many individuals and many groups. Neither has this attainment come about as the result of repeated successes and unimpeded progress. All along the way, hindrances and discouragements have been encountered. But always there were those who believed in the ultimate survival and success of the Association. Year in and year out, the golden thread of loyalty and faith can be traced as it passed from one group of officials and members to another, unchanged and unchangeable, undramatized but very vital. Had it not been for the fidelity and determination of these individuals, the result would have been quite different, or at least long delayed.

Through the years of the century, the Association has been blessed with good leadership. Men of the early era like George Cupples and Ashbel Smith would have emerged triumphant over any and all circumstances; they pitted their imposing cultural and medical capabilities against the ignorance and the apathy of the medical frontier and gave substance and stability to a struggling Association. In the mid-years of the medical century in Texas, the elected leaders brought the Association to the year of reorganization, from which point rapid growth and ultimate success were

438

assured. All the while, the problems of the Association were ever present and ever changing. But few of the leaders faced the distressing complications which sprang up in the path of organized medicine during the last fifteen or twenty years. At a time when general demoralization was taking place, when standards of conduct were tumbling and men were losing their way, when evil in high places was distressingly rampant, when the federal government often seemed hostile to the medical profession—at such a time as this the modern officials of the Association have brought to these problems those qualities of leadership which steered the buffeted organization to its present position of safety, strengthened and confidently awaiting the future.

The first half-century was a period of struggle and slow progress. Trial and error, personal differences, efforts at solution of the basic factors of organization—all these entered into the experiences of the early years and terminated in the reorganization recommended by the American Medical Association in 1903. The leaders of the second half-century took the dreams and the hopes and the experimental ventures of their medical forefathers and welded them into a coherent organization, strong, progressive, and fulfilling the purposes for which it was created. Thus the Texas Medical Association, as we know it, has acquired new powers and new purposes, new ambitions and new horizons. Today it stands as a monument to the vision and determination of the medical pioneers of Texas and to the unfaltering faith of those who have followed the trails they blazed. It has transformed their brave and buoyant dreams into a living, vibrant reality.

Our medical ancestors gave the best they had to the best they knew. At the beginning of the second century of the Texas Medical Association, we have a similarly compelling obligation to the century that lies ahead.

Appendix I:

CONSTITUTION AND BY-LAWS
OF THE
TEXAS MEDICAL ASSOCIATION [1]
1853

I. TITLE OF THE ASSOCIATION.

This Institution shall be known and distinguished by the name and title of the *Texas Medical Association.*

II. MEMBERS.

1. This Association shall not be limited as to numbers, but shall be open to every gentleman of the Medical Profession, residing within the State, under the terms and conditions hereinafter to be expressed.

2. The members of the Association shall collectively represent, and have cognizance of, the common interest of the Medical Profession in every part of the State.

III. OFFICERS.

Besides fellows, or members, the Association shall also consist of the following *Officers:* A Board of Counsellors, a President, two Vice-Presidents, Corresponding Secretary, Recording Secretary and Treasurer.

IV. MEETINGS.

1. A meeting of the fellows of this Association shall be held annually on the second Monday of November, at two o'clock, P.M., in the City of Austin.

---

[1] Reprinted from *Proceedings of the Texas Medical Convention,* Austin, 1853. See above, Chapter 2.

2. At such meeting, ten fellows shall constitute a quorum for the transaction of business.

3. Notice of the Annual Meeting shall be given in two of the public papers, by the Recording Secretary, at least two months previously.

V. ORDER OF BUSINESS.

1. The following shall be the order of business at the Annual Meeting of the Association:

2. The reading of the proceedings of the last Annual Meeting, by the Recording Secretary; also, of the records of the transactions of the *Counsellors*, for the preceding year; and of the names of those who have been admitted during that time to *ordinary fellowship*, or as *honorary members*.

3. The Recording Secretary shall then announce the names of Counsellors appointed by the District Societies, and the Association shall proceed to nominate Counsellors for those districts who have not yet organized themselves into District Societies, or who may have omitted to elect Counsellors.

4. Reports of Committees shall then be called for by the President.

5. Alterations in the By-Laws, proposed by any fellow, or by the Counsellors, shall next receive the attention of the Association; and these shall be submitted in writing, and not acted upon, until after having been submitted to the Counsellors; they are afterwards to be reported back to the Society.

6. Such Scientific Communications as the Counsellors may have ordered shall be laid before the Society.

7. Any propositions or suggestions which may be thought to be conducive to the general interest of Medical Science, or the welfare of the Association, may be offered by any member; the Association deciding by vote, whether to engage in the consideration of the same.

8. At eleven o'clock, A.M., on the Tuesday after the 2nd Monday, the President shall call upon the anniversary orator to deliver the annual discourse; and all unfinished business shall be suspended until after its delivery.

VI. ELECTIONS.

Counsellors.—The Counsellors shall be chosen from among the fellows residing in the several districts, in the proportion, as nearly as can be, of one Counsellor to every five fellows; *provided,* that at least one Counsellor shall be chosen for each district.

Officers.—At the first stated meeting of the Counsellors, every year, they shall choose from among the whole number of Counsellors who may be elected, a President of the Society, also two Vice-Presidents, two Recording Secretaries, a Corresponding Secretary and a Treasurer.

1. *Membership.*—No one shall be eligible to fellowship who cannot satisfy the Counsellors that his education, professional and otherwise, has been such as to entitle him to that honor.

2. All *irregular* practitioners are absolutely prohibited.—By an irregular practitioner is meant, one who is not a member of this Association, or a graduate of a reputable Medical College; or who offers to cure any disease by a medicine, the composition of which he keeps a secret, or vends, or advertises the same for sale.

3. Nominations to the Counsellors, must be made by one or more of the fellows; but no resident of any established district shall be nominated by any one out of that district.

Certificate.—Every person elected a member of this Association shall be entitled, on application to the Recording Secretary, to a certificate of the same.

Honorary Members.—There shall be Honorary members of this Association, appointed from time to time, after the manner and according to the forms prescribed for the admission of ordinary fellows.

Proxies.—Fellows or Counsellors absent from any meeting, shall, in all cases, be entitled to vote by proxy in writing; provided, that no fellow be represented otherwise than by a fellow, and a Counsellor by a Counsellor, who shall represent no more than five others.

VII. DISTRICT SOCIETIES.

There shall be also established, besides the *general* State Association, *District Societies,* to be organized according to the mode and plan hereinafter set forth.

VIII. DUTIES OF OFFICERS.

1. The President shall call special meetings of the Counsellors whenever he shall deem it expedient, or five Counsellors request it in writing; and the same notice shall be given as is required for stated meetings; except in a case not admitting of delay, when with

the consent of five Counsellors, he may convoke the Counsellors at such notice as the circumstances may permit; and in case the President refuses to comply with the request of the Counsellors, then the latter, should the necessity of the call be deemed sufficiently urgent or important, shall do it on their own responsibility.

2. Any meeting of Counsellors may be continued by adjournment, by a vote of a majority of those present.

3. Nine Counsellors shall constitute a quorum for the transaction of business; but a smaller number may adjourn the meeting to any day within one week.

4. At the first stated meeting of the Counsellors every year, they shall choose by ballot, from among the fellows of the Society, an Orator for the ensuing anniversary.

5. At the first meeting of the Counsellors, two standing committees shall be appointed, viz: a Committee on Publication, and a Committee on the Medical Topography and Diseases of the State.

6. The Committee on Publications shall have direction of a publication, which shall be issued annually, by the Association, as early after the annual meeting as practicable, to be distributed by the Secretary to each fellow or retired member. And that publication shall contain the annual discourse, unless otherwise ordered by the Association or Counsellors; such other medical communications as the Counsellors may authorize to be published; an abstract of the proceedings of the Association, and transactions of the Counsellors, excepting such as are of a private or personal nature; together with a list of the officers of the State and District Societies, of those who have become fellows or honorary members during the preceding year, or who have resigned, or been expelled.

The Committee on the Medical Topography and Diseases of the State shall consist of one member from each district, besides a Chairman, who shall also be appointed by the Counsellors. The committee shall report annually on the diseases of the previous year; each member forwarding to the Chairman a report on the Topography and Diseases of his own district, previous to the 1st December preceding the anniversary; the Chairman, from these special reports, to make a general report, to be read at the anniversary meeting; the special reports to be included in an appendix to the general report.

7. Nominations of Committees at the meetings of Counsellors, shall be made by the President, unless otherwise ordered.

444

8. At the stated meeting immediately preceding the annual meeting of the Association, the Counsellors shall choose a Committee to examine the Treasurer's account, on the week preceding the annual meeting, which committee shall report to the Association at its annual meeting.

9. Nominations of candidates for fellowship, shall be according to the following form:

—————, 18———

The subscriber nominates to the Counsellors of the Texas Medical Association, A. B., for admission as fellow.

He was educated by C. D., and has a respectable standing in the profession.

E. H.

10. The Counsellors at one of their stated meetings, shall appoint annually, a suitable person to deliver before the fellows, at their annual meeting, a discourse on some medical subject of his choice; and in case of his declining the service, the President with five others, may appoint another in his stead.—And every discourse so read, shall be considered the property of the Association, and a copy be required to be deposited by the author, with the Corresponding Secretary, within three months after its delivery.

They shall appoint annually, delegates to represent the Association in the *American Medical Association.*

1. *President.*—The President shall call all meetings of the Association and Counsellors; preside at the same; preserve order; regulate the debates; state and put questions; call for reports of Committees; enforce the by-laws, rules and orders; have the casting vote, and perform such other duties as may be assigned him.

2. *Vice-President.*—In case of the absence, from any cause whatever, either from the meetings of the Association or Counsellors, of the President, one of the Vice-Presidents shall perform all of the duties incidental to the Presidency. And in case of the absence of all these officers, the duties shall devolve upon the senior Counsellor present.

3. *Corresponding Secretary.*—The Corresponding Secretary shall receive and have the custody of all communications to the Association and Counsellors, and prepare and transmit answers to the same, in such form or language as the Counsellors may direct; he may cause letters or communications in a foreign language to be trans-

lated into English, or vice versa; report to the Counsellors at their meetings those who had become fellows at the preceding meeting; transmit to the Treasurer of the Association, a fortnight before its annual meeting, the names of the new fellows for the preceding year; and perform all such other duties as may be assigned him. Letters and communications should be addressed to him.

4. *Recording Secretary.*—The Recording Secretary shall keep the Seal of the Association, together with its records, and those of the Counsellors, and all papers required to be filed; supply elected members with their diplomas, signed by the President, and with his own signature, and with the seal of the Association duly affixed, and to the officers of the Association such other blank certificates as the by-laws may render necessary or proper; notify and attend the meetings of both; keep a fair record of their respective proceedings; read their minutes, and all such communications as the Counsellors may require to be made; receive and record nominations for election into the Association, and cause them to be laid before the Counsellors at their stated meetings; notify Chairmen of Committees appointed by the Association or Counsellors, specifying in each case, the commission and names of the Committee; keep a copy of the By-Laws ready for subscription; and perform all such other duties as may be assigned him.

Either of the Secretaries being absent from the meetings of the Association or Counsellors, his duties shall be performed by the other, if present; and a transfer, as soon as possible, be made to the absent Secretary, of the papers, orders or records, belonging to his department.

The records of the Association and of the Counsellors shall be produced at every annual meeting of the former, and be otherwise at all times conveniently accessible to every fellow.

5. *Treasurer.*—The Treasurer shall have the care and management of the fiscal concerns of the Association; keep an accurate account of receipts and expenditures; furnish an annual statement of the same and the funds in his hands, or other property, at the annual assembly of the Association; subject his accounts to such examination as the Counsellors may order; receive all donations or bequests, as well as money due to the Association; and, under the direction of the Counsellors, sue for all fines, assessments, sell or lease any estate, and execute the necessary papers. He shall also examine all charges and accounts against the Association, and present them for payment,

446

if correct, to the President; but shall not pay any money out of the Treasury, without an order from that officer; and when the Counsellors shall deem it requisite, and the funds admit of his being compensated, due security shall be required for the trust reposed in him, and a suitable per centage or salary be given for his services.

6. Officers may resign for sufficient reasons, or be removed by the Counsellors for inattention, neglect or misconduct. In either instance, or a vacancy occasioned by death, the Counsellors shall fill up the vacancy as soon as may be convenient.

IX. ASSESSMENTS.

Every fellow shall contribute $5 annually to the funds of the Association, and pay the same to the Treasurer; and if not paid at the Annual Meeting, the Treasurer shall collect it as soon thereafter as possible, and always, if practicable, within the year. Legal measures to enforce it may also be taken by him, under the direction of the Counsellors.

X. RESIGNATIONS.

Any member may resign from the Association, provided his arrears be paid.

XI. RETIRED MEMBERS.

Members at 60 years, resigning from the Association, shall be designated as *Retired Members,* and be freed from assessments and liabilities of office, at the same time that they are suffered to retain all the other privileges of membership. But they shall conform to all the requirements of the Association, and be subjected to its penalties.

XII. EXPULSION.

Any member may be expelled from the Association, or having resigned, be deprived of his privileges, by a majority of two-thirds of the fellows present, for notorious and gross immorality; infamous crime under the laws of the land; attempt to destroy this Association; violation of any of its by-laws, of which expulsion is the penalty; and false certificates of studies, or character of Students of Medicine. The expulsion may be made at any annual meeting. The charge or charges, however, must have been first considered by the Counsellors, and brought forward by them; or have been made at a

447

preceding annual meeting. And ample opportunity shall be afforded for refutation or defence before the Association.

XIII. FORM OF SUBSCRIPTION.

The subscribers agree to comply with the By-Laws of the Texas Medical Association.

XIV. SCIENTIFIC COMMUNICATIONS.

1. Scientific Communications shall be made to the Counsellors, who are authorized to receive and consider them, and dispose of them as they may judge most expedient.

2. Inquiries on professional topics may, through or by them, be also submitted to the fellows, and communications requested relative to the same. And such of these as they may select, or from the Association as they may judge proper, or from their own Board, or which they may think conducive to the welfare of Medical Science, they may cause to be published, at the expense of the Association, within the limit of its funds.

XV. CODE OF ETHICS.

The Association adopts, as its Code of Ethics, the one which has been commended and adopted by the American Medical Association.

XVI. FEE BILL.

It shall be the duty of each District Society to establish a Fee-Bill to govern its own members.

XVII. DISTRICT SOCIETIES.

1. It being important that there should be but one medical organization throughout the State, that the District Societies should be collateral branches of one parent Society, and that distinct associations, with equal powers opposing each other, defeating the objects of a medical organization and bringing contempt upon the whole body of the profession, should be avoided. [*Sic.*] The following are the restrictions under which this Association shall proceed, whenever called upon to institute them.

2. The whole State shall be divided into ——— Medical Districts, as experience or expediency may determine.

3. Whenever any district is desirous of organizing a District Medical Society, it shall apply in writing to the Counsellors, stating the extent of territory and the number of practitioners intended to be

comprehended by it, and the village, town or place where it is proposed to hold the meetings.—And upon their acceding to the application, the Counsellors shall cause to be forthwith issued a charter to the following effect:

STATE OF TEXAS

[L. S.] By the Counsellors of the Texas Medical Association.
To ———

Fellows of the said Society—Greeting:

Your application, made in due form, requesting the institution of a subordinate District Medical Society, to consist of fellows of the Texas Medical Association, residing in the   in the District of   , was duly considered at a meeting of the Counsellors held at   , on the   day of   , A.D. 18   , and it was thereupon voted that your request should be granted.

Be it, therefore, known that pursuant to an act of the Legislature of this State, authorizing the Counsellors of the Texas Medical Association thereunto, A District Subordinate Society, by the name of   , is hereby established, to consist of those fellows of the Texas Medical Association, now resident within the limits aforesaid, for the purpose of electing officers and transacting such other business as they shall deem expedient.

In testimony whereof, the President, pursuant to the aforesaid vote of the Counsellors, has hereunto subscribed his name and affixed the seal of the Association, this   day of   , A.D. 18   .

A. B., *President.*

Attest: C. D., *Recording Secretary.*

Election of Officers.

1. Every District Medical Society, shall elect, annually, a President, Secretary, Treasurer, Librarian, and such other officers as it may see fit, who shall examine all communications made to that Society, and direct the Secretary thereof to transmit to the Corresponding Secretary of the Association such communications, copy thereof or extracts from, as they may judge deserving the inspection of the Counsellors.

Secretary. Each District Secretary, immediately after the election of officers, shall annually transmit to the Recording Secretary, a list of the officers chosen; have custody of all communications made to that Society; keep a fair record of their proceedings, and transmit an account of the same to the Corresponding Secretary; and from time to time, transmit also to the same Secretary, whatever com-

449

munications the district officers may think worthy of being brought to the notice of the Counsellors, and any change that may occur in his district, by the death or removal of a fellow of the Society, and any omission of duty he may be requested by the Corresponding Secretary to fulfill, on the authority of this by-law.

2. Previous to the annual meeting in each year, every District Society shall elect the number of Counsellors to which it is entitled, and make known the same, through its Secretary, to the Recording Secretary, before the annual meeting of the Association.

3. Any village, town, &c., adjoining a Medical District, but not included within its limits, in which there are fellows wishing to connect themselves with the District Society they adjoin, may receive authority to do so upon application to the Counsellors, provided they have the concurrence of that Society, expressed by a majority of votes taken at one of their regular meetings.

XVIII. DECISIONS.

All questions requiring to be settled in the Association, Board of Counsellors, or District Societies, not otherwise specially provided for, shall be settled by ballot, by a majority of the fellows or members present.

XIX. PENALTIES.

1. All improprieties on the part of officers or fellows, for which no special penalty has been provided, shall be punishable in such a manner as the Counsellors, after deliberation, may think proper to inflict, in the way of suspension or expulsion, after due admonition and opportunity of exculpation.

2. Any fellow not conforming to the Code of Ethics, shall be expelled.

3. The same penalty of expulsion shall be inflicted upon any fellow violating the fee bill.

Appendix II:

AN ACT TO REGULATE THE
PRACTICE OF MEDICINE [1]
1873

SECTION 1. Be it enacted by the Legislature of the State of Texas, That no person shall be permitted to practice medicine in any of its branches, or departments in this State, as a means of livelihood, without first having attended a regular course of study and lectures at some regularly established and well accredited medical college, and received the degree of "Doctor of Medicine," or without having a certificate of qualification from some authorized board of medical examiners, as hereinafter provided.

SECTION 2. That every person heretofore engaged in the practice of medicine, in any of its branches or departments, in this State, shall, within twenty days after the organization of the "Board of Medical Examiners" for the county in which the person so practicing may reside or sojourn, furnish to the clerk of the District Court of such county, his "Diploma" or certificate of qualification; and every person who may hereafter so engage in the practice of medicine in this State shall, within twenty days after entering upon such practice, furnish, in like manner, to the clerk of the District Court of the county in which such practitioner may sojourn or reside, his diploma or certificate of qualification; and said clerk shall enter the name of said person in a well bound book, kept in his office for

---

[1] "The foregoing act was presented to the Governor of Texas for his approval on the nineteenth day of May, A.D. 1873, and was not signed by him, or returned to the house in which it originated, with his objections thereto, within the time prescribed by the Constitution, and thereupon became a law without his signature.—James P. Newcomb, Secretary of State."—*The Laws of Texas,* H. P. N. Gammel, comp. (Austin, 1898–1914), VII, 526–28.

that purpose, together with the time when, where, and by whom such diploma or certificate of qualification was given, after which he shall return the said diploma or certificate to the owner thereof. For which service said clerk shall be entitled to receive from each, any, and every such applicant, the sum of one dollar.

SECTION 3. That the county courts of the several counties in this State shall, at their first regular term after the passage of this act, or as soon thereafter as practicable, severally appoint a board of medical examiners for their respective counties, to be composed of not less than three practicing physicians of known ability, and graduates of some medical college, recognized by the American Medical Association, who shall, immediately after accepting such appointment, select one of their number president, and one as secretary, and adopt all necessary rules and regulations for their guidance and control in the examination of applicants for certificates of qualification as required by section one of this act. Any two of them shall have authority to grant certificates; provided, that in counties where no medical boards are formed, physicians practicing therein may apply to the nearest medical board to their respective counties, and if entitled to them, receive their certificates as in other cases. Such board of examiners shall be entitled to receive the sum of ten dollars for each and every such examination made, to be paid by the applicant or party so examined; and whenever a vacancy occurs in any of said boards, the same shall be filled by appointment by the County Court of the county in which such vacancy occurs.

SECTION 4. Said board shall meet regularly semi-annually, and shall give at least three weeks' public notice of such meetings, specifying the time and place of meetings; provided, that any member of any of said boards shall have authority to grant to an applicant a temporary license or certificate, upon examination, until the regular meeting of the board, at which time said applicant must apply for a thorough examination. Each and every one of said boards shall procure a seal as soon as practicable after the organization, which seal shall be impressed upon every certificate granted.

SECTION 5. That any person violating any of the provisions of this act shall be guilty of a misdemeanor, and, on conviction thereof, before any court having competent jurisdiction, shall be fined in any sum not less than fifty ($50) dollars nor more than five hundred ($500) dollars for every such offense; one-half of said fine to be paid

452

to the prosecutor, and the other half into the county treasury; provided, that nothing in this act shall be so construed as to apply to those who have been regularly engaged in the general practice of medicine in this State, in any of its branches or departments, for a period of five consecutive years in their respective counties; nor to females who follow the practice of midwifery strictly as such.

SECTION 6. That this act take effect six months from and after its passage.

Passed May 16, 1873.

Index

Campbell, M.: 42

Campbell, Thomas M.: 253, 255, 267, 276

Cancer: 176, 198, 262, 276, 294, 298, 317, 332, 348–49, 355, 376

Cantrell, C. E.: 234, 235, 243, 248, 257, 260, 262, 265, 288, 289

Capps, E. D.: 246

Carcinoma: 225

Carhart, J. W.: 165, 167

Carlsbad Sanatorium: 217

Carnes, A. W.: 331

Carothers, A. E.: 65, 67

Carpenter, [William B.]: 184

Carper, William M.: 5, 118

Carrel-Dakin system of wound irrigation: 303–304

Carroll, B. H.: 35

Carroll, James: 98

Carter, Henry R.: 241

Carter, William S.: 225–26, 236, 261, 276

Cartoons as medical publicity: 266–67

Cartwright, H. H.: 384

Cary, E. H.: 251, 272, 290, 299, 304–305, 316, 318, 349, 372, 398, 401, 402, 410, 435

Cary, Mrs. E. H.: 305

Case, James T.: 308

Cases, reporting of: 40

Castration: of criminals, 195, 195 n.; nonaseptic, 199 n.; see also sterilization

Caton, J. H.: 360

Caulk, John R.: 354

Caxton, William: 68

Cellular pathology: 96

Central Texas Conference of the Methodist Episcopal Church: 344

Century of Medicine in Jacksonville and Duval County, A, by Webster Merritt: 115 n.

Century of Medicine in San Antonio, A, by Pat I. Nixon: ix

Cerf, Bennett, Try and Stop Me: 364

Cerna, David: 175, 176, 181, 183, 196, 206

Chaillé, S. E.: 78

Chandler, Paul A.: 419

Chapman, J. B.: 329

Chapman, [Nathaniel]: 131

Chase, Hope: 365

Chase, I. C.: 225, 243, 245, 247, 248, 250, 252, 253, 255, 257, 258, 263, 267, 269, 271, 274–75, 278, 292, 299, 300, 302, 303, 304, 307, 309, 311, 313, 315, 331, 359, 437

Chilton, Horace: 168

Chilton, P. H.: 324

Chilton, R. H.: 124, 132

Chinn, R. H.: 5

Chiropractics and chiropractors: 266, 295, 297, 315, 317, 326–27, 335–36, 339, 385

Chloral hydrate: 63

Chloroform: 46, 63, 232

Cholecystenterostomy: 261

Cholecystotomy: 195

Cholera: 4, 27

Christian Science: 237–38, 258, 283

Christie, A. C.: 376

Citron, Julius: 276

Civil Works Administration: 355

Clagett, O. Theron: 397

Clark, I. E.: 156

Clark, Jean: 421

Clark, Joe A.: 400

Clark, S. M. D.: 290

Clayton, J. B.: 303

Cline, John W.: 417–18, 419, 428

Clingman, A. M.: 32

Clopton, A. G.: 57, 58, 60–61, 119, 129, 153, 170, 174, 206

Cocaine: 121

Cocke, W. E.: 35

Cocke, W. J.: 37, 39, 42, 44

Code of ethics: 13, 39, 40

Cod liver oil: 69

Cody, C. C.: 326, 333, 341, 358, 376, 387, 393, 401, 405, 424

Coke, Richard: 59

Coleman, P. C.: 168, 186, 191, 193, 195, 196, 235

Coleman, S. D.: 386, 430

Coles, J. W. T.: 9, 18

Coles, William T. F.: 5

Colgin, M. W.: 276, 277

College of Physicians and Surgeons: 206, 260

Collins, Bonnie: 320

Collins, Ira W.: 268

Collins, W. B.: 259

466

469